D0119695

Reviews in Macromolecular Chemistry

Reviews in Macromolecular Chemistry

edited by

GEORGE B. BUTLER
Department of Chemistry
University of Florida
Gainesville, Florida

KENNETH F. O'DRISCOLL
Department of Chemical
  Engineering
University of Waterloo
Waterloo, Ontario, Canada

MITCHEL SHEN
Department of Chemical
  Engineering
University of California
Berkeley, California

Volume 7

1972

MARCEL DEKKER, INC., New York

Contents

RHEOLOGY OF ADHESION   85
D. H. Kaelble
Science Center
North American Rockwell Corporation
Thousand Oaks, California

SOLVATION OF SYNTHETIC AND NATURAL POLY-
ELECTROLYTES 113
B. E. Conway
Universities of Southampton and Newcastle upon Tyne
England

J. P. Kennedy
Institute of Polymer Science
The University of Akron
Akron, Ohio
and
T. Otsu
Department of Applied Chemistry
Osaka City University
Sumiyoshiku, Osaka, Japan

Linear Polyquinoxalines

PAUL M. HERGENROTHER
Polymer Sciences Laboratory
Boeing Scientific Research Laboratories
Seattle, Washington

I. INTRODUCTION

The need for new improved structural resins which meet the requirements of advanced aircraft, space, and deep submergence vehicles has served as the impetus for research in this area. During the last 10 years, a significant amount of effort has concentrated on

1

new thermally stable organic and heterocyclic polymers. The polyquinoxalines (PQ) have evolved from this effort and represent one of
the most promising heterocyclic polymer systems currently known
for potential use in structural application which demand high thermal,
oxidative, and hydrolytic stability. The following discussion will be
confined to the linear nonladder-type PQ.

II. SYNTHESIS AND CHARACTERIZATION

A. Polyquinoxalines

Quinoxalines were initially prepared independently by Körner [1]
and by Hinsberg [2] from the cyclocondensation of an aromatic o-
diamine with 1,2-dicarbonyl compounds:

$$+ \ 2H_2O \qquad (1)$$

This reaction proceeds in quantitative yield and was proposed in 1961
at a meeting by Sorenson [3] as a potential route to PQ. At that time,
Stille commented on the status of his work, already underway, on PQ
which led to a series of papers [4-6]. Concurrent with Stille's effort,
researchers [7,8] at the Institut Français du Petrolé were also investigating PQ through the same synthetic route. This involved the
reaction of aromatic bis(o-diamines), such as 3,3'-diaminobenzidine
(DAB), with aromatic bisglyoxals, such as p,p'-oxybis(phenylenegly-
oxal hydrate) (OBPG):

DAB   OBPG

$$(2)$$

Monoether PQ

It is apparent that the reaction of an aromatic bisglyoxal with an aromatic bis(o-diamine) can yield a mixture of isomers (-2,2'-, -2,3'-, and 3,3'-). This was investigated by Stille and co-workers who concluded, as a result of ultraviolet spectroscopic study on model compounds [4a] and X-ray diffraction patterns [5] on the PQ formed from the reaction of DAB and p-phenylenediglyoxal dihydrate, that the 2,2'-isomer was predominantly formed. However, it should be noted that in predicting the isomer predominantly formed from the reaction of an aromatic bis(o-diamine) with an aromatic bisglyoxal, consideration must be given to several factors such as the relative nucleophilicity of the o-amino groups and the relative reactivity of the aldehyde versus the ketone carbonyls in the aromatic bisglyoxals. For example, the p-amino groups of 3,3',4,4'-tetraaminodiphenyl ether (TADE) should be more nucleophilic than those of DAB and, accordingly, provide predominantly the 3,3'-isomer when reacted with an aromatic bisglyoxal such as OBPG; whereas, when DAB is reacted with OBPG, the 2,2'-isomer should predominate:

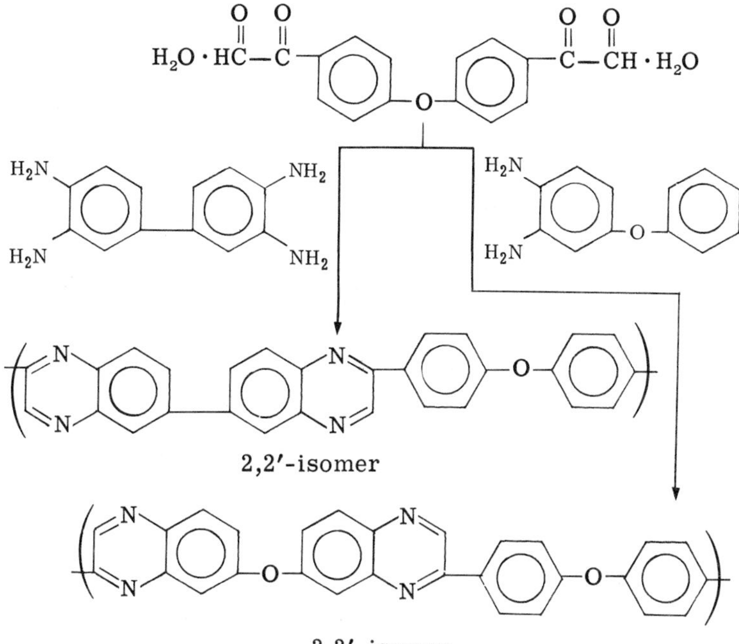

2,2'-isomer

3,3'-isomer

(3)

In 1963, work on **PQ** was initiated at Whittaker Research and Development (formerly Narmco) under Navy sponsorship to demonstrate the potential of **PQ** as a high-temperature structural resin [9]. Since an effort of this type required a significant quantity of polymer, it was necessary to develop a polymerization method which would provide an adequate supply of processable, reproducible polymer. A synthetic study [10] which is summarized in Table 1 was conducted using TADE and OBPG.

As indicated in Table 1, poor polymer was obtained when a m-cresol solution of OBPG was used for polymer synthesis under the indicated reaction conditions. However, when OBPG was used as a m-cresol slurry, good polymer was formed as indicated by its inherent viscosity, isothermal weight loss, and film properties. The difference was apparently due to a concentration factor; too much OBPG in solution reacts rapidly with the TADE to yield a cross-linked or branched polymer as indicated by its solubility and film properties. In the slurry form there is essentially no excess of bis-glyoxal in solution, and, consequently, the less reactive keto group of the intermediate has the opportunity to react intramolecularly to form the desired product (A):

(4)

Table 1

Polymerization Study of Diether Polyquinoxaline

Method No.	Mode of Addition[a]	Intermediate polymer[b]			Final polymer[f]			
		η_{inh},[c] dl/g	PST,[d] °C	Volatile content,[e] %	η_{inh},[c] dl/g	Isothermal wt loss (%)[g] at 600°F in air after		Film[h]
						100 hr	200 hr	
1	TADE slurry to OBPG solution	0.50	~270	5.3	Insol.	4.5	14	Fails fingernail crease
2	OBPG solution to TADE slurry	0.51	~260	3.8	Insol.	23.0	44	Fails fingernail crease
3	OBPG slurry to TADE slurry	0.73	~265	1.9	1.68	0.5	2.0	Tough and flexible
4	TADE slurry to OBPG slurry	0.68	~265	1.7	1.59	1.0	2.0	Tough and flexible

[a] Addition time ~3 min at 55° ± 3°C, followed by stirring to 75° ± 3°C during 4 hr; reaction scale, 0.10 mole, and concentration of 20% solids in m-cresol.

[b] Isolated by dilution with methanol and drying 1 hr at 170°C under pump vacuum.

[c] Inherent viscosity (0.5% H_2SO_4 at 25°C).

[d] Polymer softening temperature.

[e] Determined by heating for 1 hr at 400°C under nitrogen.

[f] One hour at 400°C under nitrogen.

[g] Particle size <30 mesh.

[h] Prepared by doctoring m-cresol solution onto glass plate and drying to 200°C during 8 hr, under vacuum.

With the bisglyoxal completely in solution, the opportunity arises for
the more reactive aldehyde portion of the glyoxal group to react intermolecularly with an unreacted amino group and, consequently,
leads to cross-linking (brittle films) and to poorer oxidative stability
because of unclosed rings.

Other modes of addition were also investigated where OBPG as
a fine powder was added to the tetraamine slurry and also where a
dilute solution of OBPG was added slowly to the tetraamine slurry.
Good polymer was also obtained by these methods.

Although methods numbered 3 and 4 in Table 1 provided essentially identical polymer, method 3 was selected for large-scale polymer synthesis due to the relative ease of manipulation. The m-cresol
solutions of the polymers so formed were used directly in application work for film casting or prepreg and tape preparation.

An m-cresol solution of the diether PQ exhibited excellent shelf
life as shown by characterizing the polymer solution and isolated
polymer therefrom periodically up to 90 days. The film-forming
ability of the solution and certain physical properties such as ηinh
and polymer softening temperature (PST) of the isolated polymer
remained essentially constant which indicated no apparent change
in the characteristics of the polymer. In addition, prepreg and tape
prepared from an m-cresol polymer solution provided good laminates
and adhesive panels after being stored in a polyethylene bag up to
120 days at ambient temperature. This further demonstrated the excellent stability of the PQ not only in solution but also in a more
applied state. The evaluation of PQ as a high-temperature laminating
resin and adhesive will be discussed later in this paper.

A variety of PQ have been prepared by reacting various aromatic
tetraamines, as listed in Table 2, with the bisglyoxals, as shown in
Table 3. As previously indicated, early PQ work was conducted
principally at the University of Iowa, the Institut Français du Petrolé,
and the Whittaker Research and Development. It is difficult and un-
just to compare the properties of one PQ with that of another when
the two polymers were prepared and characterized under different
conditions.

A valid comparison of the properties of a series of PQ containing
p-phenylene ether and p-phenylene moieties is shown in Table 4.
These polymers were recently prepared [16] under essentially identical conditions in m-cresol. The intermediate polymer was obtained
by quenching the m-cresol solution with methanol. The final polymers
were obtained by introducing a polymerization tube containing the intermediate polymer under argon into a preheated oil bath at 350° C

Table 2

Aromatic Bis(o-diamines)

H_2N \ / NH_2 H_2N / Ar \ NH_2 Ar =	Compound No.	Mp, °C	Ref.
	I	276-277	11
	II	179-180	11
	III	150-151	12
	IV	102.5-103	6
	V	173-174	13
	VI	217	14

and maintaining this temperature for 1 hr. This work was performed to determine the extent to which the processability and certain physical properties, such as the glass transition temperatures (T_g), of the PQ could be synthetically altered. As indicated in Table 4, as the amount of p-phenylene ether character in the polymer increased, PST and T_g decreased. Although no definite trend was observed in the polymer decomposition temperatures (PDT) as determined by thermogravimetric analysis (TGA) (Fig. 1; Table 5), isothermogravimetric analyses (ITGA) (Fig. 2) at 400°C in air showed a difference.

Table 3

Aromatic Bisglyoxals

H₂O·OHCOC—Ar—COCHO·H₂O where Ar =	Mp, °C	Mp Ref.	Tetraamine from Table 2 used in polym. synthesis	Polym. Ref.
(1,4-phenylene)	110–111	15	II	4,7,8,9,16,17, 20,25
(biphenylene)	(140–150 dec.) (162–164 dec.)	(4) (9,16)	III; V, VI	5,8,17,20,25; 18
 (naphthalene)	—	5	II, III	5
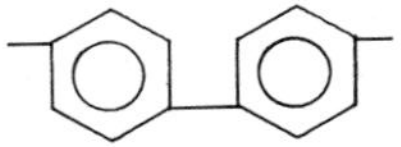 (diphenyl ether, —O—)	163–166 dec.	16	II; III	16,19; 19
(diphenyl sulfide, —S—)	122	7	II	5,7,8,10,16,17, 25
(diphenyl sulfone, O=S=O)	(118–120 dec.) (141–143 dec.)	(5) (9,16)	III; V, VI	5,8,10,19,20,25; 18
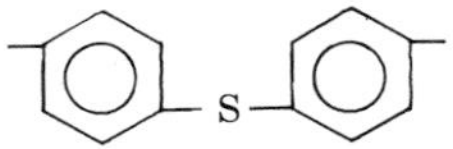 (diphenyl ...)	100–100.5	6	III, IV, V	6
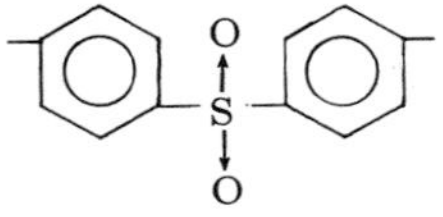 (diphenyl sulfone)	138–139	6	III, IV, V	6

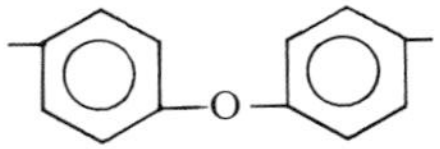

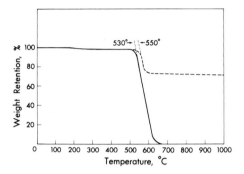

Fig. 1. Thermogram of polyquinoxaline (polymer IP); (——) in air; (– – –) in nitrogen; $\Delta T = 7°C/min$; particle size, < 60 mesh.

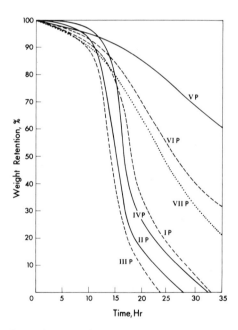

Fig. 2. Isothermal weight loss of polyquinoxalines in static air at 400°C: Particle size, < 60 mesh.

Table

Quinoxaline

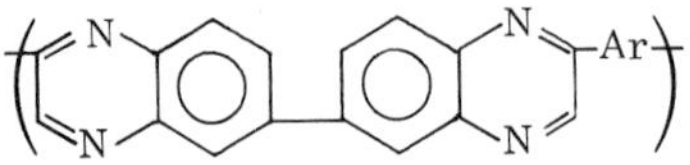 where Ar =	Polymer No.	Intermediate polymer η_{inh}, dl/g[a]	PST,[b] °C	η_{inh}, dl/g[a]
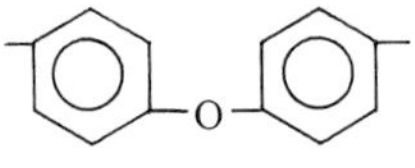	I	1.00	~315	1.62
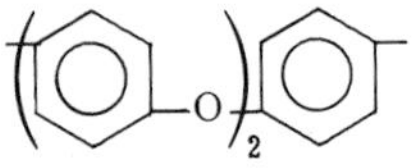	IIP	0.58	~262	1.21
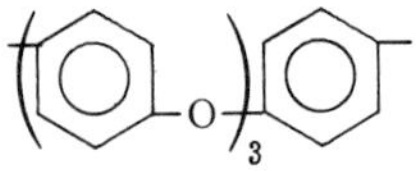	IIIP	0.62	~240	1.27
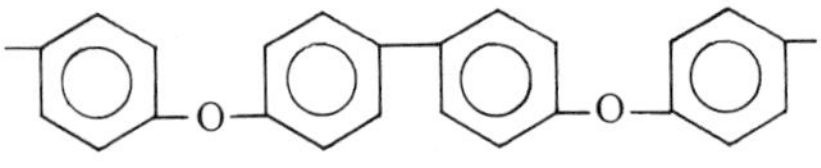	IVP	0.35	~253	0.82
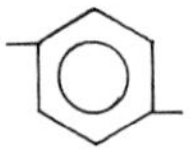	VP	0.61	>350	1.07
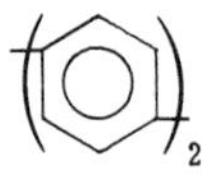	VIP	0.73	~330	1.03
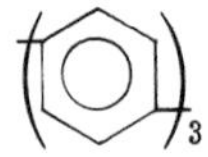	VIIP	0.44	~340	0.91

[a] 0.5% solution in H_2SO_4 at 25°C.
[b] Polymer softening temperature, determined on Fisher–John melting point becomes completely transparent upon applying slight pressure with a spatula.
[c] Glass transition temperature determined by dielectric loss measurements.
[d] Theoretical values reported in parenthesis.
[e] Obtained on sulfuric acid solutions using a Cary Model 14 recording spectro-

4

Polymers

		Final polymer						
		Elemental analysis[d]			Ultraviolet spectrum[e]		Visible spectrum[e]	
$T_g,{}^b{}^\circ C$	Formula	% C	% H	% N	$\lambda_{max}, m\mu$	$\epsilon \times 10^{-3}$	$\lambda_{max}, m\mu$	$\epsilon \times 10^{-3}$
280	$(C_{28}H_{16}N_4O)_n$	(79.25) 79.23)	4.01 (3.80)	13.10 (13.20)	280 331	22.0 35.2	590	47.0
195	$(C_{34}H_{20}N_4O_2)_n$	78.98 (79.06)	3.88 (3.90)	10.84 (10.85)	283 333	29.9 42.3	584	47.5
133	$(C_{40}H_{24}N_4O_3)_n$	77.89 (78.93)	3.95 (3.97)	8.99 (9.20)	284 333	30.0 46.0	585	48.0
213	$(C_{40}H_{24}N_4O_2)_n$	80.64 (81.07)	4.22 (4.08)	9.28 (9.45)	280 327	34.0 48.5	–	–
350	$(C_{22}H_{12}N_4)_n$	79.27 (79.50)	3.85 (3.64)	16.61 (16.86)	292	29.0	515	47.0
305	$(C_{28}H_{16}N_4)_n$	80.82 (82.34)	4.09 (3.95)	12.86 (13.72)	275 330	20.0 34.0	600	53.0
–	$(C_{34}H_{20}N_4)_n$	82.20 (84.28)	4.22 (4.16)	10.48 (11.56)	284 365	24.0 36.0	675	37.5

apparatus; PST taken as temperature when sample between cover slips

photometer.

Table 5

Polymer Decomposition Temperatures of
Polyquinoxalines

Polymer	PDT,[a] °C		Residue at 1000°C in nitrogen, %
	Air	Nitrogen	
IP	530	550	71.6
IIP	510	530	71.2
IIIP	510	520	61.4
IVP	535	560	74.0
VP	535	575	72.5
VIP	515	565	81.8
VIIP	525	600	80.8

[a]$\Delta T = 7$°C/min.

The p-phenylene PQ exhibited better oxidative stability than the p-phenylene ether PQ, but, as expected, they also displayed poorer solubility and higher PST. In comparing the oxidative stability by ITGA of one polymer with that of another, it is important that the many variables that influence the ITGA, such as sample size, sample form, atmosphere, and furnace design, be held constant. The ITGA of the individual groups of polymers compared in this paper were performed under essentially identical conditions. An isothermal weight loss curve of several PQ is shown in Fig. 3. Again, the p-phenylene PQ (polymer A) exhibited better oxidative stability at 371° C in air than the other PQ.

B. Polyphenylquinoxalines

The general route for PQ formation was extended [19,21] by reacting dibenzils such as p,p'-oxydibenzil (ODB) with aromatic bis(o-diamines) such as DAB to yield polyphenylquinoxalines (PPQ):

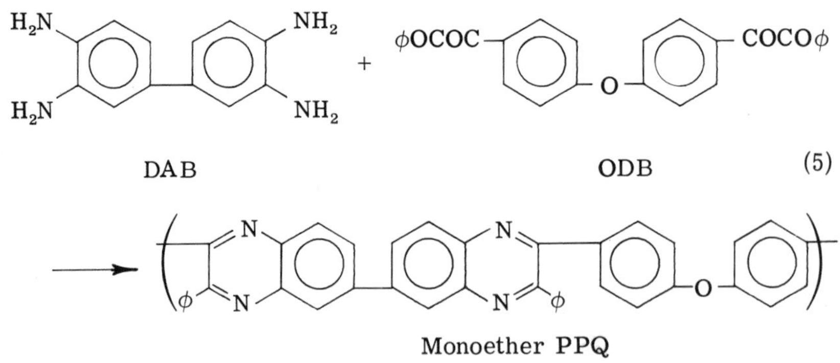

DAB   ODB   (5)

Monoether PPQ

A number of PPQ have been prepared from the reaction of various combinations of the aromatic tetraamines shown in Table 2 and the dibenzils listed in Table 6.

As in the PQ, isomeric units can also be formed in the PPQ. In fact, the possibility of isomer formation in PPQ is greater than in PQ. The relative reactivity of the adjacent carbonyl groups in the dibenzils is not influenced by a steric factor as with the diglyoxals but arises principally from electromeric effects. For example, different isomers would be expected to predominate when DAB is reacted with p-bis(phenylglyoxalyl)benzene and with ODB:

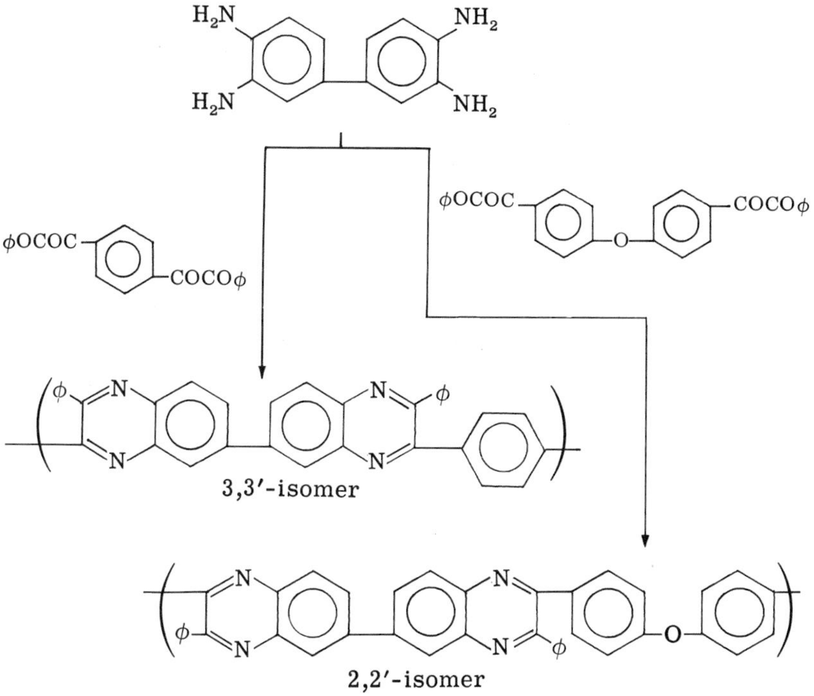

$$(6)$$

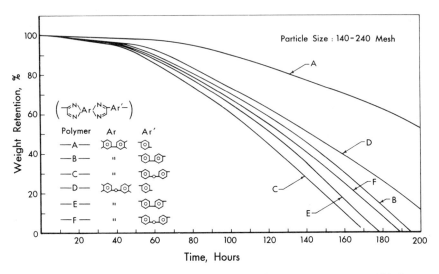

Fig. 3. Isothermal weight loss of polyquinoxalines in static air at 371°C.

In general, the PPQ exhibited several advantages over the PQ such as improved oxidative stability, better solubility, and greater amenability to processing (better flow and wetting). The improved oxidative stability is readily apparent as shown in the isothermal weight loss curves in Fig. 4. However by TGA, the PQ and PPQ are essentially the same. The difference in solubility of PPQ versus PQ is illustrated in Table 7.

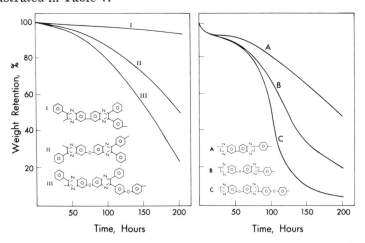

Fig. 4. Isothermal weight loss of PQ and PPQ in static air at 400°C [20].

Table 6

Dibenzils

Compound	Mp, °C	Mp Ref.	Tetraamine from Table 2 used in polymer synthesis	Polymer Ref.
ϕOCOC—$(CH_2)_6$—COCOϕ	63-64	21	II, III	21
 ϕOCOC—⬡—COCOϕ	125-126	22	I II, III V VI	20 17,20,25 18 18
 ϕOCOC—⬡—COCOϕ	98-99.5	17	I II III	20,25 17,25 17,20,25
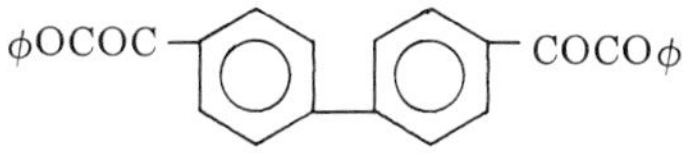 ϕOCOC—⬡—⬡—COCOϕ	203-204	23	II, III	19
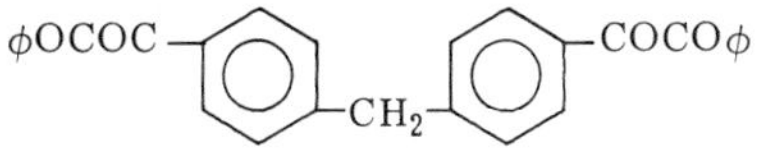 ϕOCOC—⬡—CH_2—⬡—COCOϕ	144.0-144.5	23	II, III	24
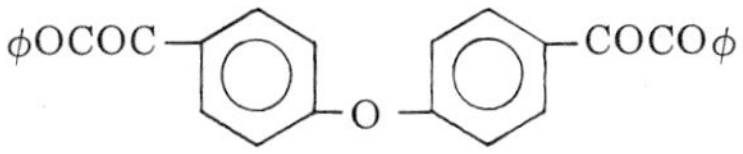 ϕOCOC—⬡—O—⬡—COCOϕ	106.4-107.4	23	II III V, VI	17,19 17,19,20, 25 18
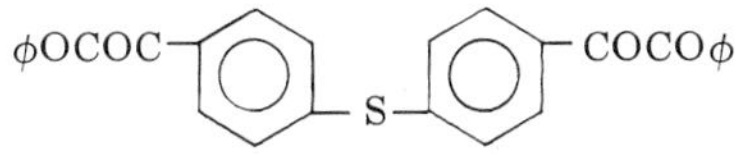 ϕOCOC—⬡—S—⬡—COCOϕ	90.0-91.6	23	II	24
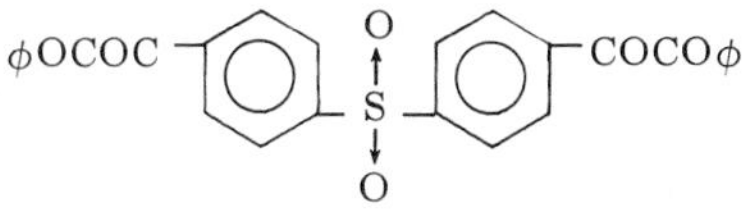 ϕOCOC—⬡—$\overset{O}{\underset{O}{S}}$—⬡—COCO$\phi$	164-166	18	V, VI	18
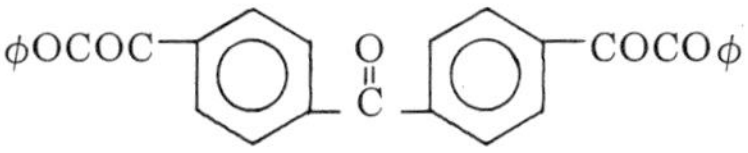 ϕOCOC—⬡—$\overset{O}{\underset{}{C}}$—⬡—COCO$\phi$	128-130	24a	II	24b

Table 7

Solubility of Polyquinoxalines[a]

X	Y	Ar	η_{inh},dl/g[b]	Chlorinated[d] solvents	Phenolic[e] solvents
Nil	C_6H_5	m,p-Phenylene	0.9, 2.1	Soluble	Soluble
Nil	H	p-Phenylene	0.8	Insoluble	Insoluble
O	C_6H_5	m,p-Phenylene	0.5, 1.3	Soluble	Soluble
O	H	p-Phenylene	0.6	Insoluble	Partially soluble
Nil	C_6H_5	p,p'-Oxydiphenylene	2.0	Soluble	Soluble
Nil	H	p,p'-Oxydiphenylene	0.8	Insoluble	Soluble
O	C_6H_5	p,p'-Oxydiphenylene	2.1	Soluble	Soluble
O	H	p,p'-Oxydiphenylene	1.8	Insoluble	Soluble

[a]From Ref. 17.
[b]0.5% H_2SO_4 at 25°C.
[c]1.00 g/10.0 ml solvent at room temperature.
[d]Chloroform and sym-tetrachloroethane.
[e]m-Cresol, phenol, anisole, and o-methoxyphenol.

To determine the effect of stoichiometry imbalance in PPQ synthesis, a study was conducted using the reaction of DAB with ODB. As shown in Table 8, even when the stoichiometry is upset by 2.5% in favor of DAB or ODB, relatively high molecular weight polymer, as indicated by η_{inh} of 0.98 and 0.78 dl/g, respectively, were still formed. The films of the polymers were tough and flexible. Unfortunately, the effect of the end groups on other polymer properties such as oxidative stability was not determined.

The T_g's of several PPQ of which the thermal histories were essentially identical are reported in Table 9. The T_g's were determined by dielectric loss measurements on films under vacuum at a heating rate of 10°C/min and at a frequency sweep from 100 to 1000 cps. A typical dielectric loss curve is shown in Fig. 5. The T_g was taken as the temperature at the intercept of the temperature versus dissipation factor curve at 1 kc/sec. The T_g's obtained in this manner agreed well with those obtained by torsional braid analysis (TBA), dynamic mechanical measurements, and differential scanning calorimetry (DSC). For example, the T_g of poly[2,2'-(p,p'-oxydiphenylene)-6,6'-di(3-phenylquinoxaline)] by the dielectric loss, dynamic mechanical method, and DSC were 285, 290, and 284°C, re-

Table 8

Effect of Stoichiometry on PPQ from the Reaction of DAB and ODB

Mole of ODB/1.000 mole of DAB	Solution color	Film properties	η_{inh}, dl/g[a]
0.900	Dark red	Brittle, orange	0.33
0.950	Red	Flexible, yellow	0.59
0.975	Reddish orange	Tough and finger-nail creasable	0.98
1.000	Yellowish orange	Tough and finger-nail creasable	1.48
1.025	Yellow	Tough and finger-nail creasable	0.78
1.050	Yellow	Flexible, yellow	0.52
1.100	Yellow	Brittle, yellow	0.33

[a] 0.5% H_2SO_4 at 25°C.

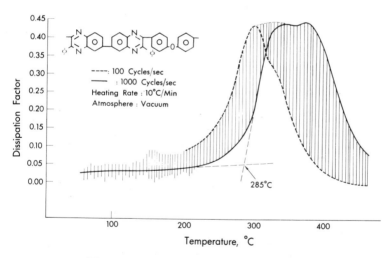

Fig. 5. Dielectric loss spectrum of PPQ.

spectively at a heating rate of 10° C/min, whereas TBA gave a maximum dispersion peak of 305° C as shown in Fig. 6 (curve 2). The
other curves (3, 4, and 5) in Fig. 6 are also of the same polymer
sample after cycling. The shift in the maximum dispersion peak is
attributed to polymer degradation. The dynamic mechanical relaxa-

Table 9

Glass Transition Temperatures of PPQ

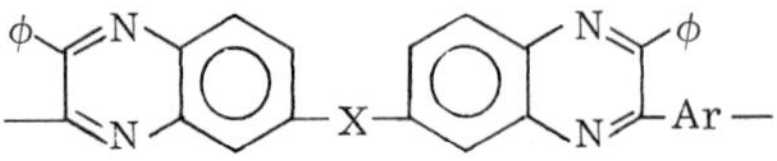

X	Ar	η_{inh},dl/g^a	T_g,^{b} °C
Nil		2.1	325
Nil		0.9	320
Nil	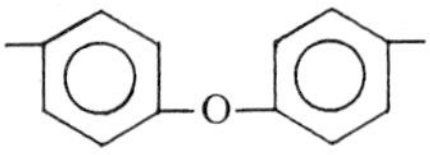	1.8	285
Nil	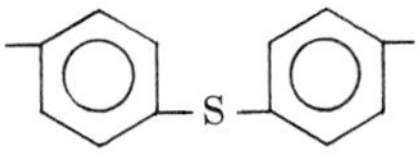	1.7	260
O		1.3	298
O	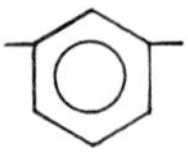	0.5	253
O	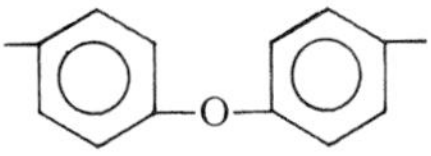	2.0	268
$-SO_2-$		1.7	212
$-SO_2-$	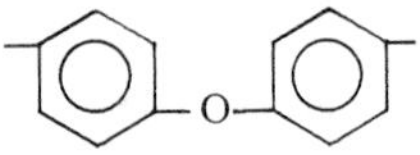	1.5	195

(continued)

Table 9 (continued)

Glass Transition Temperatures of PPQ

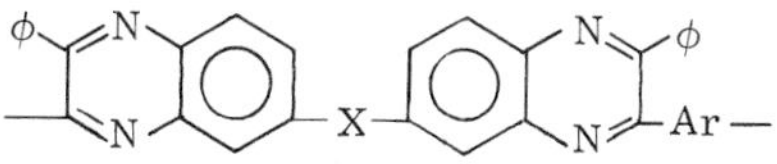

X	Ar	η_{inh}, dl/g[a]	T_g,[b] °C
	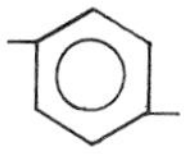	1.9	258
	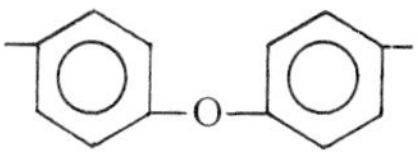	1.0	243

[a] 0.5% H_2SO_4 at 25°C.
[b] Determined by dielectric loss measurements on films dried at 200°C under vacuum.

tion spectrum (Fig. 7) was obtained using a dynamic viscoelastometer (Vibron Model DDV-II) at 110 cps on films in nitrogen employing a modified high-temperature furnace.

III. APPLICATION

A. Films and Fibers

Quinoxaline polymers have undergone only preliminary evaluation in film and fiber application. No optimization of film or fiber preparation has been performed. Films of the monoether PQ and monoether PPQ of which the structures are shown in Eqs. (2) and (5), respectively, were prepared by doctoring a solution (~18% solids content) of the polymer in m-cresol onto a glass plate. The solvent was removed by drying in a forced-air oven at 70°C for 18 hr followed by heating to 200°C under vacuum for 2 hr and maintaining at 200°C for 4 hr. After curing an additional 1 hr at 300°C under vacuum, the clear lemon yellow films provided the test results reported in Table 10.

Fibers of poly[3,3'-(p-phenylene)-6,6'-di(2-phenylquinoxaline)] prepared by wet spinning technique gave the following mechanical properties at room temperature: tenacity, 6.5 g/denier; initial modulus, 60 g/denier; and elongation, 3.2%.

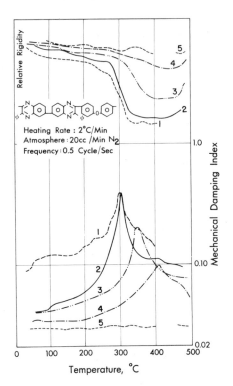

Fig. 6. Torsional braid analysis of PPQ. (Courtesy of N. J. Johnston, Chemistry and Physics Branch, NASA Langley Research Center.)

Table 10

Mechanical Properties of Quinoxaline Polymer Films

Property	Temp.,°C	Monoether PQ	Monoether PPQ
Tensile strength, psi	RT [a]	18,000	17,000
	177	14,000	12,000
Tensile modulus, psi	RT [a]	400,000	380,000
	177	280,000	240,000
Ultimate elongation, %	RT [a]	4.5	8.5
	177	21.0	25.0

[a]Room temperature.

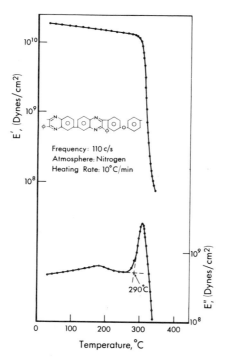

Fig. 7. Dynamic mechanical relaxation spectrum of PPQ. (Courtesy of
W. J. Wrasidlo, Polymer Sciences Laboratory, Boeing Scientific Research
Laboratories.)

B. Composites

Polyquinoxalines are noteworthy for their processability when
compared to other aromatic heterocyclic polymers. The most significant advantage is the retention of processability while having low
volatile content. For example, laminates have been fabricated from
prepreg (resin pickup 32%) containing only 0.8% total volatiles under
500 psi at 371°C. When the prepreg total volatile content was adjusted to 2-3%, high-density laminates were fabricated under 200 psi.
Generally, laminates were fabricated from prepreg (resin pickup
36-42%) having a total volatile content of 6 to 9% under 200 psi pressure starting at 232°C and increasing the press temperature to 371°C.

With such a low volatile content level (e.g., ~0.8%), it is necessary for the polymer to be of substantially high molecular weight
and also almost totally ring closed; this was indicated by η_{inh} ~0.8.

The processability of the polymer apparently results from the presence of tenaciously held m-cresol which serves as a plasticizer. This was indicated by analysis of the trapped volatiles evolved from prepreg varying in total volatile content from 0.8 to 9.0%. A piece of the prepreg was placed in a polymerization tube under argon and heated at 400°C for 1 hr. The evolved volatiles were collected by means of cooling in a Dry Ice-acetone bath and analyzed by vapor phase chromatography. The composition of the volatiles from prepreg (resin pickup 32%) having a total volatile content of 0.8% was 0.3% water and 0.5% m-cresol. This corresponded to a volatile content of 2.5% for the resin of which 0.8 and 1.7% were water and m-cresol, respectively.

Initial heating in the press removes the remaining m-cresol, but the porous resin matrix is still sufficiently thermoplastic to be compressed prior to complete loss of condensation volatiles. Such behavior provides the polyquinoxalines with superior processability and heat aging performance superior to that anticipated from TGA and ITGA evaluations.

Although several quinoxaline polymers have undergone preliminary evaluation in high-temperature structural application, this work has concentrated on the monoether and diether PQ.

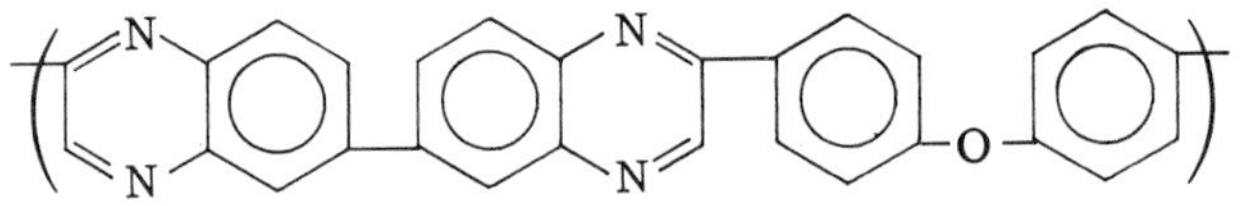

monoether PQ

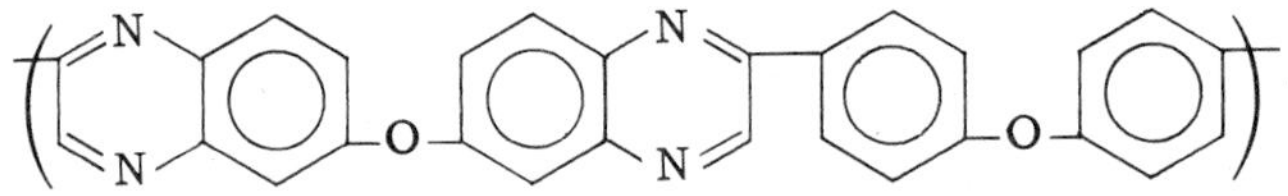

diether PQ

A quinoxaline copolymer of the following idealized structure has also undergone preliminary application work:

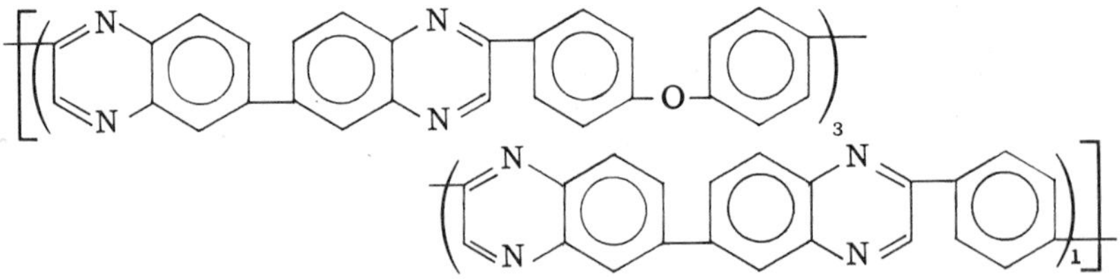

quinoxaline copolymer

Unless indicated otherwise, all composites were prepared with 1581 Style AF-994 glass having an HTS finish. The dimensions of the laminates were 4.5 in. × 6 in. × 7 ply, and all test data are reported as averages of triplicate tests and followed ASTM procedure.

Prepreg was prepared from a diether PQ solution (16.8% resin) by using three dip coats with forced air drying for 10, 15, and 60 min at 130°C, respectively. This prepreg was used to make a 7-ply laminate by curing for 10 min at 232°C followed by raising the temperature as rapidly as possible (~45 min) to 407°C and maintaining at 407°C for 4 hr (all at 200 psi). The entire laminate was postcured for 4 hr each at 205° and 232°C, 10 hr at 260°C, 8 hr at 288°C, and 4 hr each at 316°, 344°, 371°, and 398°C (all under nitrogen). The final laminate had a resin content of 24.8%, a density of 1.92, and a calculated void content of 4.0%. Test data are shown in Table 11.

Table 11

Flexural Strength and Modulus of Diether
Polyquinoxaline Glass Laminate

Test condition[a]	Flexure,[b] psi	Modulus, psi × 10^{-6}
Room temp.	111,500	4.87
1 hr/371°C	55,900	3.49
50 hr/371°C	35,750	2.62
10 min/538°C	29,800	3.20

[a]Tested at temperature.
[b]All values are averages of triplicate tests.

Prepreg prepared with monoether PQ solution (16.6% resin) was used to fabricate a 7-ply laminate by the same cure cycle as described for the diether polymer. Following the postcure as previously indicated, the laminate was postcured an additional 8 hr at 371°C in nitrogen. The final laminate of which the test data are reported in Table 12 had a resin content of 33.1%, a density of 1.71, and a calculated void content of 8.6%.

Examination of the monoether PQ flexure specimens tested at 538°C after 10 min at 538°C in air indicated that some thermoplastic failure had occurred. In an attempt to overcome this thermoplasticity, an exploratory copolymer was synthesized using 75 mole %:25 mole % of OBPG and p-phenylenediglyoxal with DAB.

As anticipated, the resultant polymer was less soluble in m-cresol and, therefore, was used as 12% solution to prepare prepreg. Seven

Table 12

Flexural Strength and Modulus of Monoether
Polyquinoxaline Glass Laminate

Test condition	Flexure, psi	Modulus, psi $\times 10^{-6}$
Room temp.	99,600	3.64
1 hr/371°C	61,600	2.44
50 hr/371°C	44,000	2.51
10 min/538°C	16,900	2.19

dip coats were needed, using forced air drying for 10 min at 130°C
between coats and a final dry of 1 hr at 130°C. The resulting prepreg was used to fabricate a 7-ply laminate which was cured and
postcured as for the monoether PQ. The laminate had a resin content of 27.8%, a density of 1.77, and a calculated void content of
9.2% and provided the mechanical properties presented in Table 13.

Table 13

Flexural Strength and Modulus of Quinoxaline
Copolymer Glass Laminate

Test condition	Flexure, psi	Modulus, psi $\times 10^{-6}$
Room temp.	105,600	3.45
1 hr/317°C	75,000	3.09
200 hr/317°C	57,700	3.35
1 hr/371°C	50,800	2.49
50 hr/371°C	49,900	2.83
10 min/538°C	31,750	3.23
60 min/538°C	12,700	1.97

Preliminary data were obtained on a unidirectional boron filament composite with diether PQ as the resin matrix. The cure was
accomplished by a 5-min contact time at 382° to 394°C followed by
maintaining at 394°C for 4 hr under 500 psi in air. The postcure
was performed using the same schedule as previously indicated for
the diether PQ laminate (Table 1). The test data reported in Table 14
were obtained after 3 min at temperature.

During the last 2 years, composite work utilizing PQ as the resin
matrix has concentrated on new high-performance reinforcement
such as Morganite "Modmor II." The prepregs were prepared using

Table 14

Flexural Strength and Modulus of Monoether Polyquinoxaline,
Boron Filament, Unidirectional Composite

Test temp.,°C[a]	Flexure, psi	Modulus, psi × 10^{-6}
Room temp.	253,000	42.3
133	197,000	36.2
177	200,600	37.5
212	180,000	37.0
316	220,800	24.2
361	241,500	12.1

[a]Tested at temperature after 3 min at temperature.

meter lengths tows which were applied to a wet PQ film on a Teflon-coated substrate. Multiple coats of PQ solution were applied starting with a coat of a dilute PQ solution. Each coat was dried for 10 min at 90°C followed by 1 hr at 130°C in a forced air oven. The final coat was dried 10 min at 90°C, 1 hr at 130°C, and 1 hr at 190°C under vacuum. Curing was accomplished in a mold starting with a cold press and raising the temperature under 250 psi pressure to 232°C. The press temperature was maintained at 232°C for 10 min, bumping twice and then increased to 316°C during ~20 minutes. The temperature was held at 316°C for 2 hr with bumping and increased to 395°C (during ~20 min) for 1 hr. The postcure was accomplished essentially the same as previously reported for the glass-reinforced laminates with the final postcure temperature and time being 4 hr at 395°C in nitrogen. The 4.5 in. × 6 in. × 9 ply laminate of which the test data are reported in Table 15 had a resin content of 34.3%, a density of 1.50 g/cc, and a calculated void content of 4.3%.

C. Adhesives

Efforts directed toward the demonstration of the PQ as a high-temperature structural adhesive were less extensive than the composite work. Nevertheless, the following discussion indicates a definite potential for the PQ as a high-temperature structural adhesive.

Adhesive prepreg tapes were prepared from the polymer solutions in m-cresol formulated with amorphous boron (50 phr) using 112 E glass fabric with A-1100 finish as the carrier and dried in a forced air oven at elevated temperature to a volatile content of 12.1% for the diether PQ and 11.3% the monoether PQ. Adhesive

Table 15

Mechanical Properties of Unidirectional Modmor II Monoether PQ Laminate[a]

Test conditions	Flexural strength, psi (modulus, psi $\times 10^{-6}$)	Straight beam[b] shear strength, psi
Room temp.	122,100 (15.5)	12,800
315°C after 1 hr at 315°C	118,200 (15.2)	8,600
315°C after 100 hr at 315°C	116,200 (15.1)	8,400
315°C after 200 hr at 315°C	94,300 (14.6)	7,000
371°C after 1 hr at 371°C	108,400 (15.1)	8,900
371°C after 50 hr at 371°C	103,400 (14.5)	8,800

[a]Tensile strength, psi (modulus, psi $\times 10^{-6}$): 128,700 (19.1). Compressive strength, psi (modulus, psi $\times 10^{-6}$): 74,200 (14.8).
[b]Tested at span-to-depth ratio of 8:1.

panels were fabricated using 17-7 stainless steel substrate given the phosphate etch. The diether PQ panels were cured for 1 hr each at 426° and 455°C under 200 psi in nitrogen, whereas the cure for the monoether PQ panels was 1 hr each at 344°, 426°, and 455°C under 200 psi in nitrogen. There was no postcure, and the test specimens provided the data reported in Table 16.

Table 16

Polyquinoxaline Tensile Shear Strength on Stainless Steel

	Tensile shear, psi	
Test condition[a]	Diether PQ	Monoether PQ
Room temp.	3320	3350
1 hr/316°C	–	2930
200 hr/316°C	–	2280
1 hr/371°C	1567	1870
50 hr/371°C	1670	2540
10 min/538°C	1283	1325
1 hr/538°C	826	–

[a] Tested at temperature.

Obviously, a postcure effect is responsible for the higher tensile shear strength after aging for 50 hr at 371°C versus that after 1 hr at 371°C.

It is obvious that the processing conditions employed for the fabrication of the composites and adhesive bonds previously discussed are stringent and accordingly not compatible for extensive use with present-day industrial processes and equipment. However, it should be noted that past work has been concerned primarily with demonstrating the potential of the PQ as a high-temperature structural resin. Since this has now been done, it is readily apparent that future attention should focus on the process development of the PQ into a useful multipurpose structural resin. The processing parameters of temperature, time, and pressure must be greatly reduced for extensive use as a structural resin. In addition, the economics of quinoxaline polymers must become more attractive for wide acceptance beyond specialty applications. Until this is done, quinoxaline polymers will remain materials of great potential but limited use.

Additional information on polyquinoxalines can be found in the final summary reports [26,27] of work performed under Navy sponsorship, and in a review [28] by Stille.

References

[1] V. Körner, Ber. Dent. Chem. Ges., 17, 573 (1884).

[2] O. Hinsberg, Ber. Dent. Chem. Ges., 17, 318 (1884).

[3] W. R. Sorenson, Polymer Preprints, 2 [2], 226 (1961).

[4] (a) J. K. Stille and J. R. Williamson, J. Polymer Sci., A2, 3867 (1964);
    (b) J. Polymer Sci., B2, 209 (1964).

[5] J. K. Stille, J. R. Williamson, and F. E. Arnold, J. Polymer Sci., A3, 1013 (1965).

[6] J. K. Stille and F. E. Arnold, J. Polymer Sci., (A-1) 4, 551 (1966).

[7] G. P. deGaudemaris and B. J. Sillion, J. Polymer Sci., B2, 203 (1964).

[8] G. P. deGaudemaris, B. J. Sillion, and J. Prévé, Bull. Soc. Chim. France, p. 1763 (1964).

[9] P. M. Hergenrother, W. J. Wrasidlo, and H. H. Levine, High Temperature Structural Adhesives: Final Summary Report, U.S. Navy Bureau of Naval Weapons, Contract NOw 63-0420-c, San Diego, California, April 1964.

[10] P. M. Hergenrother and H. H. Levine, J. Applied Polymer Sci., 14, 1037 (1970).

[11] H. Vogel and C. S. Marvel, J. Polymer Sci., 50, 511 (1961).

[12] R. Foster and C. S. Marvel, J. Polymer Sci., A3, 417 (1965).

[13] T. Matsukawa, B. Ohta, and T. Imada, J. Pharm. Soc. Japan, 70, 77 (1950).

[14] P. J. Montagne, Ber. Dent. Chem. Ges., 48, 1034 (1915).

[15] P. Ruggli and E. Gassenmeier, Helv. Chim. Acta, 22, 496 (1939).

[16] P. M. Hergenrother and D. E. Kiyohara, Macromolecules, 3, 387 (1970).

[17] W. Wrasidlo and J. M. Augl, *J. Polymer Sci.*, (A-1)7, 3393 (1969); *J. Polymer Sci.*, **B7**, 281 (1969).

[18] W. J. Wrasidlo and J. M. Augl, *Macromolecules*, 3(5), 544 (1970).

[19] P. M. Hergenrother and H. H. Levine, *J. Polymer Sci.*, (A-1)5, 1453 (1967).

[20] W. J. Wrasidlo and J. M. Augl, *Polymer Preprints*, 10 [2], 1353 (1969).

[21] P. M. Hergenrother, *J. Polymer Sci.*, (**A-1)6**, 3170 (1968).

[22] J. Schmitt, P. Comoy, J. Boitard, and M. Suguet, *Bull. Soc. Chim. France*, p. 636 (1956).

[23] M. A. Ogliaruso, L. A. Shadoff, and E. I. Becker, *J. Org. Chem.*, **28**, 2725 (1963).

[24] (a) P. M. Hergenrother, and D. E. Kiyohara, *J. Macromol. Sci.*, **A5**(2), 365 (1971); (b) unpublished work.

[25] W. Wrasidlo, *J. Polymer Sci.*, (A-1)8, 1107 (1970).

[26] P. M. Hergenrother and H. H. Levine, High Temperature Structural Resins, Contract NOw 66-0144-c, July, 1966; Contract N60921-67-C-0221, June, 1968.

[27] R. T. Rafter, High Temperature Polymer Development, Contract N60921-69-C-0073, November, 1969.

[28] J. K. Stille, in *Encyclopedia of Polymer Science and Technology*, Vol. 11 (H. F. Mark, N. G. Gaylord, and N. M. Bikales, eds.), Wiley (Interscience), New York, 1969, p. 389.

Nylons-Known and Unknown.
A Comprehensive Index of Linear Aliphatic Polyamides of Regular Structure

H. K. LIVINGSTON, MITRA SAED SIOSHANSI, and
MILTON D. GLICK
Department of Chemistry
Wayne State University
Detroit, Michigan

I. INTRODUCTION

Until recently, there was a considerable body of opinion that polymers could not be systematically indexed. This opinion grew out of the feeling that polymers were inherently ill-defined compositions of matter that could probably only be described in terms of the process by which they were made.

It is now recognized that the polymers of regular structure are well-defined compositions of matter and can be described in terms of the structural repeating unit (SRU). This unit, repeated many times, makes up the bulk of the polymer. The question of how many times a SRU is repeated (i.e., the degree of polymerization), although interesting, is not fundamental to indexing. In fact, a great many substances (e.g., liquid water, many inorganic solids) are commonly described by their simplest chemical representation without any contention that one must know exactly how many of these simplest units are associated in the ultimate structure of minimum energy and maximum stability that corresponds to a thermodynamic standard state.

With the decision of Chemical Abstracts to include polymers in both Formula Index and Subject Index sections of Chemical Abstracts, a decision that became effective with the subject indexes of 1967, it is possible to consider the initial argument as settled—polymers can be indexed.

We have been intrigued with the analogy between polymers and ring compounds. Ring compounds since 1925 have had their own particular index, The Ring Index prepared by Chemical Abstracts. This analogy has been examined and a general method for indexing polymers has been proposed [1]. An important feature of our proposal is the elimination of the distinction between known and unknown compounds. The Ring Index has been limited to rings that have been reported in the literature covered by Chemical Abstracts. This provides an invaluable record of what is known, but what is unknown is indicated only by implication. Our earlier proposal included the concept that, with modern computer-based methods of handling information, it would be possible also to index the unknown. The present review represents the first attempt to do this.

A. Historical Background

The subject that we have chosen is the polymer class of the polyamides and, more specifically, the aliphatic polyamides. Naturally our interests are limited to the polymers of regular structure (i.e., those in which a single structural repeating unit, repeated a sufficient number of times to form a high polymer, will represent the entire structure, except for the end groups). Polyamide is defined in the usual way, requiring at least one methylene group between adjacent imino groups and either two carbonyl groups or one carbonyl and at least one methylene* between adjacent imino groups. Thus, hydrazides and ureas are explicitly excluded.

The aliphatic polyamides were discovered by Carothers [2] and commercialized internationally under the generic name nylon. This term also applies to aromatic and heterocyclic polyamides, but the scientific and commercial investigation of these came somewhat later than that of the aliphatic polyamides and they are excluded from this review.

Within a surprisingly short time after the issuance of the first patent on polyamides, commercial development of two members of the class was proceeding rapidly. These were poly(hexamethyleneadipamide) (I) and poly(iminocarbonylpentamethylene) (II). These have the trivial names, 66 nylon and 6 nylon, respectively.

$$(-NHCH_2CH_2CH_2CH_2CH_2CH_2NHCCH_2CH_2CH_2CH_2C-)_n$$
$$\underset{O}{\overset{\|}{}} \qquad \underset{O}{\overset{\|}{}}$$

I
poly(hexamethyleneadipamide)
66 nylon

$$(-NHCCH_2CH_2CH_2CH_2CH_2-)_n$$
$$\underset{O}{\overset{\|}{}}$$

II
poly(iminocarbonylpentamethylene)
polycaprolactam
6 nylon

For many years these were the most important synthetic polymers for textile applications, although they are now yielding first place to newer fibers. If we were to prepare an index of linear aliphatic polyamides that had been extensively studied, there would only be these two entries. More recently, the following nylons have been commercialized: poly(iminocarbonylheptamethylene), poly-

*We have found no example of a —NHCH$_2$NH— segment in a polyamide chain; since two carbon atoms are required between nitrogens if there are carbonyl groups, we have limited the index to structures with at least two carbons between nitrogens.

(iminocarbonyldecamethylene), poly(iminocarbonylundecamethylene), and certain polyamides with cycloaliphatic and aromatic rings in the skeleton which are beyond the scope of this review. Poly(hexamethylenesebacamide) has had some small commercial use for many years, primarily in plastics use where it is used to modify the properties of 6 and 66 nylon.

The amount of research time and effort that has been devoted to the aliphatic polyamides since Carothers' invention is quite large. One might well believe that all the aliphatic polyamides would have been made and fully characterized during the past 33 years, at least all those with polymethylene sequences in the range that is usually studied thoroughly in organic chemistry $[CH_2$ to $(CH_2)_{10}]$. For this reason these polyamides provide an interesting test of our thesis that it is important to index unknown structures as well as known structures. As we shall show, there are significant number of aliphatic polyamides that are still unknown or at least unreported in the journal and patent literature.

II. SYNTHESIS OF ALIPHATIC POLYAMIDES

Although the polymer index that we are developing is based on structure, not synthesis, chemists generally find it useful to think in terms of methods of synthesis, as well as structure. For this reason we shall give a brief review of the synthetic routes that have yielded aliphatic polyamides of regular structure.

Carothers and Hill [3] first demonstrated linear polycondensation in the polyester series and soon thereafter the polyamides. The common method for preparing polyamides is by high-temperature polycondensation, e.g., the reaction of diamines with dibasic acids. Two steps are involved in this kind of polymerization—the salt preparation step and the polymerization step.

In the salt preparation step, diamine and dibasic acid are combined in exactly molecular proportions by bringing together alcoholic solutions of equivalent amounts of reactants. In the presence of a small amount of water the reaction is vigorous and heat is given off, which is the result of neutralization of a base by an acid to form a salt. The crystalline salt is separated from the cooled solution and can be used directly in the polymerization or can be purified further.

In the polymerization step heat is required to eliminate water and form amide bonds. This can be done either by fusing the salt or by heating the salt in an inert solvent for the polymer such as cresol or xylenol. These are two convenient methods out of many possible ones.

The nylon salt method is used mostly with polyamides and intermediates which are thermally stable to at least 200°C. There are
two principal methods for low-temperature polycondensation—interfacial and solution polymerization [4]. In the interfacial polycondensation method, two fast-reacting intermediates (typically a diamine
and a halide of a dicarboxylic acid) are dissolved in two different,
immiscible liquids. The polymerization takes place at or near the
liquid interface. Solution polymerization is carried out in a single
liquid, inert to both intermediates with no reactive functional group.
The polymer may remain in the solution or may precipitate. These
low-temperature methods are very convenient and have made the
preparation of a nylon a simple matter for any chemist who has the
necessary intermediates.

Although polycondensation of ω-amino acids at low or high temperature yields nylons, ring-opening polymerization of lactams is
usually preferred. The ring-opening can be induced by the presence
of a small amount of water or may occur by ionic mechanisms in the
presence of strong acids or bases in the absence of water.

The nylons with very small SRU's [2 nylon (**III**) and 3 nylon (**IV**)]
cannot be formed by ring-opening. The simplest polypeptide is **III**,

$$(-\text{NHCCH}_2-)_n \qquad\qquad (-\text{NHCCH}_2\text{CH}_2-)$$
$$\underset{\text{O}}{\|} \qquad\qquad\qquad\qquad \underset{\text{O}}{\|}$$

III   **IV**
poly(iminocarbonylmethylene)   poly(iminocarbonylethylene)
polyglycine   poly-β-alanine
nylon 2   nylon 3

which can be prepared by many of the synthetic methods used in biochemistry. The anionic polymerization of acrylamide was discovered
by Matlack [5] to form **IV**. Kagiya [6] recently made the same polymer (**IV**) by the alternating copolymerization of ethylenimine and
carbon monoxide.

The methods described above are applicable to the synthesis of
nylons of regular structure in which the SRU contains one or two
amide groups. Recently methods have been devised for nylons with
four amide groups in the SRU. These are alternating copolymers
that can also be considered homopolymers with extended SRU.
Sheremeteva et al. [7] have obtained regular polyamides from bissuccinimides and diamines, and Kagiya et al. [8] from bisimidazoline
and dicarboxylic acid.

III. PROCEDURE FOR FORMING POLYMER INDEX
BY COMPUTER

The generation of the polymer index involves the listing of all different SRU's containing only carbon and nitrogen atoms in the main chain up to an arbitrary maximum repeat unit and subject to certain chemical restrictions. The simplest chemical restriction in this problem is that any two nitrogens in the chain must be separated by at least two carbons. Since we are dealing with only two kinds of atoms in the chain we have a binary problem, which is thus uniquely suited to the bit structure of a digital computer. If we represent each nitrogen by a "1" and each carbon by a "2" (or "0" and "1", "on" and "off", "+" and "−", or "yes" and "no"), the problem is to determine all the independent combinations and permutations of "1" and "2" subject to the following restrictions: (1) two "1"s must always be separated by at least two "2"s; (2) the direction of the chain is irrelevant (i.e., 122 = 221); and (3) since we are dealing with high molecular weight, linear polymers, SRU's that are equivalent by cyclic permutation form equivalent polymers (i.e., 122 = 212).

Carbonyl placement provides isomeric possibilities that increase the number of nonequivalent symbols. Thus, if we use an asterisk to indicate the carbon atom containing the carbonyl function, 12*2 is equivalent to 122*, whereas 122*2 is not a polyamide. But 122122 cannot be eliminated as being equivalent to $(122)_2$. However, 12*212*2 is equivalent to $(12*2)_2$ (and, of course, to $122*)_2$), and 12*2*122 represents a different polyamide. For this reason our listing includes among the longer symbols multiples of all the shorter symbols.

For a repeat unit of length N, the total number of permutations and combinations of "1" and "2" is 2^N. If we consider a repeat unit of length 3, the eight possible combinations and permutations are 111, 112, 121, 122, 211, 212, 221, 222. These eight numbers are simply derived from the binary representation of the decimal numbers 0 through 7_{10} (i.e., 0 through 2^3-1) by replacing each "0" in the binary representation with a "2". Similarly, the sixteen combinations and permutations for N = 4 are derived from the four-place binary representations of the decimal numbers 0 through 15 (0 through 2^4-1), and for N = 16, the 65,536 possibilities are derived from the binary representations of 0 through $2^{16}-1$.

For each value of N, the program calls for the storage of the values of 0 through (2^N-1) in the usual integer form in the computer. This corresponds to storage of all the combinations and permutations of N "0"s and "1"s in binary form. It is then necessary to sort out those that violate our previously defined principles and output the remaining numbers in binary format.

Principle (1) must be tested by actual bitwise comparison. Principles (2) and (3) are tested by finding all cyclic permutations of the binary representation of each decimal number and by discarding any decimal number if any of these cyclic permutations, when read in either direction, represent the binary equivalent of a decimal number smaller than the original number. The "0"s are then replaced by "2"s and the results listed in the increasing numerical order.

The program was written in FORTRAN IV. This language does not provide bit operations, so it was necessary to simulate bit operations by modular arithmetic. The FORTRAN language is not very satisfactory for dealing with this problem (and for many others in information retrieval) and the authors would not recommend this language for extensive work in this area. The use of either assembler language or higher-level languages which include bit operations, such as PL1, is recommended.

This program requires very little storage. Total storage requirements of the program exclusive of input, output, and system utilities of an IBM-360 was 2588 bytes (or 647 32-bit words).

Table 1 lists only the skeletons of the various polyamides with twenty or fewer chain atoms in the SRU. Each skeleton provides the basic index for many polyamides. The skeleton must contain one adjacent carbonyl for each nitrogen in order to form a polyamide structure. It may contain any other substituents. The symbolism that has been proposed for indicating complete structures via a polymer index [1] lists in order: (1) the atomic formula for the chain atoms, e.g. N_2C_9; (2) the order of atoms in the skeleton,* e.g., 12222122222; (3) the substituents, giving position on the skeleton and formula, e.g., 2-O, 5-O, 11-CH..

The program that we have used could be used to extend the index to nineteen or more chain atoms. As will be shown later, the number of index entries that have not yet been synthesized becomes quite large for such large repeating units. We have, therefore, only listed indexes for known polyamide skeletons with nineteen or more chain atoms (Table 2).

In the actual development of experimental investigations of polyamide chemistry, almost invariably the unsubstituted polyamides (i.e., the skeleton with carbonyl substitution only) have been prepared and studied before there was any work reported on related polyamides containing noncarbonyl skeletal substitution. The number of polyamides for any given skeleton that can exist is limited

---

*It is our custom to write out the index with a symbol for each chain atom, rather than condense the index, e.g., $1(2)_4 1(2)_5$. The condensed version is not convenient for computer processing.

Table 1

Index of Polyamides with from 3 to 18 Chain Atoms per Structural Repeating Unit

```
POLYAMIDES WITH   3 CHAIN ATOMS/SRU
1 2 2
POLYAMIDES WITH   4 CHAIN ATOMS/SRU
1 2 2 2
POLYAMIDES WITH   5 CHAIN ATOMS/SRU
1 2 2 2 2
POLYAMIDES WITH   6 CHAIN ATOMS/SRU
1 2 2 1 2 2
1 2 2 2 2 2
POLYAMIDES WITH   7 CHAIN ATOMS/SRU
1 2 2 1 2 2 2
1 2 2 2 2 2 2
POLYAMIDES WITH   8 CHAIN ATOMS/SRU
1 2 2 1 2 2 2 2
1 2 2 2 1 2 2 2
1 2 2 2 2 2 2 2
POLYAMIDES WITH   9 CHAIN ATOMS/SRU
1 2 2 1 2 2 1 2 2
1 2 2 1 2 2 2 2 2
1 2 2 2 1 2 2 2 ?
1 2 2 2 2 2 2 2 ?
POLYAMIDES WITH  10 CHAIN ATOMS/SRU
1 2 2 1 2 2 1 2 2 2
1 2 2 1 2 2 2 2 2 2
1 2 2 2 1 2 2 2 ? 2
1 2 2 2 2 1 2 2 2 2
1 2 2 2 2 2 2 2 2 2
POLYAMIDES WITH  11 CHAIN ATOMS/SRU
1 2 2 1 2 2 1 2 2 2 2
1 2 2 1 2 2 2 1 ? 2 2
1 2 2 1 2 2 2 2 2 ? 2
1 2 2 2 1 2 2 2 ? 2 2
1 2 2 2 2 1 2 2 2 2 2
1 2 2 2 2 2 2 ? 2 2 2
POLYAMIDES WITH  12 CHAIN ATOMS/SRU
1 2 2 1 2 2 1 2 2 1 2 2
1 2 2 1 2 2 1 2 2 2 2 2
1 2 2 1 2 2 2 1 ? 2 2 2
1 2 2 1 2 2 2 2 2 2 2 2
1 2 2 2 1 2 2 2 1 2 2 2
1 2 2 2 1 2 2 2 2 2 2 2
1 2 2 2 2 1 2 ? 2 ? 2 2
1 2 2 2 2 2 1 2 ? 2 ? ?
1 2 2 2 2 2 2 2 2 2 2 2
POLYAMIDES WITH  13 CHAIN ATOMS/SRU
1 2 2 1 2 2 1 2 2 1 2 2 2
1 2 2 1 2 2 1 2 ? 2 2 2 2
1 2 2 1 2 2 2 1 ? 2 2 2 2
1 2 2 1 2 2 2 2 1 2 2 2 2
1 2 2 1 2 2 2 2 2 2 2 2 2
1 2 2 2 1 2 2 2 1 2 2 2 2
1 2 2 2 2 1 2 2 ? 2 2 2 2
1 2 2 2 2 2 1 2 ? 2 ? 2 2
1 2 2 2 2 2 1 2 ? 2 ? 2 2
1 2 2 2 2 2 2 2 ? 2 2 2 2
```

```
POLYAMIDES WITH  14 CHAIN ATOMS/SRU
1 2 2 1 2 2 1 2 ? 1 2 2 2 2
1 2 2 1 2 2 1 2 ? 2 1 ? ? 2
1 ? ? 1 2 2 1 2 ? ? 2 ? ? ?
1 2 2 1 2 2 2 1 ? 2 1 2 ? ?
1 2 2 1 2 2 2 1 ? 2 2 2 2 2
1 2 ? 1 2 2 2 2 1 ? ? 1 2 2 ?
1 2 2 1 2 2 2 2 2 2 2 2 2 2
1 2 2 2 1 2 2 2 1 2 2 2 2 2
1 2 2 2 1 2 2 2 ? 1 ? ? ? ?
1 2 2 2 1 2 2 2 ? 2 1 2 2 2 2
1 2 2 2 2 1 2 2 ? ? 1 2 2 2
1 2 2 2 2 2 1 2 ? 2 2 2 2 2
1 2 2 2 2 2 2 1 2 2 2 2 2 ?
1 2 2 2 2 2 2 ? ? ? ? ? ? ?
POLYAMIDES WITH  15 CHAIN ATOMS/SRU
1 2 2 1 2 2 1 2 ? 1 2 2 1 2 2
1 2 2 1 2 2 1 2 ? 1 ? 2 2 2 2
1 2 2 1 2 2 1 2 ? 2 1 2 2 2 2
1 2 2 1 2 2 1 2 ? 2 2 2 2 2 2
1 2 2 1 2 2 2 1 ? ? 1 2 2 2 2
1 2 2 1 2 2 2 1 ? ? 2 1 2 2 2
1 2 2 1 2 2 2 1 ? ? 2 2 2 2 2
1 2 2 1 2 2 2 2 1 2 2 2 2 2 2
1 2 2 1 2 2 2 2 ? 1 2 2 2 2 2
1 2 2 1 2 2 2 2 ? 2 1 2 2 2 2
1 2 2 2 1 2 2 2 ? 1 ? ? ? ? ?
1 2 2 2 1 2 2 2 ? 1 ? ? ? ? ?
1 2 2 2 2 1 2 2 ? 2 1 2 2 2 2
1 2 2 2 2 2 1 2 ? ? 2 1 2 2 2 2
1 2 2 2 2 2 2 1 ? ? 2 2 2 2 2
1 2 2 2 2 2 ? ? ? ? ? ? ? ? ?
POLYAMIDES WITH  16 CHAIN ATOMS/SRU
1 2 2 1 2 2 1 2 ? 1 2 2 1 ? ? ?
1 2 2 1 2 2 1 2 ? 1 2 ? 2 2 2 ?
1 2 2 1 2 2 1 ? 2 ? 1 ? ? ? 2 ?
1 ? ? 1 ? ? 1 2 ? ? ? ? 2 2 2 ?
1 2 2 1 2 2 1 2 ? 2 1 2 2 2 2 2
1 2 2 1 2 2 2 1 ? ? 2 1 2 2 2 2
1 2 2 1 2 2 2 1 ? ? 2 2 1 ? 2 2
1 2 2 1 2 2 2 2 1 2 2 1 2 2 2 2
1 2 2 1 2 2 2 2 1 2 2 1 2 2 2 2
1 2 2 1 2 2 2 2 ? 1 ? ? 2 2 2 2
1 2 2 1 2 2 2 ? ? 1 ? ? 2 2 2 2
1 ? ? 1 2 2 2 2 ? ? ? ? ? ? 2 ?
1 2 2 2 1 2 ? ? ? 1 ? ? ? 1 ? ? 2
1 2 2 2 1 2 2 2 ? 2 1 2 2 2 2 ?
1 2 2 2 2 1 2 2 2 2 1 2 2 2 2 2
1 2 2 2 2 1 2 2 2 2 2 1 2 2 2 2
1 2 2 2 2 2 1 2 2 2 2 2 2 2 2 2
1 2 2 2 2 2 ? ? 1 ? ? ? ? ? ? ?
1 2 2 2 2 2 2 2 1 ? ? 2 2 2 2 ?
1 2 2 2 2 2 2 ? 2 ? ? ? ? ? ? ?
```

(continued)

Table 1 (continued)

```
POLYAMIDES WITH 17 CHAIN ATOMS/SRU        POLYAMIDES WITH 18 CHAIN ATOMS/SRU
1 2 2 1 2 2 1 2 ? 1 ? ? 1 ? 2 ? 2         1 2 2 1 2 2 1 2 ? 1 ? ? 1 2 2 1 2 2
1 2 ? 1 2 ? 1 2 ? 1 ? ? 2 1 ? ? ?         1 2 2 1 2 2 1 2 ? 1 ? 2 1 ? ? ? ? ?
1 ? 2 1 ? ? 1 2 ? 1 ? ? ? ? ? ?           1 2 2 1 2 2 1 2 ? 1 2 2 2 1 2 ? ? 2
1 2 2 1 2 ? 1 2 ? ? 1 ? ? 1 ? ? ?         1 2 2 1 2 2 1 2 ? 1 ? ? ? 2 2 ? ? 2
1 ? 2 1 2 ? 1 2 ? ? 1 ? ? ? 2 ? ?         1 2 2 1 2 ? 1 ? ? ? 1 2 2 1 2 ? 1 ? ?
1 2 2 1 2 2 1 2 ? ? ? 1 ? ? ? ? ?         1 2 2 1 2 ? 1 2 ? ? 1 ? ? ? 1 ? ? ?
1 2 ? 1 2 2 1 2 ? ? ? 2 ? ? 2 ? ?         1 2 2 1 2 ? 1 2 ? ? 1 ? ? ? ? ? 2 ?
1 2 2 1 2 2 2 1 ? ? 1 ? 2 ? 2 ? 2         1 2 2 1 2 2 1 2 ? ? 2 ? 1 ? ? ? ? ?
1 2 2 1 2 2 2 1 ? ? 2 1 2 ? ? ? ?         1 2 2 1 2 2 1 2 ? ? 2 2 1 2 ? ? ? ?
1 2 2 1 2 2 2 1 ? ? ? ? ? 1 2 ? ?         1 2 2 1 2 2 2 1 ? ? 2 1 ? ? ? 1 ? ?
1 2 2 1 2 2 2 1 ? ? ? ? ? ? 1 2 ?         1 2 2 1 2 2 2 1 ? ? 2 1 ? 2 1 ? ? 2
1 2 2 1 ? 2 ? 1 ? ? ? ? ? ? ? ? ?         1 2 2 1 2 2 ? 1 ? 2 ? 1 ? ? ? ? ? ?
1 2 2 1 2 2 2 2 1 ? ? 1 ? ? ? ? ?         1 2 2 1 2 2 2 1 ? 2 ? 1 2 2 ? ? ? ?
1 ? 2 1 ? ? ? 2 1 ? ? ? 1 ? ? ? ?         1 2 2 1 2 2 2 1 ? ? 2 2 1 2 ? ? ? ?
1 ? ? 1 ? ? ? 2 1 ? ? ? ? ? ? ? ?         1 2 2 1 2 2 2 1 ? 2 ? ? ? 1 ? ? ? ?
1 2 2 1 2 ? ? 2 ? 1 ? ? ? ? ? ? 2         1 2 2 1 2 2 2 1 ? ? 2 2 2 1 ? ? ? ?
1 2 2 1 2 2 2 2 ? 1 ? ? ? ? ? ? ?         1 ? ? 1 ? ? ? 1 ? ? ? ? ? ? 2 ? ? ?
1 2 2 1 2 2 2 2 ? ? 2 ? ? ? ? ? ?         1 ? ? 1 ? ? ? ? 1 ? ? ? 1 ? ? ? ?
1 2 2 2 1 2 2 2 1 ? ? ? 1 ? ? ? ?         1 ? 2 1 2 2 2 2 1 ? ? ? ? 1 ? ? ? ?
1 2 2 2 1 ? 2 2 1 ? ? ? ? 2 ? ? ?         1 2 2 1 2 2 2 2 1 ? ? 1 ? ? ? ? ?
1 2 2 2 1 2 ? ? ? 1 ? ? ? ? ? ? ?         1 2 2 1 2 2 2 2 ? 1 ? ? 1 ? ? ? ?
1 ? ? ? 1 ? 2 ? ? 1 ? 2 ? ? ? ? ?         1 2 2 1 2 2 2 2 ? 1 ? ? ? ? 2 ? ? ?
1 2 2 2 1 ? 2 ? 2 ? 1 ? ? ? ? ? ?         1 2 2 1 2 2 2 2 ? 1 ? ? ? 1 ? ? ? ?
1 2 2 2 1 2 ? ? 2 ? 1 ? ? ? ? ? ?         1 2 2 2 1 2 2 1 ? ? 2 1 2 ? ? ? ?
1 2 2 2 ? 1 2 ? ? ? ? ? ? ? ? ? ?         1 2 2 2 1 2 2 2 1 ? ? 2 ? 1 ? ? ? ?
1 ? 2 2 2 2 ? 1 ? ? ? ? ? ? ? ? ?         1 ? 2 2 1 2 2 2 1 ? ? 2 2 1 ? ? ? ?
1 2 2 2 2 2 2 2 ? ? ? ? ? ? ? ? 2         1 ? 2 2 1 2 2 2 ? 1 ? ? ? ? 1 ? ? ?
                                          1 2 2 2 1 2 2 2 ? 1 ? ? ? ? ? 1 ? ? ?
                                          1 ? 2 2 1 2 2 2 2 1 ? ? 2 2 ? ? ? ?
                                          1 ? 2 2 1 2 2 2 2 ? 1 ? ? ? ? ? ? ?
                                          1 ? 2 2 1 2 2 2 ? 1 ? ? ? ? ? ? ? ?
                                          1 2 2 2 1 2 2 2 2 ? 1 ? ? ? ? ? ? ?
                                          1 2 2 2 1 2 2 2 ? ? 1 ? ? ? ? ? ? ?
                                          1 2 2 2 2 1 2 2 ? ? 1 ? ? ? ? ? ? ?
                                          1 2 2 2 2 1 2 2 2 ? 1 ? ? ? ? ? ? ?
                                          1 ? 2 2 2 2 1 ? ? ? ? 1 ? ? ? ? ? ?
                                          1 ? 2 2 2 2 2 ? 1 ? ? ? ? ? 1 ? ? ?
                                          1 2 2 2 2 2 1 2 ? ? ? ? 1 ? ? ? ? ?
                                          1 2 2 2 2 2 2 1 ? ? ? ? 2 1 ? ? ? ?
                                          1 ? ? ? ? ? 1 ? ? ? ? ? ? 1 ? ? ? ?
                                          1 ? ? ? ? ? ? 1 ? ? ? ? ? ? ? ? ?
                                          1 ? ? ? ? ? ? ? 1 ? ? ? ? ? ? ? ?
```

Table 2

Known Linear Aliphatic Polyamides with Regular Structure
Having More Than 18 Chain Atoms per Structural Repeating Unit

	Polymer index	1st Ref.	IR Data
N_2C_{17}:	1222221222222222222, 8-O, 19-O	2	
	1222222122222222222, 8-5, 6, 9-O, 19-O	9	
	1222222212222222222, 10-O, 19-O	10	11
	1222222221222222222, 2-O, 9-O	12	
	1222222222122222222, 11-O, 19-O	11	
N_2C_{18}:	12222221222222222222, 2-O, 7-O	10	
	12222221222222222222, 9-O, 20-O	13	
	12222222122222222222, 10-O, 20-O	13	
	12222222212222222222, 2-O, 9-O	13	
	12222222221222222222, 11-O, 20-O	2	
	12222222222122222222, 2-O, 10-O	10	11
N_4C_{16}:	1221222212222221222, 5-O, 8-O, 17-O, 20-O	7	14
N_2C_{19}:	122222122222222222222, 8-O, 21-O	2	
	122222222212222222222, 2-O, 10-O	12	12
	122222222212222222222, 12-O, 21-O	10	
N_2C_{20}:	1221222222222222222222, 5-O, 22-O	18	
	1222222221222222222222, 11-O, 22-O	15	
	1222222222122222222222, 12-O, 22-O	13	
	1222222222212222222222, 2-O, 11-O	2	16
N_4C_{18}:	1222212222122221222222, 7-O, 10-O, 17-O, 22-O	7	17

(continued)

Table 2 (continued)

Polymer index	1st Ref.
N_2C_{21}: 1222222222122222222222, 12-O, 23-O	12
122222222222212222222222, 2-O, 11-O	10
N_2C_{22}: 122222222212222222222222, 11-O, 24-O	13
1222222222122222222222222, 12-O, 24-O	13
122222222221222222222222, 2-O, 11-O	10
122222222221222222222222, 13-O, 24-O	10
N_4C_{20}: 122122222212212222222222, 5-O, 10-O, 15-O, 24-O	19
N_2C_{23}: 1222221222222222222222222, 8-O, 25-O	2
N_2C_{24}: 1222222222212222222222222, 13-O, 26-O	13
N_2C_{26}: 12222221222222222222222222, 9-O, 28-O	15
N_2C_{28}: 1222222221222222222222222222, 11-O, 30-O	15
1222222222221222222222222222, 13-O, 30-O	13
N_2C_{30}: 122222222222122222222222222222, 13-O, 32-O	15

only by the number of substituents that the synthetic chemist can affix to carbon and nitrogen atoms. However, in all but one of the cases known to us, the unsubstituted, fully saturated polyamide was the first of any given index to be synthesized and characterized.

IV. REVIEW OF POLYAMIDE LITERATURE

Early summaries listing numerous nylons by numeric code were little more than restatements of the data given in Carothers' broadest patent [2]. The most comprehensive of these appears in a book by Hopff, Muller, and Wenger [20]. There are also several earlier reviews [21-23]. These summaries and the articles in a recent encyclopedia [24-26] have provided references to the earliest disclosure of most of the known nylons listed in the present review. However, all the major polymer journals have been read systematically from the first volume through 1969 to obtain background for the review.

The patent literature is very difficult to cover completely. We feel that complete coverage has been approached through the search of the older review articles referred to above, followed by the use of Chemical Abstracts Subject Index to cover the period since that index began to include specific entries for polymers (i.e., Vol. 66 through to the most recent index, Vol. 69).

V. INDEXING KNOWN POLYAMIDES

In The Ring Index, each ring skeleton becomes an index entry with an accompanying citation of the first reference in which the ring skeleton was proposed. Frequently the citation refers to a compound in which the ring is substituted, rather than to the "parent ring" compound (i.e., a compound having hydrogen substituents only).

We propose to present a similar index for the polyamides, based on the literature described in the previous section. There will be two differences between our index and The Ring Index. First, there will be an index number available for polymer skeletons that have not yet been reported. Second, for each fundamental polyamide structure, references will be cited in which the earliest pertinent structure proof is given. Reasons for needing a structure proof are given in the next section.

The results of our literature studies appear as an index of known polyamides with eighteen or fewer chain atoms per repeating unit (Table 3), and a list of polyamides with larger repeating units (Table 2).

Table 3

Known Polyamides

Polymer index	1st Ref.	IR Data
1 2 2, 2-0	27	28
1 2 2 2, 2-0	29	12
1 2 2 2 2, 2-0	30	12
1 2 2 1 2 2, 2-0, 3-0	31	
1 2 2 2 2 2, 2-0	32	
1 2 2 2 2 2 2, 2-0	33	34
1 2 2 1 2 2 2 2, 5-0, 8-0	14	14
1 2 2 2 2 2 2 2, 2-0	35	12
1 2 2 1 2 2 2 2 2, 5-0, 9-0	18	
1 2 2 2 2 2 2 2 2, 2-0	35	12
1 2 2 1 2 2 2 2 2 2, 2-0, 3-0	12	12
1 2 2 1 2 2 2 2 2 2, 5-0, 10-0	8	8
1 2 2 2 1 2 2 2 2 2, 2-0, 4-0	2	
1 2 2 2 2 2 2 2 2 2, 2-0	35	16
1 2 2 2 1 2 2 2 2 2 2, 2-0, 4-0	36	
1 2 2 2 2 2 2 2 2 2 2, 2-0	37	11
1 2 2 2 2 1 2 2 2 2 2 2, 2-0, 5-0	14	14
1 2 2 2 1 2 2 2 2 2 2, 7-0, 12-0	2	
1 2 2 2 2 1 2 2 2 2 2, 2-0, 6-0	2	12
1 2 2 2 2 2 2 2 2 2 2, 2-0	37	12
1 2 2 1 2 2 2 2 2 2 2 2, 5-0, 13-0	38	38
1 2 2 2 2 1 2 2 2 2 2 2 2, 7-0, 13-0	10	
1 2 2 2 2 2 1 2 2 2 2 2 2, 2-0, 6-0	12	12
1 2 2 2 2 1 2 2 2 2 2 2, 8-0, 13-0	2	12
1 2 2 2 2 2 2 2 2 2 2 2, 2-0	38	38
1 2 2 1 2 2 2 2 2 2 2 2 2 2, 2-0, 3-0	2	
1 2 2 1 2 2 2 2 2 2 2 2 2 2, 5-0, 14-0	2	38
1 2 2 2 2 1 2 2 2 2 2 2 2 2, 2-0, 5-0	31	
1 2 2 2 2 1 2 2 2 2 2 2 2 2, 7-0, 14-0	2	
1 2 2 2 2 2 1 2 2 2 2 2 2 2, 8-0, 14-0	2	12
1 2 2 2 2 2 2 2 1 2 2 2 2 2, 2-0, 7-0	2	39
1 2 2 2 2 2 2 2 2 2 2 2 2 2, 2-0	31	
1 2 2 2 1 2 2 2 2 2 2 2 2 2 2, 6-0, 15-0	18	
1 2 2 2 2 1 2 2 2 2 2 2 2 2 2, 7-0, 15-0	2	37
1 2 2 2 2 2 1 2 2 2 2 2 2 2 2, 8-0, 15-0	2	
1 2 2 2 2 1 2 2 2 2 2 2 2 2 2, 2-0, 7-0	10	16
1 2 2 2 2 2 2 1 2 2 2 2 2 2 2, 9-0, 15-0	10	12
1 2 2 2 2 1 2 2 2 2 2 2 2 2 2 2, 7-0, 16-0	2	
1 2 2 2 2 2 1 2 2 2 2 2 2 2 2 2, 8-0, 16-0	2	
1 2 2 2 2 2 2 1 2 2 2 2 2 2 2 2, 2-0, 7-0	2	11
1 2 2 2 2 2 2 1 2 2 2 2 2 2 2, 9-0, 16-0	10	11
1 2 2 2 2 2 2 2 1 2 2 2 2 2 2 2, 2-0, 8-0	10	38
1 2 2 2 2 1 2 2 2 2 2 2 2 2 2 2, 7-0, 17-0	10	
1 2 2 2 2 2 1 2 2 2 2 2 2 2 2 2, 8-0, 17-0	18	
1 2 2 2 2 2 2 1 2 2 2 2 2 2 2 2 2, 9-0, 17-0	10	16
1 2 2 2 2 2 2 2 1 2 2 2 2 2 2 2 2, 2-0, 7-0	10	38
1 2 2 2 2 2 2 2 1 2 2 2 2 2 2 2 2, 10-0, 17-0	38	38
1 2 2 2 2 1 2 2 2 2 2 2 2 2 2 2 2, 7-0, 18-0	40	
1 2 2 2 2 2 1 2 2 2 2 2 2 2 2 2 2, 8-0, 18-0	2	
1 2 2 2 2 2 2 1 2 2 2 2 2 2 2 2 2, 2-0, 7-0	37	12
1 2 2 2 2 2 2 1 2 2 2 2 2 2 2 2 2 2, 9-0, 18-0	2	12
1 2 2 2 2 2 2 2 1 2 2 2 2 2 2 2 2 2, 2-0, 8-0	38	38
1 2 2 2 2 2 2 2 1 2 2 2 2 2 2 2 2 2, 10-0, 18-0	11	11
1 2 2 2 2 2 2 2 2 1 2 2 2 2 2 2 2 2, 2-0, 9-0	10	11
1 2 2 2 2 2 2 2 2 2 2 2 2 2 2 2 2 2, 2-0	35	

A. Factors Influencing Structural Regularity

Materials that cause undesirable effects in step-reaction polymerization, such as premature termination, cross-linking, cyclization, and cleavage of polymer chains during the polymerization process, destroy the homogeneity of the polymer which, if it is truly a regular polymer, has only a single kind of SRU between end groups. Small quantities of linear and cyclic oligomers are accepted to be a part of the normal, random, molecular weight distribution. The cyclic oligomers may occur to an appreciable extent as the reaction proceeds intramolecularly. For example, as the solvent phase is made more dilute, the amount of oligomers will increase.

Polyamides derived from aliphatic primary diamines can participate in branching reactions because of a secondary reaction of the amide group to yield an imide structure, as follows:

$$\wedge\!\wedge\!\wedge \; R-CONH-R \; \wedge\!\wedge\!\wedge \; RCOOH + HOOCRCOOH \longrightarrow$$

$$\wedge\!\wedge\!\wedge \; R-CON-R \; \wedge\!\wedge\!\wedge \; RCOOH$$
$$\begin{array}{c} | \\ CO \\ | \\ R \\ \lessgtr \end{array}$$

However, branching will not occur if the acid acceptor fails to form an active adduct with the amide group. Polyfunctional monomers with more than two functional groups per molecule also produce branched or cross-linked polymers. On the other hand, monofunctional monomers which can be introduced as impurities or formed by side reactions give only low molecular weight products.

Configuration of polymers is another important structural factor. If monomer molecules have no element of symmetry they can give a random sequence due to head-to-tail or head-to-head polymerization.

In chain-reaction polymerization, e.g. certain ring-opening reactions or the anionic polymerization of acrylamide, branches can be formed either by copolymerization of the monomer with its lower polymers or by chain transfer. Chain transfer can also occur with solvent that terminates the polymer chain. Low-symmetry monomers can add to the growing chain head-to-head or head-to-tail. As substituents are usually arranged in head-to-tail fashion, the chain segment follows the Emil Fischer projection. Steric hindrance in the polymer chain, as a result of interaction between substituents of successive units, can give isotactic or syndiotactic configuration if the chain atoms include atoms that are centers of chirality.

B. Proof of Structure in Polyamide Chemistry

The factors mentioned in the previous section make it important to prove the structure of polyamides wherever possible. The modern polymer chemist cannot emulate Carothers and assert the structure of a polymer based on the known structure of starting materials and the experimenter's expectations as to the course of the reaction. If he does, he cannot expect to be believed.

In the Carothers era, polymer scientists relied to some extent on melting point data to characterize their products. Some early references give melting points as the only characterization. In our own laboratories, when we began to use interfacial polymerization to synthesize some known but little-studied nylons, we were alarmed by the fact that our melting points did not agree with those in the literature for these same nylons. The literature work was based on nylons made by high-temperature condensation. We gradually realized that the differences between the melting phenomenon in low molecular weight materials and the melting of polymers are so great that melting point cannot be used as a proof of structure in polymers. This point has been most extensively investigated by Arakawa and Nagatoshi [41] for 6 nylons. They found a 50° spread in the melting temperature for this nylon. There was a linear relation between the absolute temperature of melting and the specific volume of the nylons. This shows clearly that melting point does not characterize the chemical structure of a nylon, unless the specific volume is also known. Specific volumes were not known for the nylons of which the melting points were listed by Carothers and other early workers. Therefore the various compilations of nylon melting points must be considered to be of no value. Fortunately, better methods of characterization are now available.

Polymer structure proof requires some analytical method that is reasonably sensitive to foreign SRU's. Degradative methods (pyrolysis followed by gas chromatography or mass spectrometry is one example; hydrolysis with paper chromatography is particularly applicable to polyamides) will detect a foreign SRU in a ratio of 1:10 or thereabouts. Under special circumstances it is more sensitive.

Spectroscopic methods are reasonably sensitive and have been used successfully in polymer science. Infrared and nuclear magnetic resonance (NMR) spectroscopy are preferred. In the case of the nylons, only infrared spectroscopy has been used extensively. Hummel provides a recent summary [42]. In the very best work, that

done on 4, 6, 7, 8, and 11 nylons at the Institute for Macromolecular
Studies in Prague, virtually every absorption maximum was assigned
to a vibration of the parent macromolecule and also for some of its
deuterated derivatives [43]. We consider a polyamide to have had
its structure proven when the infrared spectrum has had reasonable
assignments made for the NH stretch and for the amide I, II, III, V,
and VI maxima and when there are no puzzling and unexplained maxima.

An important aspect of the infrared spectroscopy of polyamides
is the sensitivity of the frequency of certain absorptions to the crystal structure of the nylon. It has been established through the work
of Kinoshita [16] and Miyake [11] that the amide II, V, and VI maxima
shift in frequency depending on whether the polyamide is in the α-
or γ-form. With this background, it is possible to identify the chemical structure of polyamides from infrared spectra and avoid confusion that might otherwise result because of physical changes in the
polymer.

The quantitative identification of irregularities in polymer chain
from the infrared spectra of the polymer is a subject that is just
beginning to be investigated. Opaskar and Krimm [44] have given
the theory and applied it to polyethylene and poly(vinyl chloride). In
the former case, weak absorptions observed in the infrared spectrum
of low-density polyethylene have been interpreted in terms of defects
(i.e., structural irregularities). The absence of significant unassigned
peaks in the careful analyses of the spectra of nylons [12,43,45] indicate that these nylons have a low concentration of defects. For
the other nylons, the spectra of which have been less thoroughly investigated, we can only say that no unexplained absorptions have been
noted. In our survey of polyamide infrared spectra, some worthwhile
references [46-51] have been noted that are included neither in Hummel's excellent bibliography [42] nor cited in our own tables.

Nuclear magnetic resonance spectroscopy of polymer solutions
is in general a very useful way of characterizing polymers and obtaining information about structural irregularities. The earliest
NMR studies devoted to structure proof using nylon solutions were
made by Kagiya et al. [19]. It seems reasonable to predict that this
method will become more widely used for structure determination
in the polyamides.

Another criterion of the structural regularity of a polymer is the
formation of crystals with sharp outlines and a maximum dimension
of 10 μm or more. We have shown elsewhere [52] that such crystals
are only formed from polymers that are considered from other evidence to be quite regular in structure. They have been observed for

6, 66, and 610 nylons. To date, no other aliphatic nylons have yielded such large polymer single crystals. Nylons 4, 7, and 8, on the contrary, have been observed to form small irregular objects that are considered to be characteristic of polymers with somewhat irregular structure.

In summary, infrared spectroscopy has been the most thoroughly exploited of the various methods that could be used to prove the structure and structural regularity of nylons. It is for this reason that we have based Tables 2 and 3 solely on infrared data in providing references to the best available structure proofs for the various polyamides that have been reported. Absence of a reference to infrared data in these tables indicates there is no meaningful structure proof (known to us) for the polyamide skeleton in question. If a polyamide has been reported, it can only be said that the investigators mixed together what they believed to be the proper intermediates to yield the polymer with the structure that they assigned.

C. Alternative Classifications

Formal indexing tends to stress the mathematical. This sometimes disturbs the physical scientist, who may be interested in features that are not directly expressed in mathematical terms. For example, the chemist prefers to think of aromatic rings as a group, but The Ring Index makes the number and size of rings prime considerations in indexing, not the presence or absence of aromaticity.

We are using a polymer index that stresses the size of the repeating unit. The chemist who is investigating polyamides is likely to be most interested in the number of amide groups in the repeating unit. He usually thinks in terms of two series. One series has one amide group per repeating unit and the usual synthesis involves ring-opening polymerization. These are the 2, 3, 4, 5, 6, etc. nylons (also called "n-nylons"). The other series has two amide groups per repeating unit (the "nn-nylons") and is usually made from diamines and dicarboxylic acids or their derivatives. Crystallographic differences that grow out of the special significance of hydrogen bonding between imino and carbonyl groups make it reasonable to classify these as "even-even series" (22, 24, 26, ... 66, etc.), "odd-odd series" (33, 35, 37, ... 55, etc.), and "odd-even series" (23, 32, 43, 34, ... 56, etc.). Our index includes all of these, of course, but groups together those with the same number of chain atoms in the repeating unit. For each number of chain atoms, the last index entry is the n-nylon. The other entries can contain two or more nitrogens, and the order in Table 1 will be the conventional mathematical one from smallest number to largest. The same polymer index will, for example, represent 46 nylon and 64 nylon, since these have the same skeleton and differ only in carbonyl placement. To continue with this example, this same skeleton will also represent a structure in which 4 nylon and 6 nylon units alternate. This particular example is worked out in detail in Table 4. In this table are given the only three regular structures that correspond to the skeleton 122221222222. Two are well known in the literature; the third has not been reported.

Table 4

Polyamides with Polymer Index 122221222222

Index	Chemical structure	Nylon code
N_2C_{10}, 122221222222, 2-O, 5-O	$(-NHCCH_2CH_2CNH(CH_2)_6-)_n$ $\quad\quad\, \| \quad\quad\quad \|$ $\quad\quad O \quad\quad\quad O$	64
N_2C_{10}, 122221222222, 2-O, 7-O	$(-NHC(CH_2)_3NHC(CH_2)_5-)_n$ $\quad\quad \| \quad\quad\quad\quad \|$ $\quad\quad O \quad\quad\quad\quad O$	–
N_2C_{10}, 122221222222, 7-O, 12-O	$(-NH(CH_2)_4NHC(CH_2)_4C-)_n$ $\quad\quad\quad\quad\quad \| \quad\quad\quad\quad \|$ $\quad\quad\quad\quad\quad O \quad\quad\quad O$	46

For the polyamides with two amide groups per SRU, two cases used to be considered. Those in which the index has the same number of 2's in each group can represent only one unsubstituted polyamide. This is true because as nn-nylons, the two n's are equal, and if a carbonyl is placed after each nylon, the structure contains two identical halves and is really an n-nylon. However, if one of the polymethylene sequences is substituted and the other is not, additional polyamides will be formed. For those in which the two groups of 2's are of different size, there are two unsubstituted nn-nylons and one unsubstituted alternating n-nylon/n-nylon. Presumably the last of these can be made by a selective ring-opening polymerization. This series of unknown nylons may be of some interest, as is discussed in a later section.

Polyamides with three amide groups per SRU have not been reported to date. As can be seen from Table 1, this group has 122122122 as its smallest listed representative. It is not possible to place three carbonyl groups in this structure without either forming ureas or forming a $[(-NHCCH_2-)_3]_n$ structure. However, if at least one of
$\quad\quad\quad\quad\quad\quad\quad \| $
$\quad\quad\quad\quad\quad\quad\quad O$

the three methylene groups in $(-NHCCH_2-)_3$ is substituted, this be-
$\quad\quad\quad\quad\quad\quad\quad\quad\quad\quad\quad \| $
$\quad\quad\quad\quad\quad\quad\quad\quad\quad\quad\quad O$

comes a valid (but as yet unreported) structure.

We conclude this brief perusal of chemical classes in the polyamide index by mentioning the polyamides with four amide groups per SRU (122122122122 is the smallest representative). Within the last few years, these have been reported. As mentioned in the earlier section on synthesis, Sheremeteva et al. [7] have made such polyamides by the reaction of bissuccinimides with diamines. Most of the species made have such large SRU's that they do not appear in Table 1. The Sheremeteva nylons are listed in Table 2 with the other known polyamides with especially large repeating units. So is the large four-amide nylon made by Kagiya et al. [8].

VI. UNREPORTED POLYAMIDES

The compilation of known chemical structures can be done in a perfectly satisfactory fashion, even where computer processing is required, by assigning registry numbers, serial numbers in order of accession, etc. An added virtue of a comprehensive index is its ability to assign index entries to classes that have never been reported. Lederberg [53] has been most persuasive in pointing out methods for doing this for ring compounds. The stimulus to chemists provided by a list of unmade rings could be quite significant, as witness the recent history of "on-demand synthesis" of cubane, congressane, etc.

We should stress the fact (which can be derived from a cross-comparison of Tables 1 and 3) that, of the 172 skeleton structures with eighteen or fewer chain atoms per repeating unit, 117 have not yet been reported. This suggests that much more synthetic work could be done in the polyamide area.

Reasons for investigating these "unmade nylons" are to some extent speculative. Despite all the years of research on nylon, even the most recent reviews [24-26] contain little in the way of structure-property information except for the commercial nylons. It may be significant that some of the more subtle textile properties of nylons have been correlated with the various crystalline forms which nylons can assume, which, in turn, depend on geometric factors that prevail in the chain segments between polyamides. There might be good reason to investigate the crystallography of various polyamides with three or four amide groups per SRU. The unknown two-amide polyamides in which carbonylpolymethylene groups connect the nitrogens (the alternating n-nylon/n-nylons; see Table 4) might provide an even simpler way to construct polyamides that are regular enough to crystallize, yet do so in unusual space groups. Little work has been reported concerning the solution behavior of polyamides, but here too the unknown structures might form unconventional conformations worthy of investigation.

Note added in proof: Bailey and Okamoto recently reported [*Amer. Chem. Soc.*, *Div. Polym. Chem. Preprints*, 12, 177 (1971)] a synthesis that could be used to make any of the "unmade nylons."

VII. EXTENSION OF THE INDEX TO OTHER POLYMERS

The index of polyamides that has been developed here is also applicable to other polymers. As has been explained previously [1], the use of a numerical code for the skeleton of a polymer permits the same code to apply to all skeletons following the same pattern in the arrangement of chain atoms, regardless of which elements form the skeleton. Thus, each of the polyamides indexed above have a perfectly analogous polyester. An index of linear aliphatic polyesters of regular structure could be constructed simply by inserting the appropriate data from the literature into a table of the same form as Table 1.

If we eliminate the special consideration of carbonyl groups, the tabulation of indexed polymers becomes simpler and is directly applicable to polyamines (where "1" stands for nitrogen), polyethers (where "1" stands for oxygen), polythioethers (where "1" stands for sulfur), etc. Thus we have as an added feature of the present review of polyamides the computer-produced outline for equivalent reviews of polyesters, polyamines, polyethers, polythioethers, and other aliphatic heterochain polymers of regular structure.

VIII. SUMMARY

The linear aliphatic polyamides of regular structure can be indexed using a scheme that assigns an Arabic numeral to each chain atom in the SRU. The number of unique skeleton structures for the SRU increases rapidly, from 1 for an SRU with three or four chain atoms to 43 for a SRU with eighteen atoms. A search of the literature has located examples for only 32% of the 172 unique skeleton structures for SRU's with 18 or fewer chain atoms.

Consideration of the problems of polyamide synthesis lead to the conclusion that some structure proof is desirable before a polyamide should be indexed as representative of the reported skeleton. Infrared data are most commonly used. This criterion permits the positive assignment of structure to 27 examples of different skeletons with eighteen or fewer chain atoms and 7 different skeletons with more than eighteen chain atoms.

Of the unknown polyamides, a certain number would appear to be of interest for future synthesis, based on speculations concerning possible property advantages.

The concept of a comprehensive polymer index can be successfully applied to linear aliphatic polyamides. Indexing through eighteen chain atoms per SRU does not involve inordinate amounts of computation. The concept appears to be a promising one for extension to polyesters, polyamides, polyethers, and other polymers of regular structure.

References

[1] H. K. Livingston, *J. Chem. Doc.*, 9, 131 (1969).
[2] W. H. Carothers, U.S. Pat. 2,130,948 (1938).
[3] W. H. Carothers and J. W. Hill, *J.Am. Chem. Soc.*, 54, 1559 (1932).
[4] P. W. Morgan, *Condensation Polymers, By Interfacial and Solution Methods*, Wiley-Interscience, New York, 1965.
[5] A. S. Matlack, U.S. Pat. 2,672,480 (1954).
[6] T. Kagiya et al., *J. PolymerSci.*, (A-1) 4, 293 (1966).
[7] T. V. Sheremeteva, G. N. Larina, M. G. Zhenevskaya, and V. A. Gusinskaya, *Polymer Sci. (USSR)*, 8, 803 (1967).
[8] T. Kagiya, M. Izu, M. Hatta, T. Matsuda, and K. Fukui, *J. Polymer Sci.*, (A-1)5, 1129 (1967).
[9] K. Ueda, T. Okawara, and T. Kubo, *Chem. Abstr.*, 68, 40908 (1968).
[10] D. D. Coffman, G. J. Berchet, W. R. Peterson, and E. W. Spanagel, *J. Polymer Sci.*, 2, 306 (1947).
[11] A. Miyake, *J. Polymer Sci.*, 44, 223 (1960).
[12] C. G. Cannon, *Spectrochim. Acta.*, 16, 302 (1960).
[13] W. P. Slichter, *J. Polymer Sci.*, 35, 77 (1958).
[14] T. Kagiya, I. Maruta, T. Ichida, S. Narisawa, and K. Fukui, *J. Polymer Sci.*, (A-1)5, 1645 (1967).
[15] K. Dachs and E. Schwartz, *Angew. Chem.*, 74, 540 (1962).
[16] Y. Kinoshita, *Makromol. Chem.*, 33, 1 (1959).
[17] T. Kagiya, M. Izu, T. Matsuda, and K. Fukui, *J. Polymer Sci.*, (A-1)5, 15 (1967).
[18] W. H. Carothers, U.S. Pat. 2,130,523 (1938).
[19] T. Kagiya, M. Izu, T. Matsuda, M. Matsuda, and K. Fukui, *J. Polymer Sci.*, (A-1)6, 2059 (1968).
[20] H. Hopff, A. Muller, and F. Wenger, *Die Polyamide*, Springer, Berlin, 1954.
[21] W. Scheele, *Kolloid Z.*, 98, 222 (1942).
[22] R. Hill and E. E. Walker, *J. Polymer Sci.*, 3, 609 (1948).
[23] E. F. Izard, *J. Polymer Sci.*, 8, 503 (1952).
[24] O. E. Snider and R. J. Richardson, *Encyclopedia of Polymer Science and Technology*, Vol. 10, 1969, p. 347.
[25] E. C. Schule, *Encyclopedia of Polymer Science and Technology*, Vol. 10, 1969, p. 460.
[26] W. Sweeny and J. Zimmerman, *Encyclopedia of Polymer Science and Technology*, Vol. 10, 1969, p. 483.
[27] H. Leuchs, *Chem.Ber.*, 39, 857 (1906).

[28] W. T. Astbury, C. E. Dalgliesh, S. E. Darmon, and G. Sutherland, *Nature*, **162**, 596 (1948).

[29] R. G. Beaman, *J. Am. Chem. Soc.*, **70**, 3115 (1957).

[30] W. O. Ney, W. R. Nummy, and C. E. Barnes, U.S. Pat. 2,638,463 (1953).

[31] J. P. Pied, *Ann. Chim. (Paris)*, **5**, 469 (1960).

[32] F. Korte and W. Glet, *J. Polymer Sci.*, **B4**, 685 (1966).

[33] P. Schlack, U.S. Pat. 2,241,321 (1941).

[34] M. C. Tobin and M. J. Carrano, *J. Chem. Phys.*, **25**, 1044 (1956).

[35] D. D. Coffman, N. L. Cox, E. L. Martin, and W. E. Mochel, *J. Polymer Sci.*, **3**, 85 (1948).

[36] S. Porejko, L. Makurak, I. Glogowska, and M. Bienias, *Polimery*, **9**, 58 (1964).

[37] C. Greenewalt, U.S. Pat. 2,245,129 (1941).

[38] I. Matsubara, J. H. Magill, *Polymer*, **7**, 199 (1966).

[39] E. J. Ambrose, A. Elliott, and R. B. Temple, *Proc. Roy. Soc. (London)*, **A199**, 183 (1949).

[40] G. F. Schmidt and H. A. Stuart, *Z. Naturforsch.*, **A13**, 222 (1958).

[41] T. Arakawa and F. Nagatoshi, *J. Polymer Sci.*, **B8**, 41 (1970).

[42] D. O. Hummel and F. Scholl, *Atlas der Kunstoff-Analyse*, C. Hanser, Munich, 1968.

[43] J. Jakes, P. Schmidt, and B. Schneider, *Collection Czech. Chem. Commun.*, **30**, 996 (1965).

[44] C. G. Opaskar and S. Krimm, *J. Polymer Sci.*, (A-2)**7**, 57 (1969).

[45] C. G. Cannon, *Mikrochim. Acta*, p. 555 (1955).

[46] N. Ogata, *Makromol. Chem.*, **40**, 55 (1960).

[47] N. Ogata and T. Asahara, *J. Polymer Sci.*, **B4**, 273 (1966).

[48] S. Krimm, *Proc. Intern. Conf. Spectro.*, **2**, 278 (1967).

[49] G. Heidemann and H. J. Nettelbeck, *Faserforsch. Textiltech.*, **18**, 183 (1967).

[50] O. Vogl and A. C. Knight, *Macromolecules*, **1**, 311 (1968).

[51] H. Wexler, *Makromol. Chem.*, **115**, 262 (1968).

[52] H. K. Livingston, *Macromolecules*, **2**, 98 (1969).

[53] J. Lederberg, *The Mathematical Sciences*, M.I.T. Press, Cambridge, Mass., 1969, pp. 37-51.

Recent Advances in Polymer Fractionation

L. H. TUNG
Physical Research Laboratory
The Dow Chemical Company
Midland, Michigan

An important reference for this review is a book edited by Cantow, *Polymer Fractionation,* published in 1967. In this book various methods of polymer fractionation are discussed in depth. Some chapters contain references as late as 1966. Our attention is therefore focused on more recent developments. Cantow's book is a good source for earlier work.

Polymer fractionation experiments usually are performed either for the purpose of analyzing the molecular weight distribution of a sample or for preparing narrow molecular weight distribution materials. In analytical fractionation, the scene in recent years has been overwhelmingly dominated by gel permeation chromatography (GPC). This technique is therefore discussed first. The discussions of the other methods, however, are not arranged necessarily in the order of their importance.

Although biopolymers are high polymers, polymer fractionation has traditionally referred only to the fractionation of synthetic polymers. The same implication is followed here. Techniques especially suitable for biopolymers are not included in the discussion. Biochemical and biophysical journals have not been consulted.

I. GEL PERMEATION CHROMATOGRAPHY (GPC)

A. Introduction

A description of the basic principle and the instrumentation of GPC can be found in Altgelt and Moore's chapter in Cantow's book [1]. Articles as late as 1966 were referred to by them in that chapter. Other important reviews on GPC are a book by Determann [2]; articles by Johnson, Porter, and Cantow [3], by Altgelt [4], and by Johnson and Porter [5].

In GPC the separation of polymer molecules of different molecular weights is accomplished in a set of columns packed with porous beads. When a polymer solution is injected in the eluting solvent stream, the higher molecular weight solutes, which permeate the porous beads to a lesser degree than the lower molecular weight solutes, are eluted out first. The concentration of the solution at the exit of the columns is continuously analyzed by a recording differential refractometer. Reliable GPC chromatograms can be obtained in this manner within a 3-to-4-hr period. Consecutive samples can be injected to the columns in intervals much shorter than the total elution time required for a single sample. With the automatic sample injection attachment, it is possible to analyze more than 10 samples a day. The results, if interpreted properly, are more reliable and precise than those obtainable by other methods of molecular weight distribution determinations. All the average molecular weights of a sample can be computed once the distribution is known. Thus, in some industrial laboratories GPC is beginning to displace standard techniques of molecular weight determination, such as intrinsic viscosity measurements and osmometric pressure measurements.

B. Theory

1. Mechanism of Separation. In spite of the popularity of the technique, a comprehensive theory describing the physical processes in GPC is still in the formulative stage. Several papers proposing different mechanisms of separation for GPC have appeared since 1966.

A typical molecular weight vs. retention volume curve for GPC is shown in Fig. 1. Cantow and Johnson [6] assigned to each pore size of the substrate a specific size of the solute and assumed that molecules smaller than this assigned size could enter the pores and those larger could not. By considering a distribution of the pore sizes in the substrate, they were able to derive a molecular weight-retention volume relation in agreement with that shown in Fig. 1.

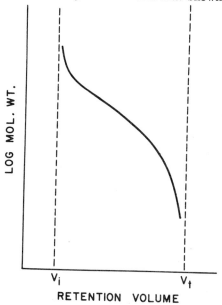

Fig. 1. A typical relation between molecular weight and retention volume for GPC.

Using the same argument of pore size distribution, Le Page, Beau, and de Vries [7] arrived at the same prediction. This relationship was derived also by Carmichael [8] using the stochastic model [9], a model which has been used successfully to describe the chromatographic separation of low-molecular-weight compounds.

In Fig. 1, v_i is the interstitial volume. All the oversized solutes are eluted out at v_i and no separation is achieved. The separation efficiency is also very poor at v_t, which can be identified as the total volume available to the solvent in the column (the volumes of the connecting tubings, the valves, and the refractometer cell are ignored). Therefore, the usable volume in the pores of the substrate v_p is equal to $v_t - v_i$. In chromatographic terminology, v_i is the volume of the mobile phase and v_p is the volume of the stationary phase. If there is a continuous equilibrium exchange of solute molecules between the mobile and the stationary phases, then for any one species in the solute the retention volume v_0 is the mobile phase volume plus a fraction K of the stationary phase volume which is available to that species.

$$v_0 = v_i + Kv_p \tag{1}$$

The parameter K is the distribution coefficient or the partition coefficient for that species. If the pores of the substrate in the column are uniform in size, then K for the species larger than this pore size is zero and K for the species very small in comparison with the pore is one. For the species of in-between sizes, K is not one but assumes a value between zero and one. This is illustrated in Fig. 2 using spheres as the model for the solute molecules. For a sphere with diameter d, the volume inside the pore available to the center of mass of the sphere is confined to the space between the parallel lines. The K value is therefore smaller than that for a smaller sphere. For flexible chain molecules one can imagine that even the longest of them is capable of entering a pore of small diameter. Of course, this event happens at a much reduced probability. The reduction of conformational entropy of flexible chains in pores of finite sizes has been treated quantitatively by Cassasa [10] and by Cassasa and Tagami [11]. These authors were able again to predict the relation shown in Fig. 1. Their theory also predicted that the separation in GPC depended primarily upon the hydrodynamic volumes of the chains regardless of whether they were linear or branched. In this respect their theory is in agreement with the experimental observation made by Grubisic, Rempp, and Benoit [12]. A similar treatment for rigid molecules has been given by Giddings et al. [13].

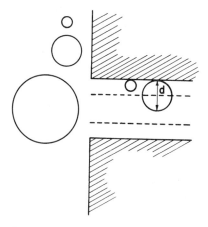

Fig. 2. A schematic sketch of spheric molecules in a pore.

Another mechanism of separation based on the flow of solution through narrow passages has been proposed by DiMarzio and Guttman [14,15]. They depicted a GPC column as a collection of fine capillary tubes in each of which the flow velocity profile was parabolic. Because of the wall effect shown in Fig. 2, larger molecules were restricted to regions where the flow velocities were higher and consequently they were eluted out of columns ahead of the smaller molecules. The contribution of the shear effect towards separation was also considered by them. Recognizing that separation by other processes must occur simultaneously with their proposed separation by flow, they nevertheless have shown that separation by flow alone could account for the molecular weight-retention volume relation given in Fig. 1.

In real chromatographic processes, true equilibrium conditions are not always achieved. Yau and Malone [16] have shown that under nonequilibrium conditions there would be a contribution to separation by the different rates of diffusion of the different molecular weight species. This diffusion process would also lead to a molecular weight-retention volume relation resembling that shown in Fig. 1. Later Hermans [17] gave a more rigorous treatment for the separation process by diffusion. Hermans did not compare his theory with experiments because, for the region of interest, he was not able to perform the inverse transform analytically for the Laplace transform solution of the partial differential equation of diffusion. Thus, the relation in Fig. 1 is predictable by nearly every separation theory. It is obvious that such a prediction is not a sufficient condition for the validity of a theory. A successful theory must also predict other GPC behaviors such as the zone spreading characteristics and the effect of flow rates on the separation and zone spreading.

2. Zone Spreading. As in all types of chromatography, there are undesirable zone spreading processes accompanying the separation processes in GPC. The extent of spreading can be expressed by the plate height parameter, H, which is defined by

$$H = L\sigma^2/v_0^2 \qquad (2)$$

where v_0 is the retention volume at the peak, σ is the standard deviation for the peak spreading, and L is the length of the column. Giddings and Mallik [18], using a spreading theory for low-molecular-weight chromatographic processes, analyzed the zone spreading in GPC. They expressed the dependence of plate height with flow rate u by the expression

$$H = B/u + Cu + f(u) \qquad (3)$$

The first term on the right in Eq. (3) accounts for longitudinal diffusion, the second term for nonequilibrium effects in the stationary phase (spreading associated with the permeation process), and the third term for flow pattern and other mass transfer effects in the mobile phase. This last term is a complex function of u.

Later Billmeyer and Kelley published a series of studies [19-21] on zone spreading in GPC. They have found experimentally that molecular diffusion described by the first term in Eq. (3) contributed negligibly in GPC zone spreading. The spreading in the mobile phase was found to vary directly with flow rate in a manner similar to the f(u) term suggested by Giddings and Mallik. The principal mechanism for the spreading in the mobile phase was attributed to the radial diffusion caused by the flow profile in the packed column. Plate height H for the mobile phase spreading was found to increase with the increase of molecular weight at low flow rates. At high flow rates spreading was found to be relatively independent of the molecular weights of the solutes. They have also found that the plate height caused by the permeation process varied linearly with flow rates as given by the second term in Eq. (3). They therefore concluded that the spreading contributed by permeation was diffusion controlled.

Biesenberger and Ouano [22,23] also investigated zone spreading in the mobile phase. Agreeing with Billmeyer and Kelley, they have found that connecting tubes and refractometer cells could cause an unusually large amount of zone spreading. By using a microrefractometer cell and by reducing the length of the connecting tubes, they have found a mild increase of plate height with the increase of molecular weight of the solute. They concluded, however, that this mild dependence of molecular weight was caused mainly by the unavoidable amount of connecting tubes in the instrument. The spreading in the packed columns, they believed, was essentially independent of molecular weight and the flow profile should conform essentially to the ideal plug flow profile.

A more detailed discussion of the zone spreading can be found in a review given by Kelley and Billmeyer [24]. Most of the works published so far have dealt mainly with the spreading in the mobile phase. When porous particles are used, the measurement of spreading using high-molecular-weight solute becomes more intricate. The main difficulty is caused by the unavailability of monodisperse high-molecular-weight polymer samples. One must isolate the true zone spreading effect from the effect of the polydispersity of the samples. If the zone spreading is Gaussian or symmetrical, then this isolation can be accomplished by the reverse flow method [25]. When a polydisperse sample is allowed to be eluted to some part of the column and then the direction of flow is abruptly reversed, the molecular weight separation process is also reversed but the zone spreading processes continue to broaden the peak. The resulting chromatogram therefore reflects only the zone spreading processes. The scheme of the reverse flow experiment is shown in Fig. 3. The zone spreading for the front half and the back half of the columns can thus be determined separately. The over-all plate height is simply the sum of the two. Figure 4 shows the over-all plate height plotted against elution volume as determined by the reverse flow method [26]. The maximum in the plate height curve has also been observed by Hendrickson [27], and by Yau, Malone, and Suchan [28]. From this zone spreading characteristic of GPC and from other experimental evidences, Yau, Malone, and Suchan [28] have arrived at the following conclusions: (a) They reasoned that the separation by flow as proposed by DiMarzio and Guttman could not have contributed significantly in GPC as the spreading in GPC was orders of magnitude smaller than what would be observed if separation by flow was the predominant mechanism. Furthermore, they could not separate styrene monomer from polystyrene in a column packed with nonporous glass beads. (b) They concluded that the equilibrium mechanism of separation by exclusion, such as the one proposed by Cassasa, must play an important part because the retention volumes of GPC were observed to be insensitive to changes of flow rates. A comparison of their single-stage batch equilibrium experiments with GPC column performances substantiated this claim.

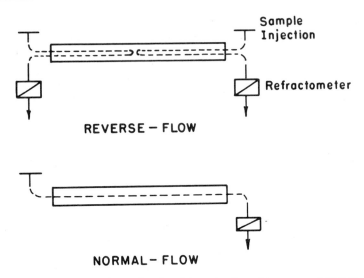

REVERSE – FLOW

NORMAL– FLOW

Fig. 3. Reverse-flow scheme for the determination of zone spreading in GPC.

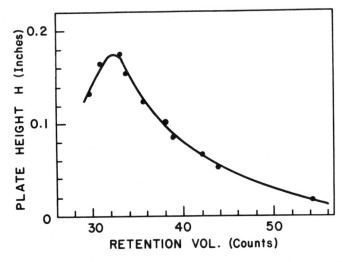

Fig. 4. The variation of plate height H with the retention volume in a typical GPC column set.

(c) Single-stage experiments indicated, however, that in GPC columns the separation by diffusion was probably also a contributing factor. In fact, the maximum spreading in the plate height curve (Fig. 4) could be explained by the diffusion mechanism. Although Hermans [17] was not able to inverse transform his solution for the diffusion equations, he did derive an explicit expression for the spreading associated with the diffusion mechanism. In the derived expression the spreading was shown to vary directly with the ratio uK/D, where D is the diffusion constant, and K and u have the meanings given before. Yau, Malone, and Suchan reasoned that in the low-molecular-weight range (high retention volume range) D decreased faster than K and there was an over-all increase in the ratio of uK/D with the increase of molecular weight. When molecular weight approached that corresponding to total exclusion, K should approach zero and thus bring about a decrease of the ratio with further increase of molecular weight. The maximum in Fig. 4 is thus explained.

C. Data Treatment

1. Calibration. In GPC it is not practical to inject internal standards simultaneously with the unknown sample. The standards tend to interfere with the shape of the chromatogram and prevent proper transformation of the chromatogram to molecular weight distribution. A separate calibration of the retention volume is usually done. When the operating conditions of GPC are not altered, such a calibration is known to remain unchanged for many repeated uses of the columns. The readily available standards for GPC calibration are the commercial anionic polystyrenes of very narrow molecular weight distribution. Unfortunately, calibrations for different polymers are different. Several proposals have been made to correlate calibration for different polymers.

An early attempt to achieve this aim was made by Moore and Hendrickson [29] who used the extended chain length vs. retention volume relation as a universal calibration curve. Later, Meyerhoff [30] proposed to use the product of hydrodynamic radius and molecular weight to the one-half power as the universal calibration parameter. The most commonly used universal calibration was introduced by Grubisic, Rempp, and Benoit [12]. They were successful in bringing the calibration curves of many random coil polymers into one relationship by correlating the retention volume with the product of intrinsic viscosity and molecular weight. This last product is a measure of the hydrodynamic volume of the chains in solution. They have found that branched polystyrene samples followed the same correlation. Confirmation of this universal calibration was reported by Boni, Sliemers, and Stickney [31] for several linear random coil polymers, and by Wild and Guliana [32] for branched and linear polyethylenes. Coll and Prusinowske [33] used the same concept to provide a formula

by which one may transform the calibration of one polymer to that of
another if the Mark-Houwink intrinsic viscosity—molecular weight
relations are known for both polymers. They advocated, however,
that the product of intrinsic viscosity and molecular weight should
be divided by a $f(\epsilon)$ function proposed by Ptitsyn and Eizner [34]:

$$f(\epsilon) = 1 - 2.63\epsilon + 2.86\epsilon^2 \tag{4}$$

where

$$\epsilon = (2a - 1)/3$$

and a is the power index in the Mark-Houwink equation. Williams
and Ward [35] used such an approach and showed experimentally
that the calibration for polyethylene could be accurately determined
from using polystyrene as standards even though the known Mark-
Houwink relations for the two polymers were in different solvents.
Finally, Provder, Woodbrey, and Clark [36] have proposed a procedure whereby GPC calibration determined by using polystyrene in
one solvent may be transformed to that for another polymer in another solvent in which polystyrene is completely insoluble. Such a
versatile universal calibration, however, may not be applicable to
polymers of stiffer chains. For instance, Dawkins [37] reported that
Meyerhoff's data for cellulose polymers were exceptions to this correlation. He argued that the true parameter for correlating GPC
calibration was the unperturbed mean square radius rather than the
hydrodynamic volume of the polymer. The unperturbed dimension
is that which a polymer would assume if it was in a θ-solvent although the solvent used in GPC for the polymer is usually a good one.
Dawkins demonstrated that when the unperturbed dimensions were
used, Meyerhoff's data on cellulose polymers merged into one relation with the data for random coil polymers.

One of the incentives for using the universal calibration is the
difficulty in obtaining narrow distribution samples for the polymer
of interest. However, broad distribution samples have also been
used for calibration. Examples for such practices have been given
by Frank, Ward, and Williams [38], and also by Weiss and Cohn-
Ginsberg [39]. Accuracy of calibration using broad distribution samples appears to be less than that using narrow distribution samples.

2. Correction for Zone Spreading. In chromatograms of monomeric compounds, the individual components appear as separate peaks
and spreading presents no problem for data treatment. For high polymers the peaks of the components are no longer separable. The chro-

matogram now represents a collection of a large number of overlapping peaks. If such a chromatogram is converted directly to the molecular weight distribution curve, then the distribution may include end sections which exist only by virtue of the spreading in the chromatogram. Such a distribution also ignores the contribution of the neighboring components to the relative amount of the component in question. If this overlapping is severe, a correction must be applied to obtain accurate molecular weight distribution.

Let the observed chromatogram be represented by f(v) where v is the elution volume in general. Let w(y) represent the chromatogram which would be observed if spreading did not exist. The variable y represents the retention volume of the individual components. Because of the large number of components involved, the function w(y) is treated as a continuous function. The relation between these two functions has been shown [40] to be describable by the convolution integral equation

$$f(v) = \int w(y)g(v - y)\,dy \tag{5}$$

where $g(v - y)$ is a function describing the spreading for the component having y as its retention volume. If the zone spreading is Gaussian, then

$$g(v - y) = (h/\sqrt{\pi}) \exp\left[-h^2(v - y)^2\right] \tag{6}$$

The parameter h may be related to the plate height H by

$$h = \sqrt{L/(2Hy^2)} \tag{7}$$

where y has the same meaning as v_0 in Eq. (2).

A number of methods for solving the integral Eq. (5) have been proposed. Most of them used one of the following three different approaches.

a. *Solution by minimization:* Aside from the method of the steepest descent in the function space used by Chang and Huang [41], other methods of minimization involve the approximation of Eq. (5) by a set of linear algebraic equations in the following form:

$$f(v_j) = \sum_{i}^{n} w(y_i)\, g_i\, (v_j - y_i)\, (\Delta y)_i \tag{8}$$

For each point on the chromatogram an equation like Eq. (8) can be written. The unknown w function is now represented by n unknown points $w(y_i)$ spaced in suitable intervals $(\Delta y)_i$ apart. The products

$g_i(v_j - y_i)(\Delta y)_i$ are known and they are the coefficients for the unknowns $w(y_j)$. The unknowns can be solved by methods of minimization if a total number of points larger than n are read from the chromatogram. This approach has been used by Hess and Kratz [42], by Tung [40], by Smith [43], and by Pickett, Cantow, and Johnson [44]. Solution by the linear algebraic equation approximation has the flexibility of using any form for the $g(v - y)$ function. The $g(v - y)$ function is not required to be constant with respect to the retention volume y. However, in such an approach long iterative steps are involved. Sometimes the solution is also sensitive to the size of the interval $(\Delta y)_i$ used.

The method of Chang and Huang [41] has been reported to involve only very short iterative steps. They used, however, only the symmetrical Gaussian function as the $g(v - y)$ function.

b. *Solution by Fourier transform:* Equation (5) has the same form as that used in X-ray diffraction for correcting the instrumental spreading. Fourier transform was the approach used by Stokes [45] for treating the X-ray diffraction data. Pierce and Armonas [46] published an attractive simplification of this approach for the correction of zone spreading in GPC. This approach has also been used by Tung [47], by Provder and Rosen [48], and by Vladimiroff [49]. The Fourier transform requires a constant $g(v - y)$ function with respect to the retention volume y. This inflexibility can be circumvented by treating the chromatogram one section at a time using the proper $g(v - y)$ for that section. Pierce and Armonas's simplification required a Gaussian $g(v - y)$ function. Any type of $g(v - y)$ function can be used in the methods reported by the other investigators using the unsimplified Fourier transform.

c. *Solution through the use of polynomials:* The functions $f(v)$ and $w(y)$ for the chromatograms can, in principle, be represented by polynomials. If the product of the polynomial representing $w(y)$ and $g(v - y)$ is integrable, then by a comparison of the coefficients of the polynomial representing $f(v)$, the coefficients for the polynomial representing $w(y)$ can be solved. Aldhouse and Stanford [50] used the Taylor series in their method of solving Eq. (5). Tung [40,47] used a polynomial of the following form:

$$f(v) = \exp\left[-q^2(v - v_0)^2\right] \sum_i U_i(v - v_0)^i \tag{9}$$

In the polynomial approach the form of $g(v - y)$ function is more restrictive. The Gaussian function works well. Some asymmetrical functions may also be used but it must be integrable when combined with $w(y)$. The polynomial method also uses a constant $g(v - y)$ function for the integration. However, as in the case of the Fourier transform approach, the chromatogram can be treated one section at a time to allow $g(v - y)$ to vary with retention volume.

Duerksen and Hamielec [51,52] have examined some of the correction methods mentioned above and reported that some degree of oscillation induced by the computation was present in all methods. Tung [53] has shown that a small variation in the slope of $f(v)$ would bring about a considerably larger variation in the slope of $w(y)$. This sensitivity of $w(y)$ varies with the breadth of the spreading function or the extent of correction. In the limiting case where there is no correction or $g = 1$, $w(y)$ becomes identical to $f(v)$. In any other cases variation in the slope of $f(v)$ is always less than that in the slope of $w(y)$. If the experimental $f(v)$ is determined to a high degree of precision and if the $g(v - y)$ function used describes the zone spreading characteristics flawlessly, then the solution for $w(y)$ can be carried out with a high degree of confidence regardless of the method used. In reality, neither of these conditions can be met fully, and as a result the uncertainties in $f(v)$ and in $g(v - y)$ are transformed into oscillations in $w(y)$. This problem is more acute when the correction is large or when the sample contains very narrow peaks. It is also more pronounced at the ends of a chromatogram where the $f(v)$ function is less precisely known. To minimize the fluctuations in the raw data, mathematical correlations are used to smooth out $f(v)$ [41]. In fact, in many of the above-mentioned methods such a data smoothing procedure is implicitly or explicitly carried out in the computer program written for the method. Whether one method of solution is better than another depends often more on this smoothing procedure than on the mathematics involved. If smoothing is done too drastically, some of the true features of $w(y)$ may be lost; if not enough smoothing is accomplished, then oscillations may show up in the solution. We may look upon the correction for zone spreading as an exchange of the accuracy in $f(v)$ for the ambiguity produced by zone spreading. If the correction demands higher accuracy in $f(v)$ than experimentally possible, then unrealistic results will be obtained.

To avoid completely the problem of oscillation, Hamielec and Ray [54] computed directly the corrected average molecular weights, assuming linear calibration and also the Gaussian spreading function. Balke and Hamielec [55] and later Hamielec [56] modified the method of Hamielec and Ray to include the cases in which the spreading is unsymmetrical. The method of Hamielec and Ray gives also the average molecular weights which are the ratios of higher moments of the distribution. If enough higher moments of the distribution are known, the distribution itself may be generated. It is possible the problem of oscillation will again appear when the corrected distribution is thus generated. Such possibilities, however, were not discussed by the above authors.

The methods of solving Eq. (5) discussed so far require high-speed digital computers to execute the calculation. Frank, Ward, and Williams [38] have used a simple method in which the calculation may be managed by a desk calculator. They separated one or more Gaussian curves from the chromatogram depending on the number of peaks in the chromatogram. The residual smooth function was left uncorrected. The Gaussian peaks were narrowed by subtracting from them the spreading effect which was also assumed to be Gaussian. These narrowed peaks were then recombined with the uncorrected residual to give the final results. In such a method no oscillation is possible and often for the very narrow distribution samples it is more practical than the more complex methods.

In correcting the zone spreading many authors used the Gaussian spreading function whereas Hess and Kratz, Smith, Pickett et al., and also Balke and Hamielec used unsymmetric $g(v - y)$ functions. It is indisputable that skewing does occur in the spreading for very high-molecular-weight polymer samples. Tung and Runyon [26] have pointed out that the shapes of the chromatograms of the currently available high-molecular-weight narrow distribution polystyrene samples could not be used to estimate the extent of skewing nor could they even be used to judge whether skewing does occur at all. These samples are themselves skewed in the distribution. When the Gaussian function is assumed, the $g(v - y)$ function can be calibrated by using the reverse flow technique [25] or methods proposed by Hamielec and Ray [54] and by Tung and Runyon [26]. Tung and Runyon reported also that the $g(v - y)$ function is the same for several random coil polymers. It appears that at this point of development it is far better to reduce the skewing as much as possible experimentally and use the Gaussian function for the correction of zone spreading. The work of Billmeyer and Kelley [19] and of Ouano and Biesenberger [23] have shown that by shortening the connecting tubings and by using a microrefractometer cell much of the skewing can be avoided.

It should be pointed out that in spite of the many different methods proposed for the correction of zone spreading, if long columns of high efficiency are used, the correction for zone spreading can be ignored for most samples of broad molecular weight distributions. For narrow distribution samples the correction nevertheless is always required.

3. Other Corrections and Sources of Errors. Standard GPC equip-
ments use differential refractometers as the concentration detector.
In most works the refractive index increment is assumed to be independent of molecular weight. This assumption was examined by Barrall and Johnson [57]. They have found that for polystyrene in toluene
the refractive index increment was significantly lower at lower molecular weight. This dependence was not found, however, when polystyrene in o-dichlorobenzene was examined by Hazell, Prince, and
Stapelfeldt [58]. Neither has the large dependence of refractive index
increment on molecular weight been reported by other workers. Barrall and Johnson suspected that their samples contained a small
amount of contaminants copolymerized in the chains or as chain ends.
Nevertheless, when samples of unknown origin are encountered, a check
for the constancy of the refractive index increment is warranted.

Sample overloading is a problem which has been recognized since
the early days in GPC development. Altgelt and Moore [1] mentioned
that samples of viscosities beyond 3 cP (centipoise) should be avoided.
Harmon [59], as well as Hazell et al. [58], reported shifts of retention
volume when sample sizes were changed. However, correction for
concentration effect as advocated by Lambert [60] and by Boni, Sliemers, and Stickney [61] has not become a practice. There apparently
exists a threshold of sample size below which the concentration effect
becomes negligible. This problem was recently examined carefully
by Moore [62] who reported that the product of the following three factors:

$$\text{(sample concn. in } mg/ml) \times \text{(sample vol. in ml)}$$

$$\times \text{ (sample intrinsic viscosity in } dl/g)$$

could serve as a guide for the safe upper limit of operation. For
standard GPC columns, using 1 ml/min as the flow rate, a value of
0.5 to 1.0 of this product should be the limit.

In early GPC works the calibration curve was often approximated
by a linear relation between the logarithm of molecular and retention
volume. Yau and Fleming [63] pointed out that such an approximation
could cause large errors in the results. They also reminded readers
that in converting the chromatogram into the distribution of molecular weight a weighing factor of $dv/d \log M$ should not be forgotten.
This factor, however, is automatically taken into consideration if an
integral distribution is constructed first as recommended in the instrument manual provided by the Waters Associates of Framingham,
Massachusetts. Numerical differentiation is then used to derive the
differential molecular weight distribution.

D. New Developments

Recent improvements in GPC instrumentation have been summarized by Barrall and Johnson [64]. Most GPC users, however, tend to use the commercial instrument with only minor modifications such as the shortening of connecting tubes or the prevention of solvent evaporation in the siphoning tube as recommended by Yau, Suchan, and Malone [65]. Cross-linked polystyrene gel is still the most efficient packing for GPC columns. Other types of column packing have been discussed recently by Harmon [66].

A preparative model of GPC has been available commercially for some time [67]. Altgelt [68] has recently reported that good separation could be obtained when samples with 10 or more times as much concentration as that used in the normal running conditions were used. Altgelt reasoned that the separation was achieved at such high loadings by a secondary exclusion mechanism which could be described briefly as follows: When a concentrated solution of small and large molecules is in contact with the gels, the small molecules will rapidly diffuse into the available pores. The larger molecules, because of the slower rate of diffusion, will find most pores occupied and are excluded. The use of extrahigh concentration samples may open the way for the development of large-scale preparative GPC.

Good separation has been reported at extrahigh flow rates by Little, Waters, Bombaugh, and Pauplis [69]. The flow rates used by them were tenfold higher than normal. This greatly reduced analysis time may lead to on-line application of GPC in polymerization processes.

A recycle mode of GPC operation has been reported by Heitz and Ullner [70], and by Waters [71]. Such a mode of operation has the effect of extending the length of the column so that much higher resolution can be obtained without an excessive increase of pressure drop. Only narrow distribution samples may be used in recycle determination because the two ends of a broad distribution sample may overlap in two successive cycles.

Malone, Suchan, and Yau [72] have shown that the vacancy chromatographic technique could be applied to GPC. A differential type measurement can therefore be made in gel permeation chromatography.

The distribution of copolymer composition has been determined by GPC. For example, if one of the comonomers is uv active, such as styrene, the use of an uv photometer as a second analyzer permits the determination of the weight fraction of styrene as a function of the molecular weight of the copolymer [73,74]. Infrared photometers [75] have also been used to perform similar analysis for copolymers.

Long-chain branching determinations can be made when GPC is combined with another method of measurement. Mendelson and Drott [76] used combined GPC and intrinsic viscosity measurements to determine the long-chain branching in low-density polyethylene. Tung [77] has used combined GPC and sedimentation velocity measurements to determine the distribution of long-chain branching in polystyrene.

An exhaustive compilation of GPC publications is not given here, as it has been expertly reported by Johnson and Porter [5].

II. BATCH FRACTIONATION

Fractional precipitation, coacervate extraction, and fractionation by crystallization are all methods of batch fractionation. The separation is achieved by the partition of polymer molecules in two immiscible phases. Several days are usually required to obtain the cuts. The cuts then must be further analyzed. A decade ago batch fractionation methods were commonly used for analytical fractionation. Because of the simplicity in experimental equipment and technique, they are still used today for preparative fractionation. For example, Prime and Wunderlich [78] used a batch crystallization fractionation method to prepare narrow distribution polyethylene samples for their physical measurements but they used GPC for the analysis of molecular weight distribution. In Cantow's book the methods of batch fractionation are discussed in chapters by Kotera [79] and Elliott [80]. The partition of polymer molecules in two immiscible phases is governed by thermodynamics of polymer solutions and a background of these theories can be found in many treatises of polymer chemistry. In Cantow's book these theories are surveyed by Huggins and Okamota [81].

As the names of the methods imply, in fractional precipitation (partial precipitation) the cuts are removed from the polymer-rich precipitated phase and in coacervate extraction the cuts are removed from the polymer-lean solution phase. Recently, Koningsveld and Staverman [82] have treated the phase equilibria of polymer-solvent systems. They concluded that coacervate extraction was the more efficient method of the two. A number of other papers discussing the efficiency of batch fractionation have also appeared recently. Klein [83], Schiedermaier, and Klein [84], and Klein and Wittenberger [85] used the characteristics of polymer solubility curves to deduce the sharpness of cuts obtainable from batch fractionation. Huggins [86] discussed the role of solvent—polymer interaction in the efficiency of polymer fractionation. Kamide and Nakayama [87] used fractions computed from a digital computer to discuss the efficiency of polymer fractionation. It appears, however, that the optimization of fractionation efficiency as recommended by the above workers can easily be offset by limitations in practices. The guidelines given by Kotera [79] for the selection of solvent systems and other experimental conditions could be still more valuable to the average laboratory worker.

In fractional precipitation, the polymer is usually precipitated by the addition of a nonsolvent to the polymer solution or by the lowering of the solution temperature. Kobayashi, Okamura, and Signer [88] reported a unique observation that agitation could also cause preferential precipitation of higher molecular weight species. The system was polyoxymethylene in p-chlorophenol at 60°C. They, however, offered no explanation of the mechanism involved.

Batch fractional crystallization is not as widely used as the fractional precipitation and the coacervate extraction methods. Koningsveld and Pennings [89] have produced very sharp fractions of polyethylene by crystallization from a dilute xylene solution. Kawai [90] discussed theoretically the conditions necessary for obtaining sharp fractions by crystallization. On the other hand, Booth and Price [91] reported unsatisfactory results for fractionating polyethylene oxide by crystallization.

The most frequently used method of deriving the molecular weight distribution from data of batch fractionation is that proposed by Schulz [92]. A discussion of this and other methods of data treatment is given in a chapter by Tung [93] in Cantow's book. Recently, Ueda [94] showed that for narrow distribution samples, Schulz's method yields distributions which are narrower than the true distribution. In such cases, Ueda has demonstrated that the data treatment method proposed by Homme et al. [95] was more proficient. This latter method is similar to one proposed by Beall [96].

Various solvent systems used for batch fractionation were compiled by Cantow [97]. Some of the more recent systems which may be added to that list are given in Table 1.

III. COLUMN FRACTIONATION

Column fractionation is a method which in nature lies somewhere between the chromatographic methods and the batch fractionation methods. It resembles a chromatographic method in that it does use a packed column and that it is amenable to continuous operation. Nevertheless, like a batch method, cuts are still to be collected and analyzed. The simple column fractionation method was reported first by Desreux and Spiegel [114] who deposited polymer on a substrate of sand packed in a column. The polymer-coated sand was then eluted with solvent and nonsolvent mixtures of varying composi-

Table 1

Solvent Systems for Batch Fractionation Methods

Polymer	Method[a]	Solvent−nonsolvent	Temp (°C)	Ref.
Alkyd resins	FP	Toluene−n−heptane	30	98
Alkyd resins	FP	Acetone−water	27	99
Hydroxypropyl cellulose	CE	Anhydrous ethanol− n−heptane	30	100
Polyacenaphthylene	FP	Benzene−methanol	25	101
Polycaprolactam	CE	Phenol−(water 81.5%, methanol 18.5%)	25	102
Poly-p-chlorostyrene	FP	Benzene−methanol	25	103
Polydimethylsiloxane	FP	Ethyl acetate−methanol	30	104
Polyethylene oxide	FP	Benzene−isopropanol	60	105
Polypropylene	FP	1,2,4-Trichlorobenzene− dimethylphthalate	−	106
Polypropylene oxide	FP	Isooctane	By temp lowering	107
Polystyrene	FP	Benzene−methanol	30	108
Polystyrene, isotactic	FP	o-Dichlorobenzene− polyethylene glycol (av mol. wt. 400)	50	109
Polyvinyl carbonate	FP	DMF−methanol	20.1	110
Polyvinyl carbonate	FP	DMF−n−butanol	20.1	110
PVC	FP	THF−water	30	111
PVC	FP	Cyclohexanone−ethylene glycol	30	111
Styrene−acrylonitrile copolymer	CE	Benzene−triethylene glycol	60	112
Styrene-acrylonitrile copolymer	CE	Dichloromethane− triethylene glycol	25	112
Styrene−methylmethac- rylate copolymer	FP	Benzene−methanol	30	108
Styrene−isobutylene copolymer	FP	Benzene−isopropanol	25	113
Styrene−isobutylene copolymer	FP	Cyclohexane−n−propanol	25	113

[a]FP = fractional precipitation; CE = coacervate extraction.

tion. Later Baker and Williams [115] imposed a temperature gradient in the longitudinal direction of the column for the purpose of achieving multistage fractionation. The Desreux and Spiegel-type column fractionation is discussed in Cantow's book by Elliott [80].

The Baker and Williams column, because of the multistage effect, is also called chromatographic fractionation and is treated in Cantow's book by Porter and Johnson [116] in a separate chapter. Both of these methods reduce the time requirement for collecting the cuts to within a working day, but the time necessary for analyzing the cuts still makes them slow methods of fractionation.

The improvement of efficiency in Baker and Williams's method has been found to be less than what was expected for a multistage process [117,118]. Recently the effect of temperature gradient on the efficiency of column fractionation was examined again by Yamaguchi and Saeda [119]. They reported that temperature gradient was effective only at the high-molecular-weight region and only if the gradient of the solvent composition was steep. The behavior of their column was found to conform to a theory proposed by Schulz, Deussen, and Scholz [120].

Theoretical analysis of the Baker and Williams column was made recently by Smith [121] using the approach of Schulz et al. [120]. Smith concluded that temperature gradient could improve fractionation efficiency under favorable conditions, but under some other conditions the gradient could actually hinder the efficiency.

A preparative Baker and Williams column that could handle 45 g of polymer in a single operation was reported by Henderson and Hulme [122]. The column was only 3 in. in inside diameter and 40 in. long. The temperature gradient used by them was only 10° C total. They reported that the theory of Caplan [123] successfully helped them in achieving this optimum design.

Some other published works using column fractionation are listed in Table 2.

IV. SEDIMENTATION METHODS

Sedimentation in an ultracentrifugal field has been used extensively in the characterization of biopolymers. For synthetic polymers of flexible chain molecules, the intermolecular interference in solution causes some serious problem in the interpretation of data. Though many of these difficulties have been overcome, sedimentation methods still are not widely used by polymer chemists. A summary of the more important applications in the synthetic polymer field is given by McCormick [130] in Cantow's book. Two types of sedimentation experiments are available. In sedimentation velocity experiments the rate of sedimentation is measured, whereas in sedimentation equilibrium experiments the sedimentation process is allowed to come to equilibrium with the diffusion process. These two methods are discussed below.

Table 2

Some Solvent Systems for Column Fractionation

Polymer	Temp grad.	Solvent—nonsolvent	Temp (°C)	Ref.
Natural rubber		Benzene—methanol	25	124
Polybenzyl-L-glutamate	Yes	Methylene chloride—methanol		125
Polybenzyl-L-glutamate	Yes	Methylene chloride—methanol		125
Polyethylene	No	p-Xylene—n-butyl ether of ethylene glycol	124.5	126
Polyethylene	No	p-Xylene—n-butyl ether of ethylene glycol	124.5	127
Polypropylene	No	p-Xylene—methanol	56	128
Polypropylene	No	o-Dichlorobenzene—methyl carbitol	172	128
Polypropylene	No	o-Dichlorobenzene—butylcarbitol	166	129
Polypropylene	Yes	1,2,4-Trichlorobenzene—dimethyl phthalate		106
Styrene—acrylonitrile copolymer	No	Acetone—methanol	30	112
Styrene—acrylonitrile copolymer	No	Dichloromethane—methanol	20	112
Styrene—isobutylene copolymer	Yes	Benzene—isopropanol	60-25	113
Styrene—isobutylene copolymer	Yes	Cyclohexane—isopropanol	60-25	113

A. Sedimentation Velocity Method

One handicap of batch and column fractionation is the limited number of experimental points which can be determined for a sample. Usually 10 to 15 cuts are collected and characterized. There are, however, thousands of components in a typical polymer sample. Thus, it is difficult for a batch or a column fractionation method to determine the molecular weight distribution of a sample which contains more than one peak. In GPC a continuous curve is recorded and much higher resolution is therefore possible. Sedimentation velocity is another such method. It is also faster and more precise than any of the batch and column fractionation methods. For some unknown reason it has never been as widely used as the latter methods.

In sedimentation velocity measurements the concentration effect and the hydrostatic pressure effect must be corrected to produce the most accurate results. Kotaka and Donkai [131] recently studied these effects for the system of polystyrene in cyclohexane at 35°C. They found that there was an unexpected dependence of concentration correction on rotor speed. Such a trend could also be detected in previously published data of Billick [132] who, however, claimed that the variation was within his experimental data. The dependence of sedimentation coefficient, s, with concentration can be expressed by

$$s = s_0 / (1 + s_0 kc) \tag{10}$$

where s_0 is the sedimentation coefficient at infinite dilution, c is concentration, and k is a constant independent of molecular weight. The k value in Eq. (10) was found by Kotaka and Donkai to be 0.030, 0.032, and 0.036 for rotor speeds of 29,500, 42,020, and 59,780 rpm, respectively. The unit used for concentration was g/100 ml and for sedimentation coefficient was svedberg units. McCormick [130] re-reported a value of 0.030 for k with no mention of the dependence on rotor speed. Similar to Billick's results, values of the hydrostatic pressure correction coefficient, μ, determined by Kotaka and Donkai, were scattered. The values obtained by them covered a range from 1.2 to 2.0 $\times$ 10^{-9} cm^2/dyn.

These effects for the same system were also investigated by Closs, Jennings, and Jerrard [133]. The correction coefficients for both effects were found by them to be slightly larger than those observed by Kotaka and Donkai. Closs, Jennings, and Jerrard used only a single sample for the polystyrene—cyclohexane system, but they also reported the correction coefficients for two other systems: (a) polymethyl methacrylate in n-butyl chloride at 35°C, and (b) polyisobutylene in cyclohexane at 34°C. The last system was not at the θ-condition and the concentration correction was found to be much greater than the other two θ-condition systems. The μ value for the system PMMA in n-butyl chloride was found to be 0.45 $\times$ 10^{-9} cm^2/dyn. For the system of polyisobutylene in cyclohexane, μ was found to be approximately the same as that for polystyrene in cyclohexane. Thus, the pressure correction coefficient, μ, was primarily a function of the solvent properties as was found by Blair and Williams [134].

The standard procedure for correcting concentration dependence is by measuring the sedimentation velocity at several concentrations and then extrapolating the results to infinite dilution. Kotaka and

Donkai [131] proposed a method whereby the concentration effect
was corrected from measurement at a single concentration. They,
however, ignored the Johnston-Ogston effect of concentration on the
shape of the sedimentation velocity profile. The correction was made
only on the sedimentation coefficients. The single concentration
method proposed some time ago by Baldwin [135] took all these effects into consideration and therefore is likely to be more reliable
than the one proposed by Kotaka and Donkai. Both methods depend
on the constancy of k or a one-to-one relationship of k with molecular weights in Eq. (10). If the polymer sample contains branched
molecules, such relations are not expected to hold and correction
by extrapolation should be used.

Recently, an uv scanning optical system designed by Lamers,
Putney, Steinberg, and Schachman [136] has been made available
commercially. By using such an optical system, sedimentation velocity of polystyrene in cyclohexane can be measured at a concentration of about 0.03 g/100 ml. At such dilutions the correction for
concentration is negligible. The molecular weight distribution of a
polystyrene determined by sedimentation velocity using this optical
system was found to agree excellently with that determined by GPC
[77]. One difficulty encountered at high dilution is the interference
from convection induced principally by temperature fluctuations.
Scholte and Rietveld [137] used a thin metal shield which hid the
cell from the heat radiating directly from the heating elements. They
have demonstrated that such a shield could reduce the interference
from convection considerably.

Sedimentation velocity of branched molecules, because of their reduced hydrodynamic volumes, is faster than for linear molecules of
the same molecular weight. Thus, branched molecules behave as
higher molecular weight species when measured by sedimentation
velocity method but they behave as lower molecular weight species
when measured by GPC. The distribution of long-chain branching
therefore may be measured by comparing the results from these two
measurements [77]. Anomalous sedimentation behavior for branched
polymers, however, has been reported. Wales and Coll [138] found
that branched polymethyl methacrylate in n-butyl chloride sedimented
slower than linear chains of equivalent molecular weights. They attributed their findings to the lowering of θ-temperature by the presence of branches. Similar lowering of θ-temperature was also reported for highly branched comb-shape polystyrene in cyclohexane
[139].

B. Equilibrium Sedimentation

Equilibrium sedimentation experiments take longer times to complete and the method has less resolving power than the sedimentation velocity method. But several papers discussing its application in the determination of molecular weight distribution appeared recently. Perhaps, as stated by Scholte [140], the following two advantages may have attracted some investigators to the method:

1. The sedimentation equilibrium method is based on purely thermodynamic principles. The absolute molecular weight distribution can be determined. The sedimentation velocity method, on the other hand, requires precalibration of the relation between sedimentation coefficient and molecular weight.

2. Correction for pressure effect can be ignored in the sedimentation equilibrium method because of the lower speed of rotation used.

There are two approaches for deriving the distribution of molecular weight from sedimentation equilibrium data. One approach is to calculate the various average molecular weights first. Then, by the method of moments, the distribution is derived. However, molecular weight averages higher than the z + 1 average are extremely unreliable. Therefore, a precise description of the distribution is difficult to obtain. Recently, Kotera, Iso, Senuma, and Hamada [141] used an ultracentrifuge equipped with a magnetically suspended rotor to investigate the distribution of polyethylene by the equilibrium sedimentation method. They were successful in obtaining the weight average, the z average, and the z + 1 average molecular weights but not the precise measurement of the distribution.

Another approach for deriving the distribution is by solving directly the integral equation [142] for sedimentation equilibrium

$$\frac{dc}{d\xi} = -c_0 \int_0^\infty \frac{\lambda^2 M^2 \exp(-\xi\lambda M)}{1 - \exp(-\lambda M)} f(M) \, dM \tag{11}$$

where

$$\xi = (r_2^2 - r^2)/(r_2^2 - r_1^2)$$

$$\lambda = (1 - \bar{v}\rho)\omega^2(r_2^2 - r_1^2)/2RT$$

c = equilibrium concentration at radial distance r from the center of rotation, r_1 = radial distance of the meniscus from the center of rotation, r_2 = radial distance of the cell bottom from the center of rotation,

ρ = density of the solution, ω = rotor speed, $\bar{v}$ = partial specific volume of solute, R = the gas constant, T = the absolute temperature, M = molecular weight, and f(M) = molecular weight distribution function. As in the case of the integral equation for correcting zone spreading in GPC, numerical methods must be used to solve Eq. (11). Because of the lack of precision in the data, the solutions for Eq. (11) are, however, much more unstable. There have been several recently proposed methods of solution: (a) Donnelly [143] used the method of Laplace transform. (b) Scholte [144] used a procedure of linear programming to solve the equation by a quadrature method. (c) Provencher [145] used a numerical approach that combined the least square and the quadrature method. Finally, Lee [146] discussed the instability of the solution for the above integral equation.

A comparison of the determination of molecular weight distribution by the three methods, sedimentation equilibrium, sedimentation velocity, and GPC, was made by Donnelly [143]. He concluded that GPC offered the highest resolution and sedimentation equilibrium the least. Scholte [147] also made such a comparison and formed a similar conclusion. Scholte, however, was more optimistic about using the sedimentation equilibrium method as a practical means of determining the molecular weight distribution of polymers.

A variation of the sedimentation equilibrium method is the density gradient sedimentation. The density gradient is created by using two or more miscible solvents of different densities. As pointed out in McCormick's chapter [130], density gradient centrifugation is a highly sensitive method for the detection of density differences in polymer solutes. It is useful in the studying of the tacticity of homopolymers and the composition distribution in copolymers. Recent application of the technique was reported by Burke and Orofino [148] in their study of nylon 66 composition and by Cowie and Toporowski [149] in their study of the tacticity of poly(α-methylstyrene). Burke and Orofino used m-cresol—carbon tetrachloride and cyclohexane as the solvents. Cowie and Toporowski used chloroform and benzene.

V. TURBIDIMETRY

Turbidimetry or turbidimetric titration is less reliable than the other methods of analyzing the molecular weight distribution discussed in this review. Giesekus [150] stated in his chapter in Cantow's book that whenever possible it should not be used as the only method and that conclusions should not be drawn solely on the basis of the turbidity curves. Even more pessimistic views were voiced by Rabel and Ueberreiter [151] and also by Mencik [152], who believed that the method should not be recommended at all.

In turbidimetry a polymer sample is dissolved in a solution at a near precipitation condition. Then, by the addition of a nonsolvent or by the lowering of the solution temperature, precipitation is induced. The amount of precipitation is monitored by the turbidity developed. Two main sources of difficulties are: (a) the uncertainty between turbidity and the amount of polymer precipitated, and (b) the dependence of precipitation point on the concentration of the precipitating species. Cornet [153] recently discovered an additional complication which further made the quantitative interpretation of the turbidity curves difficult. He found by experiments and also deduced theoretically that the precipitating condition of a polymer species depended also on the presence of already precipitated fractions of higher molecular weight. Although Rayner [154] suggested later that such a complication could perhaps be overcome by new methods of calibration, no satisfactory interpretation of the turbidity curve has been offered so far. Certainly the existing methods which did not take the last effect into consideration cannot be relied upon.

Of the two methods of inducing polymer precipitation, the lowering of solution temperature seems to be preferred by recent workers. The reproducibility of the turbidity curve also seems to be enhanced by using extremely dilute solutions. The turbidity developed from such dilute solutions is often monitored by scattered light rather than transmitted light. The apparatus is therefore quite elaborate and requires careful manipulation. Using these experimental conditions, Peaker and Rayner [155] reported impressive reproducibility for the turbidity curves developed by polystyrene in cyclohexane. They found that stirring during cooling could affect the turbidity curve and was best avoided. Their solutions were in concentrations of the order of 1 mg/100 ml.

As stated in Giesekus's chapter, the more successful application of the turbidimetric method perhaps is in the analysis of copolymers. The cloud point titration method developed by Gruber and Elias [156] measures only the initial part of the turbidity curve. For sufficiently large molecular weight samples, the parameter deduced from such experiments depends mostly on the composition of the copolymer. The same method can also be used for the detection of small amounts of homopolymers in the presence of copolymers.

VI. OTHER FRACTIONATION METHODS

Some of the less-known methods of polymer fractionation which appeared in recent literature are given below.

Brewer [157] fractionated low-molecular-weight polymers by dialysis in nonaqueous solvents using rubber membranes. His membranes were surgeon's finger-cots made of natural rubber. When used with solvents that swelled the rubber, the rubber was found to be more permeable to the solvent than cellulose membranes. The polymers tested were polyisobutene and styrene—butadiene copolymers. The separation efficiency was found to be low and there was almost no separation for species having molecular weights higher than 10,000.

Baker [158] reported fractionation of polymer by ultrafiltration. The anisotropic membranes which prevented clogging of the pores appeared to make such a method suitable for preparative fractionation. His examples were, however, limited to water-soluble polymers.

Fractionation by diffusion is discussed by Burchard and Cantow [159] in Cantow's book. The limitations of this method to fractionate polymers were amply shown by them. Matsuda, Aonuma, and Kuroiwa [160] recently used the method of diffusion to fractionate polystyrene. Their result again showed that the method was not very practical.

Among the lesser-known methods of polymer fractionation, a more interesting one is thin-layer chromatography. As early as 1959, Langford and Vaughn [161] reported using it to separate polymer blends. Recently Inagaki, Matsuda, and Kamiyama [162] applied the method to determine the composition of styrene-methyl acrylate copolymers. Silica gel was used as the substrate, and a series of solvents with different dielectric constants were used as the developers. In thin-layer chromatography R_F is defined by

$$R_F = \frac{\text{distance of spot from starting point}}{\text{distance of solvent from starting point}}$$

When the solvents were used singly by these authors, R_F values were found to be either zero or greater than 0.9. Moreover, the developing power of a solvent was found to depend less on the solvent power than on the extent to which the solvent could reduce interaction between solute and the substrate. Thus, chloroform, a good solvent for the homopolymer of methyl acrylate, did not move the spot of such a homopolymer. The most successful way of developing the chromatogram was by gradient elution using chloroform and ethyl acetate. No separation according to molecular weight was observed in their work.

This technique was later successfully used by Kamiyama, Matsuda, and Inagaki [163] to analyze the random copolymers of styrene and methyl methacrylate. Block copolymers of similar comonomer composition were not moved by the solvents capable of developing the random copolymers. Alternating copolymers were found to give R_F values intermediate between the random and the block copolymers.

This was explained in terms of the differences in the extent of adsorption associated with the three types of dyads, A-A, A-B, and B-B, in the copolymer chains.

Inagaki, Miyamoto, and Kamiyama [164], using single solvents as developers, successfully separated polymethyl methacrylates according to their stereospecificities. Using silica as the substrate and ethyl acetate as the developer, they found that isotactic PMMA remained at the starting point and syndiotactic PMMA moved with the solvent.

Otocka and Hellman [165] reported the successful separation of polymers according to molecular weight by thin-layer chromatography. The separation of polystyrene according to molecular weight was accomplished by using both the 80-20 mixture of acetone and THF and the gradient elution of acetone and THF. Polyethylene oxides were also separated by them. The developers were ethyl glycol—methanol and also methanol and DMF. In both systems silica gel and alumina were used as the substrates.

References

[1] K. H. Altgelt and J. C. Moore, in *Polymer Fraction* (M. J. R. Cantow, ed.), Academic, New York, 1967, Chap. B.4.

[2] H. Determann, *Gel Chromatography*, Springer-Verlag, New York, 1968.

[3] J. F. Johnson, R. S. Porter, and M. J. R. Cantow, *Rev. Macromol. Chem.*, 1, 393 (1966).

[4] K. H. Altgelt, in *Advances in Chromatography*, Vol. 7 (J. C. Giddings and R. A. Keller, eds.), Dekker, New York, 1968.

[5] J. F. Johnson and R. S. Porter, in *Progress in Polymer Science*, Vol. 2, Pergamon, New York, in press.

[6] M. J. R. Cantow and J. F. Johnson, *J. Polym. Sci., Part A-1*, 5, 2835 (1967).

[7] M. Le Page, R. Beau, and A. J. de Vries, *J. Polym. Sci., Part C*, 21, 119 (1968).

[8] J. B. Carmichael, *J. Polym. Sci., Part A-2*, 6, 517 (1968).

[9] D. A. McQuarrie, *J. Chem. Phys.*, 38, 437 (1963).

[10] E. F. Cassasa, *J. Polym. Sci., Part B*, 5, 773 (1967).

[11] E. F. Cassasa and Y. Tagami, *Macromolecules*, 2, 14 (1969).

[12] Z. Grubisic, P. Rempp, and H. Benoit, *J. Polym. Sci., Part B*, 5, 753 (1967).

[13] J. C. Giddings, E. Kucera, C. P. Russell, and M. N. Myers, *J. Phys. Chem.*, 72, 4397 (1968).

[14] E. A. DiMarzio and C. M. Guttman, *J. Polym. Sci., Part B*, 7, 267 (1968).

[15] E. A. DiMarzio and C. M. Guttman, *Macromolecules*, 3, 131 (1970).

[16] W. W. Yau and C. P. Malone, *J. Polym. Sci., Part B*, 5, 663 (1969).

[17] J. J. Hermans, *J. Polym. Sci., Part A-2*, **6**, 1217 (1968).
[18] J. C. Giddings and K. L. Mallik, *Anal. Chem.*, **38**, 997 (1966).
[19] F. W. Billmeyer, Jr., and R. N. Kelley, *J. Chromatogr.*, **34**, 332 (1968).
[20] R. N. Kelley and F. W. Billmeyer, Jr., *Anal. Chem.*, **41**, 874 (1969).
[21] R. N. Kelley and F. W. Billmeyer, Jr., *Anal. Chem.*, **42**, 399 (1970).
[22] J. A. Biesenberger and A. Ouano, *J. Appl. Polym. Sci.*, **14**, 471 (1970).
[23] A. Ouano and J. A. Biesenberger, *J. Appl. Polym. Sci.*, **14**, 483 (1970).
[24] R. N. Kelley and F. W. Billmeyer, Jr., *Separ. Sci.*, **5**, 291 (1970).
[25] L. H. Tung, J. C. Moore, and G. W. Knight, *J. Appl. Polym. Sci.*, **10**, 1261 (1966).
[26] L. H. Tung and J. R. Runyon, *J. Appl. Polym. Sci.*, **13**, 2397 (1969).
[27] J. G. Hendrickson, *J. Polym. Sci., Part A-2*, **6**, 1903 (1968).
[28] W. W. Yau, C. P. Malone, and J. L. Suchan, *Separ. Sci.*, **5**, 259 (1970).
[29] J. C. Moore and J. G. Hendrickson, *J. Polym. Sci., Part C*, **8**, 233 (1965).
[30] G. Meyerhoff, *Makromol. Chem.*, **89**, 282 (1965).
[31] K. A. Boni, F. A. Sliemers, and P. B. Stickney, *J. Polym. Sci., Part A-2*, **6**, 1579 (1968).
[32] L. Wild and R. Guliana, *J. Polym. Sci., Part A-2*, **5**, 1087 (1967).
[33] H. Coll and L. R. Prusinowske, *J. Polym. Sci., Part B*, **5**, 1153 (1967).
[34] O. B. Ptitsyn and Y. E. Eizner, *Sov. J. Tech. Phys. (Engl. Transl.)*, 4, 1020 (1960).
[35] T. Williams and I. M. Ward, *J. Polym. Sci., Part B*, **6**, 621 (1968).
[36] T. Provder, J. C. Woodbrey, and J. H. Clark, *Separ. Sci.*, **6**, 101 (1971).
[37] J. V. Dawkins, *J. Macromol. Sci.—Phys.*, B2(4), 623 (1968).
[38] F. C. Frank, I. M. Ward, and T. Williams, *J. Polym. Sci., Part A-2*, **6**, 1357 (1968).
[39] A. R. Weiss and E. Cohn-Ginsberg, *J. Polym. Sci., Part A-2*, **8**, 148 (1970).
[40] L. H. Tung, *J. Appl. Polym. Sci.*, **10**, 375 (1966).
[41] K. S. Chang and R. Y. M. Huang, *J. Appl. Polym. Sci.*, **13**, 1459 (1969).
[42] M. Hess and R. F. Kratz, *J. Polym. Sci., Part A-2*, **4**, 731 (1966).
[43] W. N. Smith, *J. Appl. Polym. Sci.*, **11**, 639 (1967).
[44] H. E. Pickett, M. J. R. Cantow, and J. F. Johnson, *J. Polym. Sci., Part C*, **21**, 67 (1968).
[45] A. R. Stokes, *Proc. Phys. Soc.*, **61**, 382 (1948).
[46] P. E. Pierce and J. E. Armonas, *J. Polym. Sci., Part C*, **21**, 23 (1968).
[47] L. H. Tung, *J. Appl. Polym. Sci.*, **13**, 775 (1969).
[48] E. M. Rosen and T. Provder, *Separ. Sci.*, **5**, 485 (1970).
[49] T. Vladimiroff, *J. Appl. Polym. Sci.*, **14**, 1397 (1970).
[50] S. T. E. Aldhouse and D. M. Stanford, Paper presented at the 5th International GPC Seminar, London, May 1968.
[51] J. H. Duerksen and A. E. Hamielec, *J. Polym. Sci., Part C*, **21**, 83 (1968).
[52] J. H. Duerksen and A. E. Hamielec, *J. Appl. Polym. Sci.*, **12**, 2225 (1968).
[53] L. H. Tung, *Separ. Sci.*, **5**, 429 (1970).
[54] A. E. Hamielec and W. H. Ray, *J. Appl. Polym. Sci.*, **13**, 1317 (1969).

[55] S. T. Balke and A. E. Hamielec, *J. Appl. Polym. Sci.*, **13**, 1381 (1969).

[56] A. E. Hamielec, *J. Appl. Polym. Sci.*, **14**, 1519 (1970).

[57] E. M. Barrall II, M. J. R. Cantow, and J. F. Johnson, *J. Appl. Polym. Sci.*, **12**, 1373 (1968).

[58] J. E. Hazell, L. A. Prince, and H. E. Stapelfeldt, *J. Polym. Sci., Part C*, **21**, 43 (1968).

[59] D. J. Harmon, 2nd International Seminar on GPC, Preprints, Boston, 1965.

[60] A. Lambert, *Polymer*, **10**, 213 (1969).

[61] K. A. Boni, F. A. Sliemers, and P. B. Stickney, *J. Polym. Sci., Part A-2*, **6**, 1567 (1968).

[62] J. C. Moore, *Separ. Sci.*, **5**, 723 (1970).

[63] W. W. Yau and S. W. Fleming, *J. Appl. Polym. Sci.*, **12**, 2111 (1968).

[64] E. M. Barrall II and J. F. Johnson, *Separ. Sci.*, **5**, 415 (1970).

[65] W. W. Yau, H. L. Suchan, and C. P. Malone, *J. Polym. Sci., Part A-2*, **6**, 1349 (1968).

[66] D. J. Harmon, *Separ. Sci.*, **5**, 403 (1970).

[67] K. J. Bombaugh, W. A. Dark, and R. N. King, *J. Polym. Sci., Part C*, **21**, 131 (1968).

[68] K. H. Altgelt, *Separ. Sci.*, **5**, 777 (1970).

[69] J. N. Little, J. L. Water, K. J. Bombaugh, and W. J. Pauplis, *J. Polym. Sci., Part A-2*, **7**, 1775 (1969).

[70] W. Heitz and H. Ullner, *Makromol. Chem.*, **120**, 58 (1968).

[71] J. L. Waters, *J. Polym. Sci., Part A-2*, **8**, 411 (1970).

[72] C. P. Malone, H. L. Suchan, and W. W. Yau, *J. Polym. Sci., Part B*, **7**, 781 (1969).

[73] J. R. Runyon, D. E. Barnes, J. F. Rudd, and L. H. Tung, *J. Appl. Polym. Sci.*, **13**, 2359 (1969).

[74] H. E. Adams, *Separ. Sci.*, **6**, 259 (1971).

[75] S. L. Terry and F. Rodriquez, *J. Polym. Sci., Part C*, **21**, 191 (1968).

[76] R. A. Mendelson and E. E. Drott, *J. Polym. Sci., Part B*, **6**, 795 (1968).

[77] L. H. Tung, *J. Polym. Sci., Part A-2*, **7**, 47 (1969).

[78] R. B. Prime and B. Wunderlich, *J. Polym. Sci., Part A-2*, **7**, 2061 (1969).

[79] A. Kotera, "Fractional Precipitation," in *Polymer Fractionation* (M. J. R. Cantow, ed.), Academic, New York, 1967, Chap. B.1.

[80] J. H. Elliott, "Fractional Solution," in *Polymer Fractionation* (M. J. R. Cantow, ed.), Academic, New York, Chap. B.2.

[81] M. L. Huggins and H. Okamota, "Theoretical Considerations," in *Polymer Fractionation* (M. J. R. Cantow, ed.), Academic, New York, Chap. A.

[82] R. Koningsveld and A. J. Staverman, *J. Polym. Sci., Part A-2*, **6**, 305, 325, 349, 367, 383 (1968).

[83] J. Klein, *Angew. Makromol. Chem.*, **10**, 21 (1970).

[84] E. Schiedermaier and J. Klein, *Angew. Makromol. Chem.*, **10**, 169 (1970).

[85] J. Klein and U. Wittenberger, *Makromol. Chem.*, **122**, 1 (1969).

[86] M. L. Huggins, *J. Polym. Sci., Part A-2*, **5**, 1221 (1967).

[87] K. Kamide and C. Nakayama, *Makromol. Chem.*, **129**, 289 (1969).

[88] E. Kobayashi, S. Okamura, and R. Signer, *J. Appl. Polym. Sci.*, **12**, 1661 (1968).

[89] R. Koningsveld and A. J. Pennings, *Rec. Trav. Chim. Pays-Bas*, **83**, 552 (1964).

[90] T. Kawai, *Makromol. Chem.*, **102**, 125 (1967).

[91] C. Booth and C. Price, *Polymer*, **7**, 85 (1966).

[92] G. V. Schulz, *Z. Physik. Chem.*, **B47**, 155 (1940).

[93] L. H. Tung, "Treatment of Data," in *Polymer Fraction* (M. J. R. Cantow, ed.), Academic, New York, 1967, Chap. E.

[94] M. Ueda, *Makromol. Chem.*, **90**, 139 (1966).

[95] T. Homma, K. Kawahara, H. Fugit, and M. Ueda, *Makromol. Chem.*, **67**, 132 (1963).

[96] G. Beall, *J. Polym. Sci.*, **4**, 483 (1949).

[97] M. J. R. Cantow, "Additional Methods of Fractionation," in *Polymer Fractionation* (M. J. R. Cantow, ed.), Academic, New York, 1967, Chap. G.

[98] T. Nagata, *J. Appl. Polym. Sci.*, **13**, 2601 (1969).

[99] D. H. Solomon and J. J. Hopwood, *J. Appl. Polym. Sci.*, **10**, 993 (1966).

[100] M. G. Wirick and M. H. Waldman, *J. Appl. Polym. Sci.*, **14**, 579 (1970).

[101] J. Springer, K. Ueberreiter, and R. Wenzel, *Makromol. Chem.*, **96**, 122 (1966).

[102] A. Mattiussi, F. Manescalchi, and G. B. Gechele, *Eur. Polym. J.*, **5**, 105 (1969).

[103] R. B. Mohite, S. Gundiah, and S. L. Kapur, *Makromol. Chem.*, **116**, 280 (1968).

[104] N. J. Mills, *Eur. Polym. J.*, **5**, 405 (1969).

[105] W. Ring, H. J. Cantow, and W. Holtrup, *Eur. Polym. J.*, **2**, 151 (1966).

[106] M. D. Baijal, R. M. Diler, and F. R. Pool, *Macromolecules*, **2**, 679 (1969).

[107] E. Powell, *Polymer*, **8**, 211 (1967).

[108] F. C. Baines and J. C. Bevington, *Eur. Polym. J.*, **3**, 593 (1967).

[109] A. Nakajima, F. Hamda, and T. Shimizu, *Makromol. Chem.*, **90**, 229 (1966).

[110] R. C. Schulz and N. Vollkommer, *Makromol. Chem.*, **116**, 288 (1968).

[111] G. Pezzin, G. Sanmartin, and F. Zilio-Grandi, *J. Appl. Polym. Sci.*, **11**, 1539 (1967).

[112] L. Lovric, *J. Polym. Sci.*, *Part A-2*, **7**, 1357 (1969).

[113] J. Danon and J. Jozefonvicz, *Eur. Polym. J.*, **5**, 405 (1969).

[114] V. Desreux and M. C. Spiegels, *Bull. Soc. Chem. Belges*, **59**, 476 (1950).

[115] C. A. Baker and R. J. P. Williams, *J. Chem. Soc.*, **1956**, 2352.

[116] R. S. Porter and J. F. Johnson, "Chromatographic Fractionation," in *Polymer Fractionation* (M. J. R. Cantow, ed.), Academic, New York 1967, Chap. B.3.

[117] N. S. Schneider, J. D. Loconti, and L. G. Holmes, *J. Appl. Polym. Sci.*, **5**, 354 (1961).

[118] N. S. Schneider and L. G. Holmes, *J. Polym. Sci.*, **38**, 552 (1959).

[119] K. Yamaguchi and S. Saeda, *J. Polym. Sci.*, *Part A-2*, **7**, 1303 (1969).

[120] G. V. Schulz, P. Deussen, and A. G. R. Scholz, *Makromol. Chem.*, **69**, 47 (1963).

[121] W. V. Smith, *J. Polym. Sci., Part A-2*, **8**, 207 (1970).

[122] J. F. Henderson and J. M. Hulme, *J. Appl. Polym. Sci.*, **11**, 2349 (1967).

[123] S. R. Caplan, *J. Polym. Sci.*, **35**, 409 (1959).

[124] E. M. Bristow and B. Westall, *Polymer*, **8**, 609 (1967).

[125] A. Cosani, E. Peggion, E. Scoffone, and A. S. Verdini, *Makromol. Chem.*, **97**, 113 (1966).

[126] R. W. Ford and J. D. Ilavsky, *J. Appl. Polym. Sci.*, **12**, 2299 (1968).

[127] R. T. Traskos, N. S. Schneider, and A. S. Hoffman, *J. Appl. Polym. Sci.*, **12**, 509 (1968).

[128] R. S. Porter, M. J. R. Cantow, and J. F. Johnson, *Makromol. Chem.*, **94**, 143 (1966).

[129] K. Yamaguchi, *Makromol. Chem.*, **128**, 19 (1969).

[130] H. W. McCormick, "Sedimentation," in *Polymer Fractionation* (M. J. R. Cantow, ed.), Academic, New York, 1967, Chap. C.2.

[131] T. Kotaka and N. Donkai, *J. Polym. Sci., Part A-2*, **6**, 1457 (1968).

[132] I. H. Billick, *J. Phys. Chem.*, **66**, 1941 (1962).

[133] W. J. Closs, B. R. Jennings, and H. G. Jerrard, *Eur. Polym. J.*, **4**, 639, 651 (1968).

[134] J. E. Blair and J. W. Williams, *J. Phys. Chem.*, **68**, 161 (1968).

[135] R. L. Baldwin, *J. Amer. Chem. Soc.*, **76**, 402 (1954).

[136] K. Lamers, F. Putney, I. Z. Steinberg, and H. K. Schachman, *Arch. Biochem. Biophys.*, **103**, 379 (1963).

[137] Th. G. Scholte and B. J. Rietveld, *Makromol. Chem.*, **94**, 60 (1966).

[138] M. Wales and H. Coll, Paper presented at the Conference on Advances in Ultracentrifugal Analysis, New York, February 1968.

[139] D. Decker, *Makromol. Chem.*, **125**, 136 (1969).

[140] Th. G. Scholte, *J. Polym. Sci., Part A-2*, **6**, 91 (1968).

[141] A. Kotera, N. Iso, A. Senuma, and T. Hamada, *J. Polym. Sci., Part A-2*, **5**, 277 (1967).

[142] H. Fujita, *Mathematical Theory of Sedimentation Analysis*, Academic, New York, 1962, p. 281.

[143] T. H. Donnelly, *J. Phys. Chem.*, **70**, 1862 (1966).

[144] Th. G. Scholte, *J. Polym. Sci., Part A-2*, **6**, 111 (1968).

[145] S. W. Provencher, *J. Chem. Phys.*, **46**, 3229 (1967).

[146] D. A. Lee, *J. Polym. Sci., Part A-2*, **8**, 1039 (1970).

[147] Th. G. Scholte, *Eur. Polym. J.*, **6**, 51 (1970).

[148] J. J. Burke and T. A. Orofino, *J. Polym. Sci., Part A-2*, **7**, 1 (1969).

[149] J. M. G. Cowie and P. M. Toporowski, *Eur. Polym. J.*, **5**, 493 (1969).

[150] H. Giesekus, "Turbidimetric Titration," in *Polymer Fractionation* (M. J. R. Cantow, ed.), Academic, New York, 1967, Chap. C.1.

[151] W. Rabel and K. Ueberreiter, *Kolloid-Z.*, **198**, 1 (1964).

[152] Z. Mencik, *Collec. Czech. Chem. Commun.*, **24**, 3185 (1959).

[153] C. F. Cornet, *Polymer*, **9**, 9 (1968).

[154] M. G. Rayner, *Polymer*, **10**, 827 (1969).

[155] F. W. Peaker and M. G. Rayner, *Appl. Polym. Symp.*, **8**, 1 (1969).

[156] U. Gruber and H. G. Elias, *Makromol. Chem.*, 78, 58, 72 (1964); 86, 168 (1965); *J. Polym. Sci.*, *Part B*, 1, 337 (1963).
[157] P. I. Brewer, *Polymer*, 9, 545 (1968).
[158] R. W. Baker, *J. Appl. Polym. Sci.*, 13, 369 (1969).
[159] W. Burchard and H. J. Cantow, "Isothermal Diffusion," in *Polymer Fractionation* (M. J. R. Cantow, ed.), Academic, New York, 1967, Chap. C.3.
[160] H. Matsuda, H. Aonuma, and S. Kuroiwa, *J. Appl. Polym. Sci.*, 14, 335 (1970).
[161] W. J. Langford and D. J. Vaughan, *J. Chromatogr.*, 2, 564 (1959).
[162] H. Inagaki, H. Matsuda, and F. Kamiyama, *Macromolecules*, 1, 520 (1968).
[163] F. Kamiyama, H. Matsuda, and H. Inagaki, *Makromol. Chem.*, 125, 286 (1969).
[164] H. Inagaki, J. Miyamoto, and F. Kamiyama, *J. Polym. Sci.*, *Part B*, 7, 329 (1969).
[165] E. P. Otocka and M. Y. Hellman, *Macromolecules*, 3, 362 (1970).

Rheology of Adhesion

D. H. KAELBLE

Science Center

North American Rockwell Corporation

Thousand Oaks, California

I. INTRODUCTION

Adhesion is a physical-chemical phenomenon which still defies rigorous theoretical definition. At the molecular level we have the following definitions for adhesion and cohesion:

<u>Adhesion</u> - the molecular force exerted across a surface of con-

Copyright © 1971 by Marcel Dekker, Inc. *NO PART of this work may be reproduced or utilized in any form or by any means*, electronic or mechanical, including xerography, photocopying, microfilm, and recording, or by any information storage and retrieval system, without the written permission of the publisher.

tact between unlike liquids or solids which resists interfacial separation.

    Cohesion - the molecular force exerted across a surface within a liquid or solid that resists internal rupture.

These definitions describe the molecular level of response and are expressed in terms of force per unit area, or stress, rather than the conventional free energy or work terms. Adhesion and cohesion are intimately related subjects since, by definition, adhesion becomes cohesion when the physical-chemical properties of the interacting materials become identical.

    Several additional definitions describe important micro- and macroscopic aspects of adhesion phenomena. We shall employ the following definitions of an adhesive and adhesive joint:

    Adhesive - a material capable of bonding and holding adherends together by means of surface attachment.

    Adhesive joint - a composite structure whose properties depend upon the bulk properties of both adhesive and adherend and the interphases which join these bulk phases.

The above definitions introduce the subject of rheology and viscoelastic state as a fundamental proposition in micro- and macroscopic response. For an adhesive to bond it must display the viscous properties of a liquid in order to wet, spread, and penetrate the surface roughness of the adherend. To provide the holding function, the adhesive must display the elastic properties of a solid to provide strength and creep resistance to the adhesive joint. The bonding state of an adhesive is thus rheologically distinguished from the holding state. Thermal or solvolytic activation may be required to provide a bonding state for normally solid adhesives. Conversely, an adhesive may be a liquid in which case polymerization or crosslinking provide the mechanism for in situ solidification after bonding is accomplished. A very special class of materials termed pressure-sensitive adhesives provides a special balance of viscoelastic properties which permit both the bonding and holding function at ambient conditions.

    Performance of an adhesive joint is evaluated by testing of thermal, electrical, optical, acoustical, and mechanical response. Destructive mechanical testing provides the most commonly accepted standard for the evaluation of adhesive performance in adhesive joints. All types of statistical variants enter destructive test data which reflect the direct operation of Murphy's law which is approxi-

mated in the following statement: "If anything can go wrong, it will!"
While the operation of Murphy's law introduces dilemmas to the test
analyst, it provides the fundamental justification for destructive testing. Put in other words, Murphy's law states that failure proceeds
by a least stress or least work mechanism. An adhesive joint con-
sisting of N bulk phases presents the maximum number $0.5N(N-1)$
interphases for a total of $0.5N(N+1)$ mechanisms of cohesive and
interfacial failure. Stress may be distributed through the adhesive
joint in parallel or series fashion or in a complex balance between
these extremes of loading. Furthermore, the stress may be dila-
tional (hydrostatic) or deformational (shear) and the balance between
these types of stress vary with position inside the joint and also
with time during the test.

The evaluation and prediction of performance for adhesive joints
has developed as an independent discipline which is termed fracture
mechanics. Fracture mechanics is concerned with the system response at the micro- and macroscopic level. The molecular aspects
of adhesion are normally considered to describe a branch of physical
chemistry and more particularly relate to surface chemistry. Between surface chemistry and fracture mechanics exists a broad gap
in both the physical and phenomenological description of the bonding
and failure processes of adhesion. It is in this broad middle ground
that rheology, as an interdisciplinary science concerned with both
physical state, time dependence, and stress-strain response, finds
a natural position in correlating the molecular and macroscopic aspects of adhesion phenomena.

In this review of the rheology of adhesion we will introduce the
fracture mechanics viewpoint first and examine the content of this
argument. The consequences of introducing the rheological viewpoint
into fracture mechanics will be explored. Finally, the extension of
the rheological argument to include surface chemistry considerations
will be examined. In this manner we shall progress back from the
macroscopic to the molecular consideration. Although this mode of
subject development is a reversal of the usual presentation, it may
provide a new insight into the important role of rheology in adhesion
phenomena.

II. FRACTURE MECHANICS

Mechanics, in its broad definition, is the study of the responses
of bodies or systems to forces [1]. Fracture mechanics applies
stress analysis and energy balances to define the system response
to forces in terms of a definite mathematical model. Fracture me-

chanics models for adhesive or cohesive failure sometimes tend to
emphasize propositions involving mathematical simplicity at the expense of physical exactness. The advantage of viewing the fracture
process in terms of an exact mathematical model very often over-
shadows the fact that the assumptions of the model do not coincide
with real physical response.

The Griffith [2,3] theory of cohesive failure in brittle materials
provided the first formal theory which focused attention on the central role of microscopic cracks or defects in the mechanism of failure. The Griffith model for failure by crack propagation is based
upon the following assumptions:

1. The crack is an ellipse of vanishing minor axis.
2. Hooke's law holds up to the corner of the crack.
3. The plane of the crack is perpendicular to the applied load.
4. The crack will grow spontaneously when the rate of decrease
in stored elastic energy within the volume of the material equals or
exceeds the rate of surface energy increase.

The first three assumptions define a two-dimensional case for a flat
plate with an elliptical crack extending through its thickness. The
stress analysis of this case due to Inglis [4] provides the following
relation for the stress concentration at the crack tip:

$$\sigma_m/\sigma = 2(c/r)^{1/2} \tag{1}$$

where σ_m = maximum stress at the crack tip, σ = applied stress on
the plate, c = depth of surface crack or half the length of the major
axis for an ellipse cut through the interior of the sheet, and r = radii
of curvature of the crack tip.

The fourth of the above assumptions provides the following familiar
relation for the case of plane stress:

$$\sigma_c = (2E\gamma/\pi c)^{1/2} \tag{2}$$

where σ_c = critical value of the applied stress σ acting on the plate
normal to the plane of the crack, E = Young's modulus of the plate
material, and γ = surface (or interfacial) tension of the crack surface. Equation (2) provides a simple mathematical model which relates material strength (σ_c) to a rheological property (E), a surface
property (γ), and a microgeometry (c). The natural cracks which
determine the strength of brittle materials may have small dimensions where $c \leq 1$ μ and $2r$ approximates the molecular dimensions.

For materials which display slight ductility so that plastic flow occurs at the crack tip during crack propagation, Orowan [5,6] has modified the classical Griffith relation by the following expression:

$$\sigma_c = \left[\frac{2E(\gamma + W_p)}{\pi c}\right]^{1/2} \tag{3}$$

where W_p = work of plastic deformation per unit area of surface formation.

Organic and polymeric materials display solid surface tensions of γ = 6 to 50 dynes/cm as measured by critical wettability [7]. Inorganic and metallic surfaces—in the absence of organic contamination—are estimated to display surface tensions which range from γ = 500 to 5000 dynes/cm [7]. Measured values of $(\gamma + W_p)$ from fracture mechanics experiments provide the following values [8]:

Material	Experimental $(\gamma + W_p)$ (dyn/cm)
Glass	550
Polymethyl methacrylate (PMMA)	3×10^5
Steel	1×10^6

which illustrates that W_p may be a minor factor in the fracture of glass which behaves as a brittle solid. With tough solids such as PMMA and steel, the surface tension contribution to $(\gamma + W_p)$ may become negligible and the major resistance to crack propagation derives from the plastic work of surface formation. Introduction of the Orowan notion of plastic flow at the crack tip automatically complicates the analysis of the stress distribution at the crack tip. Equation (1) no longer applies within the plastically deformed zone, and other approximations are required to define the stress field in this critical region.

Irwin [1] has extended the Griffith theory to treat the case of elastic-plastic materials by a method which retains the linear-elastic assumptions and provides the Griffith equation as a limiting case. The Irwin analysis has been applied to a number of adhesive joint systems where both cohesive and adhesive fracture are recognized [1,9-11]. Williams and coworkers [12-15] have recently applied the Griffith criteria to selected cases of cohesive and adhesive failure where crack propagation occurs by pressurizing a blister following the method of Dannenberg [16].

Rivlin and Thomas [17] have applied a modified Griffith theory to crack propagation in elastomers through the following relation:

$$T = -\frac{1}{h}\left(\frac{\partial W}{\partial c}\right)_\ell \tag{4}$$

where T = tearing energy, W = elastically stored energy per unit volume available to the crack, c = crack length, h = thickness of the sheet, and ℓ = denotes that crack displacement occurs at constant sheet length with no external work input.

Greensmith and Thomas [18] have shown that the tearing energy T depends upon both rate and temperature and thus includes a viscoelastic contribution not described by the Griffith surface energy criterion. When a thin rubber sheet is torn where the material at the crack tip is under simple tension, Thomas [19] has shown that the tearing energy is defined by the following relation:

$$T \simeq W_b d \tag{5}$$

where W_b = work per unit volume to extend a specimen to failure in simple extension, and d = diameter of the crack tip.

Typical values for tear energy, such as $T \simeq 10^5$ to 10^8 dyn/cm, greatly exceed the surface tension γ = 25 to 38 dyn/cm determined for elastomers by critical wettability measurements [20,21]. Further work has shown that T correlates with W_b, assuming constant d, when the roughness of the torn surface remains unchanged [22]. When tearing is constrained and propagates in a straight line, Gent and Henry [23] show that the tearing energy data at different rates and temperatures can be superposed according to the conventions of the equation of Williams, Landel, and Ferry (WLF) [24]. For rubbery materials we are led to conclude that the tearing energy as expressed by Eq. (4) or (5) is a volumetric property primarily related to W_b [20,22].

This brief review of the Griffith model and its several variations as applied to tough solids and rubbery materials serves to illustrate the general characteristics of fracture mechanics models. The fracture mechanics model is generally based upon continuum mechanics with assumptions of linear elasticity. The work of surface formation is introduced to satisfy the energy balance relation. The work of surface formation includes a reversible part, denoted by surface or interfacial tension γ, and an irreversible part, denoted by W_p in Eq. (3). Useful structural materials, whether metal, ceramic or polymeric, require toughness and, generally speaking, we find that

$W_p \gg \gamma$ in crack propagation experiments. The Griffith Eqs. (1) and (2) become inapplicable in a strict physical sense when $W_p > 0$ and the description of the stress distribution and effective crack geometry must be approximated by other criteria. Knauss [25] provides a clear review of these complications and current continuum mechanics approaches to their resolution.

The morphology and roughness of the fracture surface provides information concerning the velocity-dependent processes which govern crack propagation in tough materials which display elastic-plastic or rubbery response [1,25,26]. The application of the scanning electron microscope (SEM) with its high resolution and depth of field provides new impetus to fracture surface analysis [11,27]. Auger electron spectroscopy (AES) is only sensitive to those elements on the surface (escape depth of 5 to 10 Å) of a freshly fractured surface held in high vacuum of 10^{-9} torr. All elements except hydrogen and helium are detected by this method [28,29]. Micro Auger electron spectroscopy (MAES) has recently been combined with SEM to correlate the two-dimensional surface chemistry with the topology of a fracture surface at a resolution diameter of about 0.8 μ [30]. It is expected that this highly resolved information concerning microsurface chemistry and topology may provide new impetus to detailed physical-chemical studies of fracture mechanics.

III. THE LOCUS OF FAILURE

An accurate definition of the locus of failure is crucial to isolate properly the role that interfacial adhesion plays in determining adhesive performance. A test for adhesion must, by definition, result in interfacial failure. Tests of adhesive joints are not adhesion tests when cohesive failure is obtained. This apparently trivial point is a source of much confusion in reporting and interpreting test results. Lacking other independent information, true interfacial failure can be indicated by bond strength data when the following factors dominantly influence bond strength [31,32]:

1. The surface density of interfacial interactions.
2. The surface chemistry and physics of the adherend.

Rate—temperature transitions between interfacial and cohesive failure have been reported by a number of workers based upon the above criteria [32-36]. These interfacial—cohesive failure transitions are observed in peel testing. Peeling involves a teartype crack propagation analogous to the visualization of the Griffith model.

A number of studies utilizing electron microscopy [37,38], wettability measurements [36,39], and interferometry [40] have illustrated that interfacial failure of a properly bonded joint does occur
and is a common rather than a rare occurrence. Many instances are
additionally reported where microzones of cohesive failure occur
where by visual inspection failure appears to be interfacial [37-39,
41,42]. In most cases, these cohesively fractured microzones—in
the adhesive or adherend phase—can be identified with a morphologi-
cal feature of surface structure which provides a cohesive weakness
near the bonded interface. The locus of failure, by following the
Murphy's law principle (see Introduction) at the micro or molecular
level, seeks out the weak points of either two- or three-dimensional
structures and operates on these weaknesses to create the fracture
surface. We conclude from this brief review that interfacial failure,
mixed failure, and cohesive failure is demonstrated in a variety of
adhesively bonded systems. Transitions in failure mechanism can
occur due to time—temperature effects, morphology, and chemical
composition effects in either adhesive or adherend.

IV. MICROMECHANICS OF POLYMER FRACTURE

Knauss [25] points out that, strictly speaking, molecular and continuum mechanics models for fracture are incompatible. The molecular or atomistic argument deals with discrete elements. The continuum mechanics argument displaces the notion of physically discrete response. Our previous discussion of the Griffith and related
theories of fracture has shown this essential difficulty when correlating the surface tensions measured by physical chemical methods
with those determined by fracture mechanics experimentation and
analysis. A fracture analysis based on a modified Griffith criterion
superimposes a mathematical visualization upon the discrete micromechanics of fracture. The operational advantages of the continuum
visualization are obvious and well documented. However, the physical chemistry of fracture is left undefined.

The design of adhesive materials evolves from physical chemical
principles. Therefore, the gap existing between the fracture mechanics argument and the molecular concepts of adhesion and cohesion
is by necessity bridged by micromechanics models which deal with
more specific aspects of fracture. Irwin [1], for example, visual-
izes an infinite series of colinear equal length cracks separated by
a uniform center-to-center distance. Knauss [25] itemizes the following types of microdefects which may initiate fracture: (a) surface
flaw, (b) cavity or void, (c) inclusion interface, (d) combined inclusion—

void interface, (e) craze crack, and (f) molecular density variation. The growth and coalescence of such defects can be viewed as a pre-requisite mechanism to the formation of a continuous crack line. The propagation of the crack line then creates the failure surface.

Microfracture mechanics would treat fracture as the resultant of a sequence of propositions:

1. Nucleation, existence, and nature of microdefects.
2. Growth of microdefects.
3. Coalescence of microdefects.
4. Crack propagation and failure surface formation.

Fracture theory developed from a micromechanics viewpoint might accommodate some special combination of physical chemical and continuum mechanics arguments. The above sequence of microfracture steps separates the analysis into a treatment of defects as structure and stress singularities in the first two stages of fracture (Steps 1 and 2). The third stage of fracture describes the tunneling process that connects stress singularities.

The fourth and final stage of fracture involves a generalized process of crack propagation as idealized by Griffith [2,3] for brittle solids and Rivlin-Thomas [17,19] for elastomers. Detailed theories which interconnect the four stages of fracture described above are not yet fully developed for polymeric solids [43] or elastomers [20].

Recent fracture theories for elastomers due to Knauss [44] and also to Bueche and Halpin [45,46] introduce viscoelastic considerations into the crack propagation criteria with good success. The simplifying assumptions of these theories largely bypass the detailed consideration of the microdefects which coalesce to form the crack tip. These and other theories of rupture in elastomers are reviewed in excellent discussions of this subject [20,47].

The phenomenon of cavitation appears to provide a major mechanism for the early stages of microfracture which precede generalized crack propagation and failure. The stresses or pressures required to induce cavitation in cross-linked elastomers were first analyzed by Gent and Lindley [48] in the "butt joint" geometry provided by bonding a short rubber cylinder between rigid adherends and loading the joint in central tension. This test procedure was refined by Lindsey and coworkers [49,50] to permit optical monitoring of cavity formation. Oberth and Bruenner [51] have studied cavity formation around solid spherical inclusions imbeded in elastomers. Gent and Denecour [52] report studies of cavitation in swollen vulcanizates where superheating of the swelling liquid provides the cavitation stress. Kaelble and Reyleck [53,54] report measured values of boundary cavitation stress in peeling of noncross-linked elastomers over a range of peeling rates.

The phenomenon of cavitation correlates with the well-known Mullins effect in filled elastomers [55-57]. During the first cycle of tensile strain in filled elastomers a volume increase is recognized which is attributed to dewetting between rubber and filler with consequent vacuole formation. The modulus of the material is lowered by the loss of interfacial contact and may subsequently be partially or completely recovered by a rebonding process. This loss of micro-continuity does not correlate directly with resistance to crack propagation and failure properties since at low stress and strain the voids fail to coalesce to form a crack tip. This dewetting phenomenon has been extensively studied and has an important influence on the performance of propellent grains where local relaxation of volumetric strain is required [25,51,58].

The role of cavitation as a primary process of fracture in simple (nonelastic) liquids is well recognized [59]. The ability of a moving liquid film to resist splitting in the nip region between rollers correlates with a property termed "tack" in the printing industry [60]. In the rubber industry the term "tack" is generally applied to describe the resistance to separation following momentary contact between two materials under light contact pressure [61]. This latter definition of tack of viscoelastic materials has been systematized in several standard test methods [62-64]. These tests involve a butt joint geometry with a controlled time or rate sequence of compressive bonding followed by tensile deformation and rupture. The definition of tack for viscoelastic materials is complicated by the fact that the short bonding times prevent relaxation of elastic stresses at the interface. The time dependence of the bonding history is thus superimposed upon the subsequent time history of fracture. For viscous liquids one may presume a simpler model for bonding and a more complete isolation between the time histories of bonding and fracture.

Examination of several models for cavitation in viscous and viscoelastic media serves to isolate some of the principal factors in this phenomenon. Hoffman and Myers [65] have analyzed the dynamics of cavity formation and growth in thin liquid films by application of a relation derived by Poritsky [66]. The Poritsky relation expressed as a pressure difference ΔP has the following form:

$$\Delta P = P_V - P_\infty$$

$$= \rho \left(ra + \frac{3v^2}{2} \right) + \frac{2\gamma}{r} + \frac{4\eta v}{r} \tag{6}$$

where P_V = vapor pressure within the cavity, P_∞ = far field pressure
in the liquid phase, r = radii of the spherical cavity, γ = liquid-vapor
surface tension of the cavity, ρ = liquid density, η = liquid viscosity,
v = cavity growth velocity = dr/dt, and a = cavity growth accelera-
tion = dv/dt. The parenthesized terms of Eq. (6) describe the kine-
matics of cavity expansion. The cavity growth rate, v, was established experimentally by cinematographic recording at 1000 frames/
sec of cavities formed in the nip region of a rotating disk-on-cone
geometry. Systems studied included low molecular weight polyisobutylene (LMW:PIB), a LMW:PIB-sulfur dispersion, and an alkyd
varnish. Evaluation of experimental data by Hoffman and Myer
showed that for cavity sizes between r = 35 to 180 μ and growth
times between t $\simeq$ 1.5 to 9.0 msec, the kinematic terms were negligible and Eq. (6) simplifies to the following form:

$$\Delta P = P_V - P_\infty$$

$$= \frac{2\gamma}{r} + \frac{4\eta v}{r} \tag{6a}$$

In Eq. (6a) only two material constants—surface tension γ and liquid
viscosity η—remain to define the restraints to cavitation. For the
liquids studied it was shown that $2\gamma/r \leq 0.07\Delta P$ and that liquid tack
is primarily determined by the viscosity—rate product ηv at constant
r.

In simple liquids the tack measure of adhesion thus appears to be
dominantly controlled by a rheological rather than a surface or interfacial property of the system. Equation (6a) further shows that ΔP
$\propto 1/r$ and therefore cavity growth proceeds with no restrictions at
constant ΔP and can thus produce generalized fracture of the liquid.
The importance of these conclusions to practical adhesion technology
is evident. Equations (6) and (6a) treat cavity growth and therefore
leave unanswered questions concerning the nature of the initial defects which provide the cavitation nuclei.

Cavity growth in elastomeric media produces a field of biaxial
tensile deformation around the cavity very similar to that produced
by inflating a rubber balloon. The symmetric expansion of a small
cavity in an incompressible (Poisson's ratio μ = 0.5) neo-Hookian
rubbery continuum can be visualized as the inflating of a balloon of
infinitely thick walls. Green and Zerna [67] have treated the continuum aspects of this problem. Gent and coworkers have successfully
applied special forms of the Green-Zerna relations to cavitation in
cross-linked elastomers [48,52]. Kaelble [68] has considered both
surface tension and elastic stress effects for cavity growth in visco-

elastic media so that expansion of a bulk cavity is described by the following relation:

$$\Delta P = P_V - P_\infty$$

$$= \frac{2\gamma}{r} + 0.5 G(t) F(\lambda) \tag{7}$$

where $F(\lambda) = 5 - 4\lambda^{-1} - \lambda^{-4}$, $G(t) =$ time dependent shear modulus, $\lambda =$ surface extension ratio r/r_0 of the cavity, and $r_0 =$ initial cavity radius. Equation (7) differs from the relation of Gent and Lindley [48] by the addition of the surface tension stress $2\gamma/r$ which is neglected in the continuum treatment. The replacement of an equilibrium shear modulus G_C with a time-dependent modulus $G(t)$ provides additional generality to Eq. (7).

The strain function $F(\lambda)$ of Eq. (7) has a value $F(\lambda) = 0$ when $\lambda = r/r_0 = 1.0$ and a positive limit of $F(\lambda) \simeq 5.0$ when $\lambda = r/r_0 \geq 10.0$. The form of the $F(\lambda)$ function relates to the special localization of the biaxial strains near the surface of the expanded cavity. When an incompressible spherical shell is expanded, it follows from the incompressibility condition that:

$$R_0^3 - r_0^3 = R^3 - r^3$$

where R_0, $r_0 =$ initial outer and inner radii; and, R, $r =$ expanded outer and inner radii. We define the outer extension ratio $\lambda(R) = R/R_0$ and the inner extension ratio $\lambda = r/r_0$, and by substitution and rearrangement obtain the following relation for $\lambda(R)$ when $R/r \geq 1.0$:

$$\lambda(R) = \left[1 - (r/R)^3 (1 - \lambda^{-3}) \right]^{-1/3} \tag{8}$$

Equation (8) can be solved to provide functions of $\lambda(R)$ vs. R/r at various levels of surface extension ratio $\lambda = r/r_0$ for the cavity. These functions show that independent of the value of $\lambda \geq 1.0$ the values of $\lambda(R)$ diminish rapidly with increased distance R away from the cavity surface to provide values of $1.00 \leq \lambda(R) \leq 1.01$ when $R/r \geq 4.0$. This rapid decay of biaxial strain (and stress) with increased R explains the form of the $F(\lambda)$ function and describes a condition of isolation between cavities when:

$$D \geq 4(r_1 + r_2) \tag{9}$$

where $D =$ center to center distance between cavities; and r_1, $r_2 =$ radii of adjacent expanded cavities. Since Eq. (7) describes an isolated cavity, it follows that Eq. (9) describes the necessary minimum distance between adjacent isolated cavities.

The cavitation theory for viscoelastic media, expressed in simple form by Eqs. (7) through (9), rationalizes the experimental result:

$$\bar{\sigma} + P_V - P_\infty \simeq 2.5 G(t) \tag{10}$$

determined for diverse modes of cavitation with a variety of rubbery polymers [48,54]. Equation (10) introduces the triaxial tension:

$$\bar{\sigma} = \tfrac{1}{3} (\sigma_1 + \sigma_2 + \sigma_3)$$

σ_1, σ_2, and σ_3 are the orthogonal principal tensile stresses on a unit cube enclosing the cavity. Very often $\bar{\sigma}$ and P_V are used interchangeably. In certain cases of cavitation, such as vacuole formation where $P_V \simeq 0$, it is important to distinguish between the effects of internal pressurization and triaxial tension as driving forces for cavity growth. Equation (7) reduces to Eq. (10) when: (a) the surface tension stress is negligible, $2\gamma/r \ll 0.5 G(t) F(\lambda)$, and (b) when the cavity surface strain $\lambda = r/r_0$ is sufficiently high that $F(\lambda) \simeq 5.0$.

The triaxial tension $\bar{\sigma}$ measure of tack characterizes the butt joint test methods [62-64]. When applied to elastomeric materials which display high extensibility, Eq. (10) would predict a correlation between $\bar{\sigma}$ and the time-dependent modulus $G(t)$. An analysis of "pressure sensitive tack" of soft elastomer adhesives by Dahlquist [69] concludes that this property is dominantly controlled by viscoelastic properties. Adhesion as measured by tack testing and a correlation $\bar{\sigma} \propto G(t)$ again points out that rheology enters the practical definition of adhesion in a fundamental manner. The correlation between tack bond strength and rheological response involves a cavitation model for failure wherein the surface tension stress $2\gamma/r$ appears as a nondominant contribution to $\bar{\sigma}$.

The important notion of an initial cavity radius r_0 appears in the cavitation model for elastomeric or viscoelastic materials described by Eq. (7) and forms the basis for defining $\lambda = r/r_0$ and the magnitude of $F(\lambda)$. The introduction of r_0 automatically introduces the notion of stable cavitation nuclei as a microscopic feature of the bulk or interfacial structure of elastomeric materials. We may note that while the term r_0 does not explicitly appear in Eq. (6) or (6a), for viscous liquids the notion of cavitation nuclei is implied by these relations. Analysis of cavitation data by Kaelble [68] reveals that the initial radius is $r_0 \geq 1.0 \ \mu$ in order that the surface tension stress $2\gamma/r$ be negligible in typical elastomers where $G(t) \simeq 1 \times 10^6$ to 1×10^7 dyn/cm^2.

The experimental confirmation of cavitation nuclei of $r_0 \geq 1.0$ μ in polymeric media has recently been shown in the studies of Murray and Hull [70,71]. Earlier studies of Kambour [72-74] had revealed that crack propagation in glassy amorphous plastics was preceded by a phenomenon termed crazing. The zone of crazing precedes the crack tip and functions to delocalize stress at the crack tip and also to produce a textured fracture surface by the irregular propagation of the crack front through the crazed region. Murray and Hull [71] detected cavity nuclei of $r_0 \geq 1.0$ μ which experience cavity growth and coalescence to produce the irregular crack front by direct observation of the optical interference effects in the crazing region of the advancing crack in polystyrene.

Finer details of the micro and molecular mechanisms of crazing and crack propagation in polystyrene of narrow and broad molecular weight distribution are reported in the studies of Hayward and Brough [75]. Fracture surfaces were created at room temperature and $-196°$C for polymers of 35,000, 82,000, and 220,000 molecular weight. For polystyrene the minimum molecular weight $M = 2M_e \simeq 40,000$ characterizes incipient entanglement network formation [76]. The lowest molecular weight polymer, with $M = 35,000$, displayed generally smoother fracture surfaces due to lack of entanglement structure. The highest molecular weight material with an average of eleven entanglements per chain gives rise to highly extended filaments on the fracture surface, apparently due to entanglement network orientation in the craze region. The high elongation and orientation of these filaments is indicative of either adiabatic heating or isothermal transition to a rubbery state response within the stressed filament.

An analytic model for cavity growth in compressible (i.e., Poisson's ratio < 0.50) solids such as glassy polymers is not presently available. The stress and strain field analysis for cavitation in the solid phase is expected to be more complicated than for either elastomers or viscous liquids. Development of such a model would contribute importantly to an improved definition of fracture toughness and cohesive strength for solid polymeric adhesives.

This brief review of microfracture mechanics indicates that a detailed description of fracture mechanisms can include several stages of microfailure which precede crack growth. The microdefects and sequence of microfracture steps outlined in the introduction to this section are experienced in studies of liquid, elastomer, and solid-state fracture. The micromechanics of adhesive bonding can be well visualized as a reverse sequence of the micromechanics steps which describe fracture. The viscoelastic theory of polymer autohesion by Anand and coworkers [77-81], for example, treats both bonding and fracture from a micromechanics viewpoint.

V. RHEOLOGY OF BONDING

The objective of adhesive bonding is to establish molecular con-
tinuity between adhesive and adherend by displacement of the intervening vapor phase through the wetting of the adherend by adhesive.
The thermodynamic work of adhesion W_a is expressed by the familiar
Young-Dupre relation for an ideally smooth solid surface [7]:

$$W_a = (\gamma_{s0} - \gamma_{sv}) + \gamma_{Lv}(1 + \cos \theta)$$

$$= \gamma_{s0} + \gamma_{Lv} - \gamma_{Ls} \tag{11}$$

where W_a = reversible work of adhesion, γ_{s0} = solid surface tension
in vacuum, γ_{sv} = solid-vapor interfacial tension, γ_{Lv} = liquid-vapor
interfacial tension, γ_{Ls} = liquid-solid interfacial tension, and θ =
liquid-solid contact angle at equilibrium.

The nominal work of adhesion W_a' defines the equilibrium between
the liquid and solid by the following relation [7]:

$$W_a' = \gamma_{Lv}(1 + \cos \theta)$$

$$= \gamma_{sv} + \gamma_{Lv} - \gamma_{Ls} \tag{12}$$

which neglects the reduction in solid surface tension $(\gamma_{s0} - \gamma_{sv})$ due to
vapor adsorption. Equation (12) thus describes the liquid interaction
with the adsorption layer of the solid surface. Zisman and coworkers
have made extensive use of Eq. (12) in the analysis of contact angle
data of organic liquids on polymeric substrates. The development of
the critical surface tension γ_c characterization of solid surface properties makes a graphical analysis of $\cos \theta$ vs. γ_L data to obtain the
critical wetting condition $\cos \theta = 1.0$ when $\gamma_L \leq \gamma_c$.

Zisman [7] and more recently Sharpe and Schonhorn [82] have
postulated that one criterion of good bonding is the requirement that
γ_{Lv} for an adhesive be equal or less than γ_c for the solid substrate
so that the contact angle $\theta = 0$ for the liquid-solid interface. A number of experimental studies have shown that the strength of an adhesive joint increases with decrease in adhesive-adherend contact
angle [83-87].

When contact angle criteria are applied to the wetting of molten
polymeric adhesives, the studies of Schonhorn, Frisch, and Kwei [88]
reveal the importance of considering the time-dependent contact angle
θ_t. In this study the kinetics of interfacial wetting was represented
by the following relation:

$$\cos \theta_t / \cos \theta = H(a_T t) \tag{13}$$

where θ_t = contact angle at time t, θ = equilibrium contact angle at t = ∞, $H(a_T t)$ = function of a reduced variable a_T multiplied by time t, $a_T = \gamma_{Lv}/L_W \eta$ is a time shift factor, γ_{Lv} = polymer surface tension, η = polymer viscosity, and L_W = a characteristic length which is a property of the polymer—substrate interaction. The reduced variables of Eq. (13) have been applied to generate master curves of $\cos \theta_t / \cos \theta$ vs. $\gamma_{Lv} t / \eta L_W$ where temperature effects are isolated in the ratio γ_{Lv}/η.

Newman has analyzed Eq. (13) in terms of a model for interfacial capillary flow and proposes an equation of the following form:

$$\cos \theta_t = \cos \theta [1 - A \exp (-ct)] \tag{13a}$$

where A = constant, and $c \simeq a_T = \gamma_{Lv}/\eta L_W$. Equation (13a) provides a more definite form for the $\cos \theta_t$ function. Cherry and Holmes [90] point out that Eq. (13a) represents the integrated form of the relation:

$$R = \frac{d \cos \theta_t}{dt} = c(\cos \theta - \cos \theta_t)$$

$$= \frac{\gamma_{Lv}}{\eta L_W} (\cos \theta - \cos \theta_t) \tag{14}$$

where R = rate of spreading. Equation (14) isolates the kinetic aspects of the wetting process between adhesive and adherend in the parameter R. In Eqs. (13), (13a), and (14) the fundamental implications of the characteristic length L_W remain unclear. Cherry and Holmes [90] apply values of c = 3.3×10^{-3} sec^{-1}, $\eta = 3 \times 10^3$ poise, and γ_{Lv} = 35 dyn/cm to calculate a value of $L_W = 3.6 \times 10^{-3}$ cm for Elvax 200 (a copolymer of ethylene with 28 wt % of vinyl acetate) on an aluminum substrate at 149°C. Schonhorn, Frisch, and Kwei [88] show that for Elvax 200 on three substrates: $(L_W)_{mica} > (L_W)_{Al} > (L_W)_{Teflon}$. Since the mica surface is the smooth cleavage plane while Al and Teflon display microroughness, it would appear that the above ordering of L_W does not correlate with surface roughness. The magnitude of L_W calculated by Holmes and Cherry is evidently too large to reflect segment jump dimensions or other kinetic features of polymer motion.

The models of Newman [89] and Cherry and Holmes [90] treat the effect of surface roughness on the kinetics of spreading. The model of Newman considers interfacial capillaries while Cherry and Holmes consider the ratio of true surface area to the ideal plane area. The kinetics of spreading of a spherical drop on an ideal smooth surface is treated in a detailed analysis by Yin [91]. The analysis of Yin

postulates that spreading is promoted by the net surface tensions at
the smooth interface rather than capillary forces. Although present
theory does not completely resolve the complicated processes of
spreading of liquids on solids, the several models for this process
do provide clearer definitions for "wetting" and "spreading." The
degree of wetting would be defined by the thermodynamic criteria of
Eqs. (11) and (12) where $\theta = \theta_\infty$. The degree of spreading would be
related to θ_t of Eqs. (13) and (14) and the kinetics of spreading defined by $R = d \cos \theta_t / dt \propto \gamma_{Lv} / \eta L_W$.

Recent experimental studies of Cherry and Muddaris [92] have
been directed toward a direct examination of whether wetting equi-
librium, defined by $\cos \theta_\infty$, or spreading kinetics, defined by $\gamma_{Lv} / \eta L_W$,
controls bond strength. The results of this study appear to show that
both variables are significant for the case of a molten polyethylene
bonding to a series of modified epoxy lacquers. Newman and co-
workers [93] also provide new experimental data on spreading kinetics of ethylene—vinyl acetate copolymers both in the form of advancing contact angles and penetration into slits representing two-dimensional capillaries. Dettre and Johnson [94] have recently demonstrated that the spreading of molten polymers may in some cases
involve a combination of a spherical cap in the center of the drop
and a projecting annular foot at the edge of the drop. The several
analyses for the kinetics of spreading visualize the spreading drop
as a spherical cap [88-93] and therefore do not analytically define
the case recognized by Johnson and Dettre.

Based on this brief review we can conclude that both the equilib-
rium and kinetic aspects of bonding as measured by θ_∞ and $\theta_t - \theta_\infty$,
respectively, have merit. The simple formulation of bonding cri-
teria in terms of contact angle measurement provides a convenient
means of studying the interfacial process of bonding through an ob-
servable microscopic variable. The molecular process of interfacial
interaction, where the adhesive is polymeric, requires a much more
detailed consideration of both thermodynamic and viscoelastic constraints to bonding. Some aspects of these molecular arguments have
now been advanced and provide an interesting insight into the phenomena of fracture and bonding already discussed.

VI. MOLECULAR CRITERIA FOR ADHESION

As mentioned in the Introduction, a definition of adhesion which
pertains to both the thermodynamics and mechanics defines a force
per unit area or stress across an interface. Statements relating to
this type of definition describe intermolecular forces and separation

distances. The review articles of Good [95], Gardon [96], and Fowkes [97] provide extensive discussions of the application of classical London-Debye-Keesom [98-100] statements for the van der Waals forces which enter into the Lennard-Jones 6-12 potential function [101] for an ideal adsorption interface. Recent modifications and extensions of the theories of Good [95] and Fowkes [97] now provide more detailed insight into the molecular mechanisms of liquid-solid interactions. Tamai, Makuuchi, and Suzuki [102] introduce the following relation for interfacial tension:

$$\gamma_{12} = \gamma_1 + \gamma_2 - 2(\gamma_1^d \gamma_2^d)^{1/2} - I_{12} \tag{15}$$

where γ_{12} = interfacial tension; γ_1, γ_2 = surface tensions for Components 1 and 2; γ_1^d, γ_2^d = dispersion part of surface tensions; and I_{12} = defines interfacial interactions of the nondispersion type. Equation (15) has been utilized by Tamai and coworker to analyze contact angle data at the hydrocarbon-water-solid interface where the solid is either metallic or polymeric. Dann [103] has applied Eq. (15) to vapor-liquid-solid interactions where the liquids are polar and the solids are polymeric.

Kaelble and Uy [104] have introduced a more detailed statement for interfacial tension which has the following form:

$$\gamma_{12} = [(\gamma_1^d)^{1/2} - (\gamma_2^d)^{1/2}]^2 + [(\gamma_1^p)^{1/2} - (\gamma_2^p)^{1/2}]^2 - \Delta_{12} \tag{16}$$

where γ_1^d, γ_2^d = dispersion part of surface tensions for Components 1 and 2; γ_1^p, γ_2^p = polar part of surface tensions; and Δ_{12} = excess interactions not defined by van der Waals forces. Equation (16) has been applied by Kaelble [105] to a system of analysis which isolates the dispersion γ_{sv}^d and polar γ_{sv}^p parts of the solid surface tension $\gamma_{sv} = \gamma_{sv}^d + \gamma_{sv}^p$ for organic monolayers and polymeric materials by analysis of vapor-liquid-solid interactions. An early application of Eq. (16) is reported by Uy and Chang [106] in a study of interfacial interactions between organic functionalities and tooth surfaces. More recently Owens and Wendt [107] and Chan [108] have applied relations similar to Eq. (16) to the analysis of interfacial interaction between aromatic liquids and fluorocarbon polymers.

One general objective in the more detailed descriptions of interfacial tension is to isolate specific molecular mechanisms of interaction at the liquid-solid or solid-solid interface. At the liquid-liquid interface the interfacial tension can be measured directly [97]. At the liquid-solid interface the value of γ_{12} is calculated from contact angle data which measure either the true or nominal value of adhesion as expressed by Eqs. (11) and (12), respectively. For the case of a nonwetting liquid, $\theta_\infty \geq 0$, interacting with a low-energy solid, a common assumption is that solid surface energy reduction due to vapor adsorption is negligible:

$$\gamma_{so} - \gamma_{sv} \simeq 0$$

in which case Eqs. (11) and (12) become identical. For this special case Eqs. (11), (12), and (16) may be combined to provide the following relation for interfacial work of adhesion [104,105]:

$$W_a = W_a' = 2[(\gamma_L^d \gamma_S^d)^{1/2} + (\gamma_L^p \gamma_S^p)^{1/2}] + \Delta_{Ls}$$

$$= W_a^d + W_a^p + \Delta_{Ls} \tag{17}$$

where W_a^d, W_a^p = dispersion and polar parts of W_a. Equation (17) points out that both liquid and solid surface tensions must possess a polar part to provide $W_a^p \geq 0$ through interfacial interaction. In other words, the polar properties of a liquid adhesive are wasted when interacting with a nonpolar solid surface. Conversely, the polar surface properties of a solid substrate do not interact with a nonpolar liquid adhesive. De Bruyne [109] first recognized this important proposition in an empirical statement concerning the effects of surface polarity upon adhesive joint strength. The implications of the de Bruyne "adhesion rule" are discussed by Zisman [7]. As indicated in earlier discussions, many other factors in addition to the equilibrium liquid–solid contact angle θ_∞ and work of adhesion W_a enter into the determination of adhesive joint strength.

A completely different approach to the definition of intermolecular and interfacial forces of adhesion is due to Lifshitz and coworkers [110,111]. The Lifshitz model bypasses the classical quantum mechanical argument [95-101] and is based directly upon macroscopic electrodynamics and fluctuation analysis. By considering the force between solids in a state of high dilution, the intermolecular force terms may be isolated. The van der Waals force is described by a generalized dispersion formula. Articles by Krupp [112] and Langbein [113] discuss some special solutions and implications of this theory which relate directly to micro- and macroscopic adhesion phenomena.

The special solution obtained by Langbein [113] for the effects of an adsorption layer on solid is of special significance. This analysis, based on the Lifshitz theory, shows that the adsorption layer acts both as a spacer and as a screen for the intermolecular reaction fields between solids. The dispersion energy of interaction appears to be dominated by the adsorbed layer when surface separation distance becomes smaller than the adsorbed layer thickness. Thus, at the condition of close approach defined by intermolecular contact and adhesive bonding, the adsorption layer rather than the substrate dominates the interaction forces of van der Waals type. This theoretical result, obtained by Langbein from the Lifshitz theory, appears to confirm the "principle of independent surface action" stated by Langmuir [114,115] which calls attention to the extreme localization of surface forces. The extensive studies of Zisman and coworkers [7] on the surface properties of oriented monolayers also show that the surface constitution of the 3 to 5 Å outer layer of the surface dominates surface wettability when the attraction field is described by van der Waals forces.

When the substrate is a high-energy solid such as inorganic glass, ceramic, metal or metal oxide, one would expect the surface properties of the virgin surface in vacuum to be dominated by long-range ionic and electrostatic forces, and to display high values of $\gamma_{s0} \gg$ 100 dyn/cm. When exposed to an ambient atmosphere these surfaces are immediately covered by an adsorption layer of either water or organic contaminants present in the atmosphere and further modified by oxidation and hydration. Thus the ambient surface properties described by γ_{sv} in Eq. (12) often bear little relation to those of the virgin surface. The dominant influence of adsorption layer on the available surface property γ_{sv} of many high energy substrates has recently been demonstrated by Zisman and coworkers [116-118]. These studies reveal that while all such surfaces are water wettable, they are not necessarily wetted by nonpolar liquids of lower surface tension. The magnitude of the critical surface tension for wetting γ_c to nonpolar liquids was shown to depend upon the relative humidity (R.H.) of the atmosphere over the solid surface. A brief summary of these results is given in Table 1. These results indicate why the "water break test" which evaluates for spontaneous retraction of a water film subsequent to immersion or spray coverage [119,120] does not necessarily indicate wettability by organic liquids or polymeric adhesives. The lowering of γ_c to nonpolar liquids with increased R.H. appears related to an increase in the thickness of the water adsorption layer on the surfaces of the high-energy substrates.

The general propositions already discussed, which are (a) extreme localization of intermolecular forces of van der Waals type, (b) screening effects of the adsorption layer, and (c) general presence of a water or organic monolayer or multilayer on high energy substrates, lead to the consideration of the role of interdiffusion as a molecular

Table 1

Dependence of Critical Surface Tension for Wetting on Relative Humidity

	R.H. in % at 20°C	
Substrate	0.5	95
	γ_c (dyn/cm) to nonpolar liquids	
Glass, fused quartz, α-alumina	37 to 40	25 to 30
99.999% pure Cr, Cu, Ag, Au, Cd	$\simeq 46$	$\simeq 38$
99.9% pure Al, Fe, Ni, Ge, Zr, Nb, Ta, Mo, W	$\simeq 46$	$\simeq 38$

mechanism of adhesion. The important role of interdiffusion in the autohesion, or self-bonding, of high polymeric materials has been extensively investigated by Voyutskii and coworkers [121] and this subject reviewed by Kaelble [122] with regard to the rheological implications of the process. When two dissimilar materials are brought into molecular contact, the adsorption step defined by Eq. (12) and the nominal work of adhesion W_a' describes the adhesive interaction with the surface layer of molecules (or functional groups of larger molecules) described by γ_{sv}. For high-energy substrates it is evident that this initial interaction is with the surface of the adsorption layer.

A thick multilayer of adsorbed material may display some of the surface and rheological properties of the bulk adsorbate. For example, a water multilayer adsorbed on glass or metal oxide may approach the surface properties of bulk water defined by Fowkes [97] as $\gamma_{Lv}^d \simeq 21.8$ dyn/cm and $\gamma_{Lv}^p \simeq 51.0$ dyn/cm. In fact, the decrease in γ_c for nonpolar wetting liquids with increased R.H. noted above appears to correlate with the dominance of the surface properties of water in reducing $\gamma_c \simeq \gamma_{sv}^d$ toward those of bulk water.

In the absence of interdiffusion the adsorption layer may act as a weak boundary phase which intervenes between the adhesive and substrate. One postulated function of coupling agents such as the reactive silanes is that they provide a bridge of covalent structure which extends through the adsorption layer to couple the adhesive to the adherend [123]. Ideally, the coupling agent should be chemically bonded to both the adhesive (or matrix in composites) and the adherend (reinforcing medium in composites) [124]. Silane coupling agents possess three hydrolyzable groups attached to silicon in the structure

$(CH_3O)_3SiR$. The trimethoxy groups bond strongly to metal, metal oxide, and silica. The specific bonding mechanism to the polymeric adhesive or matrix is obtained by designing either good cosolubility or coreaction properties in the R portion of the $(CH_3O)_3SiR$ molecule. The wide variety of silane coupling agents stems from the need for very specific structural requirements for the R radical for optimized interaction with different types of polymers used as adhesives or matrix materials. Lee [124] reports the critical surface tensions for polymerized films of polysiloxane coupling agents and qualitatively defines the surface properties in terms of low, medium, and high polarity.

Twiss [125] has pointed out the need for an adhesive which will remove, by an interdiffusion mechanism, the oily surface layer normally present on steel so as to achieve bonding without cleaning. It is reported by Coover [126] that the requirement outlined by Twiss has been met by proper adhesive design and formulation. High-energy substrates, typified by inorganic glasses, ceramics, metals, and metal oxides, are generally described by an available bonding surface, at ambient conditions, involving either an organic (normally hydrocarbon) or water adsorption multilayer. The use of silane coupling agents to bridge this layer or absorptive adhesives to solvate and remove the layer provide independent approaches to improving the strength and environmental resistance of adhesive joints [123-126].

The capacity of a polymeric adhesive to solvate the adsorption layer on a high-energy substrate or to intermix with the surface segments of a polymeric substrate is defined by the free energy of interfacial mixing:

$$\Delta F_m^\sigma = \Delta H_m^\sigma - T\Delta S_m^\sigma \leq 0 \tag{18}$$

where ΔH_m^σ, ΔS_m^σ = enthalpy and entropy of interfacial mixing; and T = absolute temperature. The free energy requirement for interfacial mixing is, of course, that ΔF_m^σ be zero or negative. The theory of regular solutions, which is redeveloped to define two-dimensional interactions at an ideal adsorption interface, has been applied by Kaelble [127,128] to define explicit relations for ΔH_m^σ and ΔS_m^σ in Eq. (18). The theory which describes van der Waals interactions appears to provide reasonable predictions for polymer-adsorption layer and polymer-polymer interdiffusion [127]. For the case of strong ionic-covalent interactions or hydrogen bonding between strong proton donors and acceptor groups, where the excess terms Δ_{12} or Δ_{Ls} of Eqs. (16) and (17) achieve substantial magnitude, a more detailed treatment of interfacial interactions such as outlined by Bolger and Michaels [129] is required.

The mechanical-rheological criterion of adhesion describes the importance of achieving a time-dependent contact angle $\theta(t) = 0$ so that cavities and voids are removed from the bonded interface. This subject is described in previous sections and relates to the micromechanics of fracture. The molecular criterion of adhesion which describes the equilibrium contact angle θ at time $t = \infty$ is dominated by the nature of physical or chemical interactions between nearest neighbors at short ranges of 3 to 5 Å distance. The formation of a continuous liquid–solid interface free of voids requires that $\theta = 0$.

Many solid surfaces are covered by an adsorption layer, which may act as a weak adsorption layer in the adhesive joint. New considerations which relate to interdiffusion phenomena, bridging by coupling agents, or other means of achieving direct interaction of polymeric adhesives with the solid substrate are necessarily introduced. Consideration of both the surface and bulk properties of adhesive, adsorption layer, and adherend is essential in providing a phenomenological definition of bonding through an adsorption layer.

VII. SUMMARY

This discussion has outlined a series of considerations which begin with engineering definitions of system response of adhesive joints and end with propositions involving molecular interactions at interfaces. Connecting these extreme aspects of the argument is the central subject of the micromechanics of bonding and fracture. Cavitation theory, as simply described by Eqs. (6a) and (7), illustrates the scale of microresponse in which both the thermodynamic and rheological aspects of adhesion phenomena achieve a parity when applied to cavities of radius $r = 0.1$ to 10 μ.

The discussion of the micromechanics of polymer fracture provides ample evidence that pure materials, polymer composites, and adhesive joints, need to be described in terms of their microdefects. The several mathematical models [1-6,17-20] for crack propagation which are imposed upon fracture mechanics data tend to oversimplify the visualization of the true micromechanisms of fracture. The fuller development of micromechanics theory and experimental analysis promises to be an important area of current developments in the better understanding of macroscopic response of filled systems, fiber reinforced composites, and adhesively bonded structures.

Recent developments in the several theories of intermolecular forces and the physical chemistry of bonding [95-129] provide new impetus to the chemist to design optimized polymeric materials with finely adjusted balances of surface and bulk properties. The fuller visualization of adsorption-interdiffusion bonding as a process involving both the two-dimensional interface and the three-dimension interphase defines bonding as both a thermodynamic and a rheological process. The microstages of bond formation are somewhat the reverse of the stages of microfracture listed earlier. The microdefects that commonly exist in polymeric materials and polymer composites tend to indicate that the viscoelastic constraints typical of polymer chains and networks play an important role in preventing equilibrium bonding in the simple thermodynamic sense as expressed by idealized liquid–liquid or liquid–solid interactions. The current development and application of a refined thermodynamic and rheological argument to both bonding and fracture processes stands as a central issue in directly correlating the molecular criteria of adhesion and performance of bonded systems. Any of the simple mathematical relations introduced in this discussion may be expressed with greater detail and precision by incorporating detailed statements concerning chemical composition, macromolecular structure, and free volume state of the polymeric adhesive [122,130].

References

[1] G. R. Irwin, in *Treatise on Adhesion and Adhesives*, Vol. 1 (R. L. Patrick, ed.), Dekker, New York, 1967, Chap. 7.

[2] A. A. Griffith, *Phil. Trans. Roy. Soc. London*, 221, 163 (1921).

[3] A. A. Griffith, *Proc. Int. Cong. Appl. Math., 2nd Delft*, 54 (1924).

[4] C. E. Inglis, *Trans. Inst. Naval Arch.*, 60, 219 (1913).

[5] E. Orowan, *Fatigue and Fracture of Metals* (MIT Symposium, June 1950), Wiley, New York, 1950.

[6] E. Orowan, *Welding J.*, 34(3), 1575 (1955).

[7] W. A. Zisman, in *Adhesion and Cohesion* (P. Weiss, ed.), Elsevier, Amsterdam, 1962, p. 176.

[8] J. P. Berry and A. M. Bueche, *Ibid.*, p. 18.

[9] E. J. Ripling, S. Mostovoy, and R. L. Patrick, *Mater. Res. Std.*, 4, 129 (1964).

[10] S. Mostovoy and E. J. Ripling, *J. Appl. Polym. Sci.*, 10, 1351 (1966).

[11] R. L. Patrick, J. A. Brown, L. E. Verhoeven, E. J. Ripling, and S. Mostovoy, *J. Adhesion*, 1, 136 (1969).

[12] M. L. Williams, *Proc. U.S. Cong. Appl. Mech.*, 5th, 451 (1966).

[13] M. L. Williams, *J. Appl. Polym. Sci.*, 13, 29 (1969).

[14] W. B. Jones and M. L. Williams, "The Measurement of Adhesive Energy for Fracture Investigations," UTEC DO 68-019, University of Utah, February 1968.

[15] J. D. Burton, W. B. Jones and M. L. Williams, "Theoretical and Experimental Treatment of an Adhesive Interlayer," presented before the Society of Rheology, Pasadena, California, February 1970 (to be published).

[16] H. Dannenberg, *J. Appl. Polym. Sci.*, 5, 125 (1961).

[17] R. S. Rivlin and A. G. Thomas, *J. Polym. Sci.*, 10, 291 (1953).

[18] H. W. Greensmith and A. G. Thomas, *J. Polym. Sci.*, 18, 177 (1955).

[19] A. G. Thomas, *J. Polym. Sci.*, 18, 177 (1955).

[20] T. L. Smith, in *Rheology*, Vol. 5 (F. R. Eirich, ed.), Academic, New York, 1969, Chap. 4.

[21] L. H. Lee, *J. Polym. Sci.*, *Part A-2*, 5, 1103 (1967).

[22] H. W. Greensmith, *J. Appl. Polym. Sci.*, 3, 183 (1960).

[23] A. N. Gent and A. N. Henry, *Proceedings of the International Rubber Conference*, Maclaren, London, 1967, p. 167.

[24] M. L. Williams, R. F. Landel, and J. D. Ferry, *J. Amer. Chem. Soc.*, 77, 3701 (1955).

[25] W. G. Knauss, *Trans. Soc. Rheol.*, 13(3), 291 (1969).

[26] S. B. Newman and I. Wolock, in *Adhesion and Cohesion* (P. Weiss, ed.), Elsevier, Amsterdam, 1962, p. 218.

[27] Symposium on Scanning Electron Microscopy of Polymers and Coatings, *Preprint Amer. Chem. Soc. Div. Org. Coatings and Plastics*, 30(1), 243-374 (1970).

[28] P. W. Palmberg and H. L. Marcus, *Trans. Amer. Soc. Metals*, 62, 1016 (1969).

[29] H. L. Marcus and P. W. Palmberg, *Trans. Met. Soc. AIME*, 245, 1664 (1969).

[30] N. C. Macdonald, H. L. Marcus, and P. W. Palmberg, *Proc. Ann. SEM Symp. 3rd Chicago* (April 1970).

[31] D. H. Kaelble, *J. Interface Colloid Sci.*, 19, 413 (1964).

[32] D. H. Kaelble, *J. Adhesion*, 1, 102 (1969).

[33] W. M. Bright, in *Adhesion and Adhesives* (J. Clark, J. E. Rutzler, and R. L. Savage, eds.), Wiley, New York, 1954, p. 130.

[34] J. R. Huntsberger, *J. Polym. Sci.*, A1, 2241 (1963).

[35] A. N. Gent and R. P. Petrich, *Proc. Roy. Soc.*, *Ser. A*, 310, 433 (1969).

[36] D. H. Kaelble and F. A. Hamm, *Adhesives Ages*, 11(7), 25 (1968).

[37] G. A. Ilkka and R. L. Scott, in *Adhesion and Cohesion* (P. Weiss, ed.), Elsevier, Amsterdam, 1962, p. 65.

[38] L. Reegan and G. A. Ilkka, *Ibid.*, p. 159.

[39] C. L. Weidner, *Adhesives Age*, 6(7), 30 (1963).

[40] J. R. Huntsberger, *J. Polym. Sci.*, A1, 1339 (1963).

[41] C. W. Hock, *Hercules Chemist*, 47, 16 (1963).

[42] V. E. Gul, Ch. In'-Si, V. L. Vakula, and S. S. Voyutskii, *Vysokomol. Soedin.*, 4, 294 (1962).

[43] A. E. Woodward, in *Rheology*, Vol. 5 (F. R. Eirich, ed.), Academic, New York, 1969, Chap. 7.

[44] W. G. Knauss, "Rupture Phenomena in Viscoelastic Materials," Ph.D. Thesis, California Institute of Technology, 1963.

[45] F. Bueche and J. C. Halpin, *J. Appl. Phys.*, **35**, 36 (1964).
[46] J. C. Halpin, *J. Polym. Sci.*, *Part C*, **16**, 1037 (1967).
[47] R. F. Landel and R. F. Fedors, in *Fracture Processes in Polymeric Solids* (B. Rosen, ed.), Wiley (Interscience), New York, 1964, Chap. 3B.
[48] A. N. Gent and P. B. Lindley, *Proc. Roy. Soc.*, *Ser A*, **249**, 195 (1958).
[49] G. H. Lindsey, R. A. Shapery, M. L. Williams, and A. Zak, "The Triaxial Tensile Failure of Viscoelastic Materials," Aerospace Research Laboratory Report ARL 63-152, Office of Aerospace Research (USAF), September 1963.
[50] G. H. Lindsey, *J. Appl. Phys.*, **38**, 4843 (1967).
[51] A. E. Oberth and R. S. Bruenner, *Trans. Soc. Rheol.*, 9(2), 165 (1965).
[52] R. L. Denecour and A. N. Gent, *J. Polym. Sci.*, *Part A-2*, **6**, 1853 (1967).
[53] D. H. Kaelble, *Trans. Soc. Rheol.*, 9(2), 135 (1965).
[54] D. H. Kaelble and R. S. Reyleck, *J. Adhesion*, **1**, 124 (1969).
[55] L. Mullins, *J. Rubber Res.*, 16, 275 (1947).
[56] L. Mullins and N. R. Tobin, *Trans. Inst. Rubber Ind.*, **33**, 2 (1956).
[57] L. Mullins, in *The Chemistry and Physics of Rubber-Like Substances* (L. Bateman, ed.), Wiley, New York, 1963, Chap. 11.
[58] J. H. Wiegand, *Amer. Rocket Soc. J.*, **32**, 521 (April 1962).
[59] G. Birkoff and E. H. Zarantonello, *Jets*, *Wakes*, *and Cavities*, Academic, New York, 1957.
[60] A. Voet, in *Adhesion and Adhesives* 2nd ed., Vol. 2 (R. Houwink and G. Salomon, eds.), Elsevier, Amsterdam, 1967, Chap. 19.
[61] W. C. Wake, *Ibid.*, Vol. 1, Elsevier, Amsterdam, 1965, Chap. 6.
[62] ASTM D1878-61T.
[63] F. H. Hammond, *Adhesion*, ASTM Spec. Tech. Publ. No. 360, Philadelphia, 1964, p. 123.
[64] J. D. Skewis, *Rubber Chem. Technol.*, 37, 689 (1964).
[65] R. D. Hoffman and R. R. Myers, *Trans. Soc. Rheol.*, **6**, 197 (1962).
[66] H. Poritsky, *Proc. 1st Nat. Congr. Appl. Mech.* (U.S.), 813 (1951).
[67] A. E. Green and W. Zerna, *Theoretical Elasticity*, 2nd ed., Clarendon Press, Oxford, 1968, p. 103.
[68] D. H. Kaelble, "Cavitation in Viscoelastic Media," Paper Presented at the Society of Rheology Meeting, St. Paul, Minnesota, October 1969.
[69] C. A. Dahlquist, *Adhesives Age*, 2(10), 25 (1959).
[70] J. Murray and D. Hull, *Polymer*, 10, 451 (1969).
[71] J. Murray and D. Hull, *J. Polym. Sci.*, *Part B*, 8, 159 (1970).
[72] R. P. Kambour, *J. Polym. Sci.*, *Part A*, **2**, 4159 (1964).
[73] R. P. Kambour, *J. Polym. Sci.*, *Part A-2*, **4**, 17, 349 (1966).
[74] R. P. Kambour and R. E. Barker, *J. Polym. Sci.*, *Part A-2*, **4**, 359 (1966).
[75] R. N. Hayward and I. Brough, *Polymer*, 10, 724 (1969).
[76] F. Bueche, *Physical Properties of Polymers*, Wiley (Interscience), New York, 1962, p. 76.
[77] J. N. Anand and H. J. Karam, *J. Adhesion*, **1**, 16 (1969).
[78] J. N. Anand and R. Z. Balwinski, *Ibid.*, **1**, 24 (1969).
[79] J. N. Anand, *Ibid.*, **1**, 31 (1969).

[80] J. N. Anand and L. Diplinski, *Ibid.*, **2**, 16 (1970).

[81] J. N. Anand, *Ibid.*, 2, 23 (1970).

[82] L. H. Sharpe and J. H. Schonhorn, *Advan. Chem. Ser.*, **43**, 189 (1964).

[83] N. A. DeBruyne, *Nature*, 180, 262 (1957).

[84] M. Levine, G. Ilkka, and P. Weiss, *J. Polym. Sci.*, *Part B*, **2**, 915 (1964).

[85] M. J. Barbarisi, *Nature*, **215**, 383 (1967).

[86] M. J. Barbarisi, *Tech. Rept. 3456*, Picatinny Arsenal, Dover, New Jersey (AD 651 093).

[87] E. A. Bourcher, *Nature*, **215**, 1054 (1967).

[88] H. Schonhorn, H. L. Frisch, and T. K. Kwei, *J. Appl. Phys.*, 37, 4967 (1966).

[89] S. Newman, *J. Colloid Interfac. Sci.*, 26, 209 (1968).

[90] B. W. Cherry and C. M. Holmes, *Ibid.*, **29**, 174 (1969).

[91] T. P. Yin, *J. Phys. Chem.*, 73, 2413 (1969).

[92] B. W. Cherry and S. E. Muddaris, *J. Adhesion*, 2, 44 (1970).

[93] H. V. Oene, Y. F. Chang, and S. Newman, *Ibid.*, 1, 54 (1969).

[94] R. H. Dettre and R. H. Johnson, Jr., *Ibid.*, 2, 61 (1970).

[95] R. J. Good, *Treatise on Adhesion and Adhesives* (R. L. Patrick, ed.), Dekker, New York, 1967, Chap. 2.

[96] J. L. Gardon, *Ibid.*, Chap. 8.

[97] F. M. Fowkes, *Ibid.*, Chap. 9.

[98] F. London, *Trans. Faraday Soc.*, 33, 8 (1937).

[99] P. Debye, *Phys. Z.*, 21, 178 (1920); 22, 302 (1922).

[100] W. H. Keesom, *Phys. Z.*, 22, 126, 643 (1922); 23, 225 (1922).

[101] J. E. Lennard-Jones, *Proc. Roy. Soc.*, *Ser. A*, **112**, 214 (1926).

[102] Y. Tamai, K. Makuuki, and M. Suzuki, *J. Phys. Chem.*, 71, 4176 (1967).

[103] J. R. Dann, *J. Colloid Interfac. Sci.*, 32, 302, 321 (1970).

[104] D. H. Kaelble and K. C. Uy, *J. Adhesion*, 2, 50 (1970).

[105] D. H. Kaelble, *Ibid.*, 2, 66 (1970).

[106] K. C. Uy and R. Chang, in *Dental Restorative Materials*, Vol. 2, P.H.S. Publication 1494, Govt. Printing Office, Washington, D.C., 1966, Chap. 3.

[107] D. Owens and R. Wendt, *J. Appl. Polym. Sci.*, 13, 1741 (1969).

[108] R. K. S. Chan, *J. Colloid Interfac. Sci.*, 32, 492, 499 (1970).

[109] N. A. de Bruyne, *Aircraft Eng.*, 18(12), 58 (1939).

[110] E. M. Lifshitz, *Sov. Phys. JETP*, *(English Transl.)*, 2, 73 (1956).

[111] I. E. Dzaloshinski, E. M. Lifshitz, and L. P. Pitaevski, *Adv. Phys.*, 10, 165 (1961).

[112] H. Krupp, *Adv. Colloid Interfac. Sci.*, 1, 111 (1967).

[113] D. Langbein, *J. Adhesion*, 1, 273 (1969).

[114] I. Langmuir, *J. Amer. Chem. Soc.*, **38**, 2286 (1916).

[115] I. Langmuir, *Third Colloid Symp. Monograph*, Chemical Catalogue Co., New York, 1925.

[116] E. G. Shafgin and W. A. Zisman, *J. Amer. Ceram. Soc.*, **50**, 50 (1967).

[117] M. K. Bernett and W. A. Zisman, *J. Colloid Interfac. Sci.*, 28, 243 (1968).

[118] K. W. Bewig and W. A. Zisman, *J. Phys. Chem.*, 68, 1804 (1964).

[119] H. B. Linford and E. B. Saubestre, *ASTM Bull.*, **190**, 47 (May 1953).

[120] D. O. Fedor and D. E. Koontz, *ASTM Spec. Tech. Publ.*, **246**, 40 (1958).
[121] S. S. Voyutskii, *Autohesion and Adhesion of High Polymers*, Wiley (Interscience), New York, 1963.
[122] D. H. Kaelble, *Treatise on Adhesion and Adhesives* (R. L. Patrick, ed.), Vol. 1, Dekker, New York, 1967, Chap. 6.
[123] E. P. Plueddemann, *J. Paint. Technol.*, **40**(516), 1 (1968).
[124] L. H. Lee, *J. Colloid Interfac. Sci.*, **27**, 751 (1968).
[125] S. B. Twiss, *ASTM Spec. Tech. Publ.*, **360**, 96 (1964).
[126] H. W. Coover, Jr., *Adhesives Age*, **11**(2), 20 (1968).
[127] D. H. Kaelble, *Physical Chemistry of Adhesion*, Wiley (Interscience), New York, 1971.
[128] D. H. Kaelble, "Interfacial Morphology and Mechanical Properties of A-B-A Triblock Copolymers," Paper Presented at the Pasadena Society of Rheology Meeting, Pasadena, California, February 1970, to be published in *Trans. Soc. Rheol.*
[129] J. C. Bolger and A. S. Michaels, *Interface Conversion* (P. Weiss, ed.), Elsevier, New York, 1968, pp. 3-60.
[130] D. H. Kaelble, *Rheology* (F. R. Eirich, ed.), Vol. 5, Academic, New York, 1969, Chap. 5.

Solvation of Synthetic and Natural Polyelectrolytes

B. E. CONWAY*

Universities of Southampton and Newcastle upon Tyne, England

*Commonwealth Visiting Professor (1969-1970). Permanent address:
Chemistry Department, University of Ottawa, Canada.

I. INTRODUCTION

In comparison with the extent to which solvation of simple ions has been studied [1-4], the present state of knowledge regarding hydration of polyions is relatively limited. The matter is, however, of great practical importance, since the ionization and resulting properties of ion-exchange resins and membranes, soil conditioners, and polyelectrolytes of biological significance depend very much on their hydration in the water medium. Further, the interactions of polyions with simple ions, and other polyions and small molecules, are of great importance in biological systems and, in general, in cytochemistry.

In this review a quantitative development of the subject is presented where possible but in some sections, e.g., where the biochemically significant polyelectrolytes are discussed, the treatment is more synoptic and qualitative.

The solvation of polyions involves most of the factors that determine the solvation of simple ions; in addition, however, important new effects arise from (a) the proximity of like charges in a chain at relatively short distances from one another; (b) the resulting counter-ion association with the chain ion together with the ionic atmosphere carried within the random polymer coil (or about a charged rodlike ion); and (c) the charge-dependent configuration of the polyion chain, an effect that depends on the chain length (degree of polymerization, z) and intrinsic molecular flexibility (length of the statistical element). At low degrees of ionization, α, the ionized centers on the polymer chain behave, to a first approximation, as isolated charge centers, the solvation of which is characteristic largely of the chemical nature, size, and charge of local ionic centers involved. The nonelectrolyte backbone of the polymer chain, however, provides an environment to the charge centers which is different from that experienced by similar free charges in corresponding monomers. In fact, the local charge centers will tend to salt-out the nonelectrolyte regions of the polymer (un-ionized side groups on the polyion backbone) and cause a modification of the polymer chain configuration.

The intermolecular forces, and structural factors which determine solvation of simple ions will manifest themselves in polyion-solvent interactions; solvation of simple ions has been the subject of a number of comprehensive reviews in the last 16 years [1-5]. More recently, the role of specific solute and solvent structure effects has been recognized in relation to structural equilibria and hydrogen bonding in the water solvent [1,6-9] and much interest has been attached to the solvation of organic ions where the local environment of the charge center can be controllably varied, e.g., at N^+ by successive alkyl substitutions of the ammonium ion [10-12] up to the tetraalkylammonium type of structure [10], and with ionized pyridine by substitution at the 2, 5, and N positions [13]. Similar, but secondary, structural changes can be effected in ionized organic acids by substitution at the α-carbon atom [14]. The behavior of such ionized centers is of considerable importance in the solvation of a number of polysalts where the ionization occurs in a side chain group, e.g., in the case of polyacrylic acid, polymeth-

acrylic acid, polyvinylpyridine, and polystyrenesulfonic acid where
the ionizable centers are, respectively:

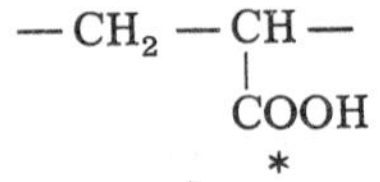

$$-CH_2-CH- \atop \underset{*}{COOH} \qquad I$$

$$-CH_2-\underset{\underset{*}{COOH}}{\overset{CH_3}{\underset{|}{C}}}- \qquad II$$

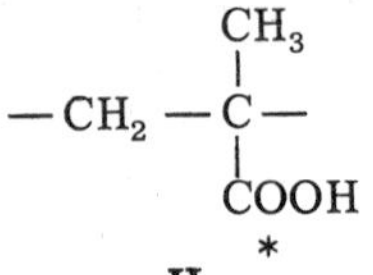

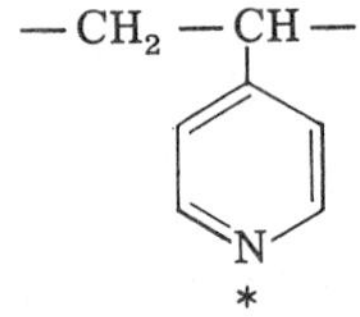

III

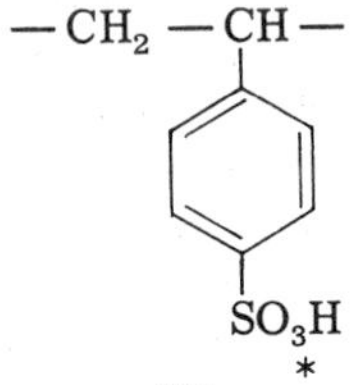

IV

as indicated by the asterisks. Rather few polyelectrolytes can be
ionized in the backbone itself but two important examples are the
linear and branched chain polyphosphates and the polyimines. These
cases are of special interest as they approach most closely to the
idealized models on the basis of which theoretical predictions can be
made about the properties of polyelectrolytes, e.g., in the case of the
rigid linear charged rod model [15]. Other substances such as
sodium deoxyribonucleate (DNA) [16,17] also approach this model
over appreciable lengths of the long, double helical chain but the
complexity of the nonionic parts of the molecule renders unrealistic
any attempt to apply the idealized rigid rod model, particularly for
short range ionic solvation effects.

In the case of the polyphosphates and poly(ethylene)imines, low
molecular weight oligomers may be synthesized [18,19] so that the
transition from simple ion to polyion properties may be followed.
The chain elements, with the ionized centers shown, are:

$$-\!\!\left[CH_2-CH_2-\underset{*}{\overset{+}{NH_2}}\right]\!\!-CH_2-CH_2-\ldots$$

V

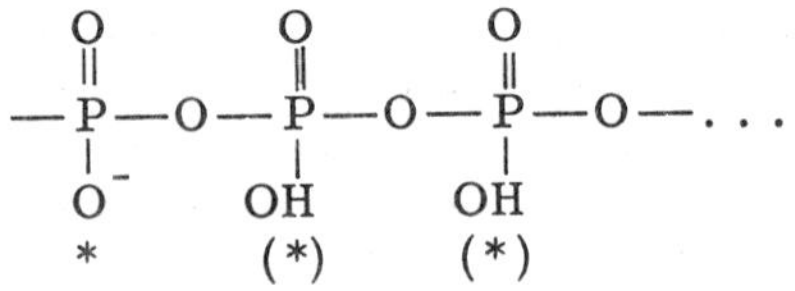

VI

In the case of the polyphosphates and polyimines, branched chain structures usually arise in the higher molecular weight preparations. Since it is anticipated that this review may be read as much by polymer chemists as by physical and electrochemists interested in ionic solutions, introductory material is provided covering the behavior of simple ions and salts but, in any case, these topics are basic to the development of principles and methods for treating polyion or polysalt-solvent interactions. It will therefore be useful first to summarize briefly the principal factors determining ionic solvation and the experimental methods that may be used for its study since they may also be employed for studies on polysalts. Detailed reviews on the solvation of simple ions are available elsewhere [1-6].

In most cases, the discussion will be restricted to "hydration" i.e., polyion-solvent interaction in the aqueous medium.

II. SUMMARY OF FACTORS
DETERMINING SOLVATION OF SIMPLE IONS

A. Structural Factors

The radius of the ion, if monatomic, or the size of the charge-bearing center [20], if the ion is polyatomic (e.g., ClO_4^-, ClO_3^-,

SO_4^{2-}, SO_3^{2-}, $H.C\diagup\diagdown\begin{smallmatrix}O\\-\\O\end{smallmatrix}$), is the primary geometrical factor in simple

ion solvation. For more complex ions, e.g., in the series $R_nNH_{4-n}^+$, accessibility of the solvent dipole to the charge center is a major factor determining the solvation. The local radius of the charge center rather than the mean radius of the whole ion must be considered. This is illustrated by the progressive change of entropy of ionization of bases in the series R_nNH_{3-n} [21,22] and by the observed progressive decrease of electrostriction (deduced from partial molal volumes) as n increases from 0 to 4 in the series $R_nNH_{4-n}^+$ [11,12]. Similarly, the entropy of hydration of complex anions is a function of the structure of the ion and the location of the charge-bearing ligand [20]. Charge delocalization effects are also of great importance, e.g., in carboxylate ions and organic ions such as tropylium$^{\oplus}$, cyclopentadienyl$^{\ominus}$, and anions and cations derived from anthracene or more complex polynuclear hydrocarbons by electrochemical reduction or oxidation, respectively. These factors also enter into the determination of the solvation behavior of many polyions.

The molecular structure of the molecules of the solvating solvent is no less an important factor in any modern appraisal of solvation effects. Early treatments of ionic solvation and ionization [23] were, however, based on models in which the solvent was treated as a structureless medium of constant dielectric "constant" For example, in the treatment of Born [24] (see below) only the dielectric constant of the solvent and the radius and charge of the ion are involved. More recent treatments take into account the finite size and dipole moment of the solvent molecules, and in more sophisticated treatments [25,26] the optimum orientation of solvent dipoles in the field of the ion, the "location" of the electric dipole in the solvent, e.g., in H_2O [27], CH_3CN, DMF, DMSO, and propylene carbonate, and the role of ion-quadrupole interactions [28] are considered. Insofar as the local dipole of the solvent molecules is involved, the role of unshared electron pairs (e.g., on O, N, S) must receive consideration in relation to the size of the charge center becoming solvated. Such factors are related to hard and soft (Lewis) acid/base concepts [29] which are also of importance in solvation. Among other factors, the location of the principal electric dipole in a solvent molecule also determines the difference of solvation energy of cations and anions since different orientations of the solvent molecules will arise at cations and anions of comparable radius at the charge-bearing center and the polar group may be more or be less accessible to the charge depending on the sign of the charge and resulting dipole orientation. A second and more general reason for differences of energy of solvation of cations and anions of the same nominal size in a given solvent arises because ion-quadrupole interactions add to the ion-dipole interaction energy at an anion while they must be subtracted from that energy in the case of cations, assuming the dipoles of the solvent are oriented towards the positive and the negative changes in mirror-image opposite directions. The latter situation is, however, not always the case, owing to H-bonding, e.g., in the water solvent.

B. Energetic Factors

1. **Thermodynamic Aspects.** Ionic solvation energies are usually comparable with crystal lattice energies or molecular bond energies. The same applies to solvation of ionic centers in polyelectrolytes. In crystal lattice dissolution the net free energy or enthalpy of dissolution is usually quite small, e.g., ±10 kcal/mole and some dissolutions, e.g., of NaCl in water, are almost athermal. Since, however, the process of dissolution in a solvent S can be represented [4] by a Born-Haber type of thermodynamic cycle:

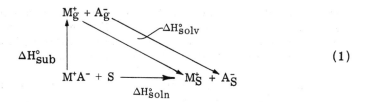

$$\text{(1)}$$

it is evident that

$$\Delta H^{\circ}_{solv} = \Delta H^{\circ}_{soln} - \Delta H^{\circ}_{sub} \tag{2}$$

where ΔH°_{solv} is the standard heat of solvation of the two types of ions per mole of salt, ΔH°_{sub} the lattice sublimation energy, and ΔH°_{soln} the experimental standard enthalpy of solution of the solid salt lattice. Since ΔH°_{soln} is usually small, ΔH°_{solv} is the same order of magnitude as $-\Delta H^{\circ}_{sub}$, the lattice energy of the salt. The standard free energies of solvation of pairs of ions are also of similar magnitude. Similar conclusions follow if a solvolytic ionization process is considered, e.g.,

$$HA + S \xrightarrow{} SH^+ + A^-$$
$$\Delta H^{\circ}_i$$

In this case the heat of ionization ΔH°_i is usually relatively small, e.g., for many acids in water, but the HA bond energy is of the order of 25-100 kcal/mole. Hence the solvation energy is determined by $D_{HA} + I_H - E_A$ where E_A is the electron affinity of the A radical. This is seen [3] from the cycle

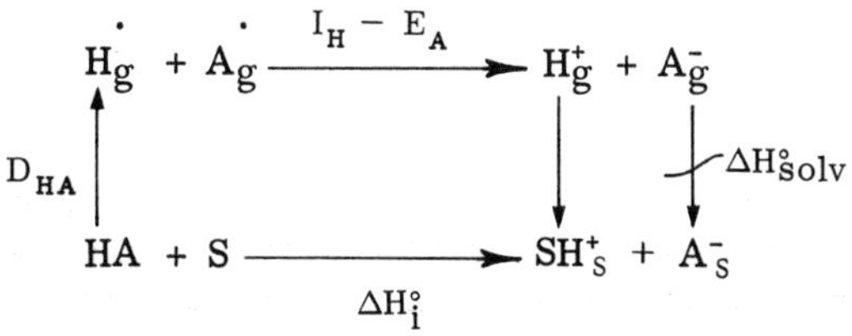

$$\begin{array}{ccc}
\overset{\textstyle\cdot}{H_g} + \overset{\textstyle\cdot}{A_g} & \xrightarrow{\quad I_H - E_A \quad} & H^+_g + A^-_g \\[2mm]
D_{HA} \Big\uparrow & & \Big\downarrow \Big| -\Delta H^{\circ}_{solv} \\[2mm]
HA + S & \xrightarrow{} & SH^+_s + A^-_s \\
& \Delta H^{\circ}_i &
\end{array} \tag{3}$$

which gives

$$\Delta H^{\circ}_{solv} = \Delta H^{\circ}_i - I_H + E_A - D_{HA} \tag{4}$$

Similar considerations apply to the free energy of solvation of SH^+ and A^- ions arising in the solvolytic equilibrium for which the ΔG_i^o corresponding to ΔH_i^o is given by $-RT \ln K_i$, where K_i is the ionization constant of HA in the solvent S. These considerations apply to the ionization of polyacids and polybases but the interaction effects arising from the proximity of like charges cause an important dependence of acidic and basic ionization constants (e.g., in polymethacylic acid, polystyrenesulfonic acid, and polyimines) on degree of ionization, α. In polyacids the pK_a decreases by 4-6 pK units as α increases from 0-0.9 due to the build up of negative charge on the polyion which inhibits (a) further release of protons and (b) increase of negative charge density on the polymer structure. The effects are, however, attenuated by metal counter-ion association as $\alpha \rightarrow 1$. The ionization behavior has been treated theoretically and evaluated quantitatively [30] for a number of polymeric electrolyte systems.

2. **Solvent Interaction Energies at Ionic Centers.** The earliest treatment of the energy of solvation of ionic centers was that of Born [24] based on the calculation of the difference of energy of "charging" the ion in the solvent (static dielectric constant ϵ_0) in comparison with that in vacuum. The charging energy for a sphere of radius r is obtained by performing an integration of the form

$$\int_0^q \left(\frac{q}{\epsilon_0 r} \right) dq$$

The result is an electrostatic free energy G_e. It is convenient to rewrite the integral in terms of the fraction λ of the final total charge q built up at a given stage of the charging so that

$$G_e = \frac{q^2}{\epsilon_0 r} \int_0^1 \lambda \, d\lambda = q^2/2\epsilon_0 r \tag{5}$$

with $dq = q \, d\lambda$ for an ion of charge q. The corresponding energy for charging in vacuum is $q^2/2r$ so that the free energy of solvation of an ion transferred from the gas phase to the medium is

$$\Delta G_{e,solv} = \frac{-q^2}{2r} \left(1 - \frac{1}{\epsilon_0} \right) \tag{6}$$

for an ionic charge q (= ze). The Born equation also follows from considering the internal compressional work. The contractive "pressure" or energy density associated with a field E is $E^2/8\pi$ and the work done on volume dv in establishing the electric polarization is

$$dw = \frac{E^2}{8\pi} dv \qquad (7)$$

for ϵ independent of E.

For a spherical particle, $dv = 4\pi r^2 dr$. Hence, for $\epsilon_0 = 1$,

$$dw = \frac{E^2}{8\pi} \cdot 4\pi r^2 dr = \frac{(ze)^2}{8\pi r^4} \cdot 4\pi r^2 dr \qquad (8)$$

Integrating this "vdp" work from ∞ to r_i gives

$$G_e = \frac{(ze)^2}{2} \int_{r_i}^{\infty} \frac{dr}{r^2} = -\frac{(ze)^2}{2} \left[\left(\frac{1}{r} \right) \right]_{r_i}^{\infty} \qquad (9)$$

$$= (ze)^2/2r_i$$

as found by the method employing integration of elements of charge $d\lambda$. We have illustrated this method since it may be applied to other more complex cases and also because the relation of the charging energy to electrostriction arises through the contractive pressure $E^2/8\pi$ [31]. The corresponding electrostatic entropy and enthalpy of solvation follow readily by the usual operation of taking the temperature derivative of $\Delta G_{e,solv}$. This gives

$$\Delta S_{e,solv} = -\frac{\partial \Delta G_{e,solv}}{\partial T} = \frac{(ze)^2}{2r} \frac{1}{\epsilon_0^2} \left(\frac{\partial \epsilon_0}{\partial T} \right)_P \qquad (10)$$

and

$$\Delta H_{e,solv} = -\frac{(ze)^2}{2r} \left[1 - \frac{1}{\epsilon_0} - \frac{T}{\epsilon_0^2} \left(\frac{\partial \epsilon_0}{\partial T} \right)_P \right] \qquad (11)$$

Since $\partial \epsilon_0/\partial T$ is usually negative, it is evident that $\Delta S_{e,solv}$ will be negative. In a real molecular dielectric this corresponds to (a) the effect of orientation of induced and fixed dipoles, and (b) to the resulting electrostriction of the solvent due to the field of the ion. In (b), the dielectric constant is in reality a function of field, and hence distance from the ion due to electric saturation effects in dipole

orientation [32]. Allowance for this effect improves the agreement
between theory and experiment using Eq. (6) for $\Delta G_{e,solv}$ or Eq.
(11) for $\Delta H_{e,solv}$. The use of Eq. (6) for evaluation of free energies of solvation is, on the whole, unrealistic, particularly for associated solvents like water. A more detailed molecular model of the
solvation sphere about an ion is usually required for satisfactory
theoretical calculations of ion-solvent interaction energies and,
even then, the more recent treatments leave much to be desired.

A substantial improvement in the calculation of $\Delta G_{e,solv}$ or
$\Delta H_{e,solv}$ over that given by Eqs. (6) and (11) is nevertheless obtained if the ion-solvent interaction is calculated over two regions
[27]: (a) a spherical annular region about the ion containing oriented solvent dipoles, and having a radius $r_i + d_S$, where d_S is the
effective diameter of the solvent molecules; and (b) a continuum
region beyond the spherical envelope of radius $r_i + d_S$ where Eqs.
(6) or (8) apply but with r replaced by $r_i + d_S$. This avoids using the Born relation in a region near the ion where the sizes and
specific orientations of the solvent molecules are critical (since in
most solvents the size of the solvent molecules is comparable with
that of the ion; this applies also, of course, to polyions even though
the polyion is over-all much larger, because most of the energy of
solvation arises from short-range interactions between the ionic
centers on the chain and the solvating solvent molecules). The difficulty of what is the effective value of the dielectric constant to be
used in Eqs. (6) or (8) (treated below for the polyion case) is also
avoided by this approach since beyond $r + d_s$ the fields at most
ionic centers are insufficiently large to cause appreciable dielectric saturation ($\epsilon \ll \epsilon_0$).

The type of model referred to above was first introduced by
Bernal and Fowler [27], developed further by Eley and Evans [25],
and provided the basis for Bockris's important distinction [33] between "primary" and "secondary" hydration, the inner region near
the ion within the annular volume $(4/3)\pi[(r_i^3) - (r_i + d_s)^3]$ constituting the "primary" hydration layer (Fig. 1) with a corresponding
"primary hydration number" characterizing the time-average coordination of the ion by oriented solvent molecules kinetically associated* with the ion, e.g., in conductance and diffusion. In the case

---

*"Permanent" association is rarely involved, except, e.g., in the case of
$(Cr.6H_2O)^{3+}$, as there is continuous interchange [34] between solvent molecules
in the primary shell and those in the bulk. The association is, however, significant over time intervals large compared with reciprocals of OH bond frequencies and H_2O or other solvent molecule libration frequencies in the liquid
solvent "lattice."

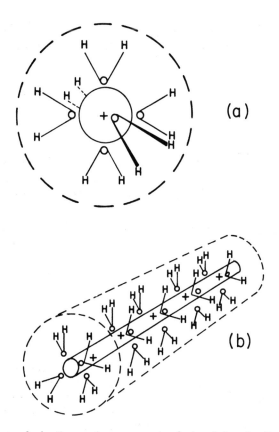

Fig. 1. Primary hydration region near a simple ion (a) and a linear polyion (b).

of polyions, the proximity of the primary solvation regions of adjacent ionized centers on the chain at high α introduces important complications (see below) in the representation and treatment of the solvation, particularly when the ionic centers are on, or near, the chain backbone as in the case of polyiminium and polyphosphate ions (Fig. 2).

In the treatments of Bernal and Fowler [27] and Eley and Evans [25], which may be applied also to polyion charge centers, the ion-dipole interaction energies $G_{i,d}$ are calculated to a first-order approximation from

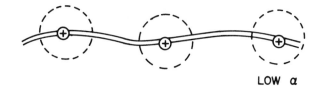

LOW α

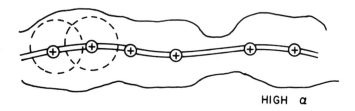

HIGH α

Fig. 2. Overlap of solvation regions in polyions with progressively increasing charge density.

$$G_{i,d} = n(ze)\bar{\mu}/(r_i + r_d)^2 \tag{12}$$

where n is the primary solvation number, $\bar{\mu}$ the time-average radial component of the dipole moment of the solvent molecules coordinating the ion, r_i the ionic radius, and r_d the effective radius of the solvent dipole. $\bar{\mu}$ and n are a function of T which enables an entropy of the primary ion-solvent interaction to be formally expressed in terms of $\partial/\partial T$ of $\bar{\mu}$ and n. In terms of a statistical mechanical treatment, the entropy of solvation was calculated rigorously by Eley and Evans [25] taking into account the free volume of the ions in solution, the librational, vibrational, and translational modes of motion of the solvent molecules in the solvent itself, and with regard to their interactions with the ion.

In addition to the free energy given by Eq. (12), three further terms must be considered: (a) the lateral dipole-dipole interactions between the dipoles oriented by the ion [27]. This depends on the dipole orientation [26] characterized by $\bar{\mu}$ and the geometry of the primary hydration shell (determined in part by r_i), but in general a term in $\bar{\mu}^2/x^3$ is involved where x is a mean lateral distance between dipoles around the ionic center. For such short distances as are involved around most charge centers, summation of point charge interactions between the dipolar molecules is preferable to use of an energy formula in terms of $\bar{\mu}^2/x^3$. (b) The ionic charge-solvent quadrupole interaction considered by Buckingham [28]. For principal quadrupole moments θ_a and θ_b, an ion of charge ze with solvent dipoles along the two principal directions experiences an energy of interaction

$$U_{i,d,q} = -ze \left\{ \frac{\bar{\mu} \cos \phi_z}{r^2} + \frac{1}{2r^3} \theta_a (3 \cos^2 \phi_x - 1) \right.$$

$$\left. + \theta_b (3 \cos^2 \phi_y - 1) \right\} \tag{13}$$

where $r = r_i + r_d$, the ion-dipole distance, and ϕ_z, ϕ_x, and ϕ_y are the angles which principal reference axes x, y, and z make in the general case [28] with the line along which r is measured. When $\phi_z = 0$ (cations) or $\phi_z = \pi$ (anions) (mirror image reversal of dipole orientations), $U_{i,d,q}$ becomes simply

$$U_{i,d,q} = \frac{-ze\bar{\mu}}{r^2} + \frac{2e(\theta_a + \theta_b)}{2r^3} \tag{14}$$

and the difference of interaction energies of the solvent dipole with cations and anions is given by

$$U_- - U_+ = \frac{-|z|e(\theta_a + \theta_b)}{r^3} - O/r^5 \tag{15}$$

where O is any residual octupole moment giving a small term in r^{-5}. Generally $\theta_a + \theta_b$ are evaluated together and, using the hydration energies of K^+ and F^- (ions of almost the same crystal radius), Buckingham [28] estimated this sum as 3.9×10^{-26} esu.

Finally (c), the primary hydration sphere about the ion will not usually fit into the remainder of the solvent structure so that an energy and entropy of reorganization is usually involved. This was first recognized by Bernal and Fowler [27] and the energy can be as large as 10 kcal/mole. The corresponding entropy change associated with this region of solvent structure reorganization was considered by Frank and Evans [35] for aqueous solutions and can be substantial. It is also significant with nonelectrolyte solutes in water (e.g., [35], the entropy of solution of 2 Ar atoms is, surprisingly, more negative than that of the two isoelectronic ions K^+, Cl^- at which appreciable electrostriction occurs) so that these factors must also be considered with regard to solvation of the un-ionized part of polyelectrolyte chains where hydrophobic interactions may be significant. The interaction of these electrostatic and nonelectrostatic kinds of effects found already [13,18] with simple organic ions will also arise in a more complex way with polyions as the degree of ionization is varied. The various regions of solvent near a simple ionic center are shown schematically in Fig. 3 according to the representation of Nemethy and Scheraga [7] and Frank and Wen [8].

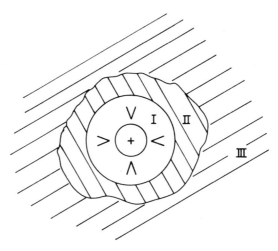

Fig. 3. Various solvation regions near an ion (according to representation of Nemethy and Scheraga [7], and Frank and Wen [8]). I = primary solvation region; II = solvent-structure reorganization region; III = bulk solvent.

C. Ionic Volumes and Compressibilities

One of the properties of ions in solution that is easily measured with considerable precision is the partial molal volume, e.g., from density measurements. The latter are usually made by means of a differential buoyancy balance, a magnetic densitometer or, at the highest dilutions (0.02-0.001 m), by means of a dilatometer. These methods are to be preferred to pyknometry. The apparent molal volume ϕ_V is obtained as

$$\phi_V = \frac{10^3(d_0 - d)}{cd_0} + M/d_0 \qquad (16)$$

where d is the density of the solution, d_0 that of the solvent, M the molecular weight of the solute, and c its concentration. The corresponding partial molal volume $\overline{V}$ is

$$\overline{V} = \phi_V + n_2 \left(\frac{d\phi_V}{dn_2}\right) \tag{17}$$

for n_2 moles of solute in n_1 of solvent. In terms of solvation of ions, ϕ_V or $\overline{V}$ is usually obtained at infinite dilution $(\overline{V}^0)$ by extrapolating $\overline{V}$ or ϕ_V with respect to $c^{1/2}$ or some other suitable function to zero concentration. $\overline{V}^0$ can then be interpreted in terms of solvation effects if it is recognized that $\overline{V}^0$ will be determined by the following four principal factors:

$$\overline{V}^0 = V_i + V_s + V_e + V_c \tag{18}$$

where V_i is the intrinsic volume of the ion under an internal pressure corresponding to the solution condensed phase (this is usually almost the same as that of the ion in a crystal lattice but is smaller than the gas-phase volume of the ion), V_s is the (positive or negative) volume due to a change of structure of the surrounding water (the hydrophobic or the so-called "structure breaking" term in aqueous solution), V_e is the (negative) volume change due to electrostriction of the surrounding solvent, and V_c (related to V_s) is the volume of cavities in the solvent occupied by the ion (a negative contribution). Usually $\overline{V}^0 < V_i$ due to electrostriction and occupation of cavities in the solvent lattice structure and to the presence of dead-space when ions of finite size fit among a coordinating region of solvent molecules of usually comparable size or, in the case of polyions, where the solvent size is comparable with the cross-sectional area of the polymer chain.

The electrostriction effect (V_e) arises from the operation of the contractive pressure or energy density $E^2/8\pi$ referred to in relation to Eq. (7). The relative electrostriction V_E/V_0 or the corresponding local relative density change ρ_E/ρ_0 can be calculated [31, 36] from electrostatic theory under conditions of field-dependent dielectric constant [32,36]. The above quantities are given by

$$V_0/V_E = \rho_E/\rho_0 = \left[\frac{A(A-1)\epsilon_0 E_r^2}{8\pi\beta D} + 1\right]^{D/1-A} \tag{19}$$

where A and D define the variation of compressibility and dielectric constant, respectively, with pressure and ϵ_0 is again the static dielectric constant. V_0/V_E can be evaluated [36] explicitly for high field and low field limiting cases, and by numerical integration for the general case over any range of field strengths.

Partial molal ionic compressibilities $\overline{K}$ can also be measured with some facility either isothermally by direct P-V measurements in high pressure apparatus with oil pumps or adiabatically by determination of the velocity of ultrasound in the solution directly by means of an interferometer [37] or differentially by phase difference methods [11,12]. A recent method employs the so-called "sing-around" technique [38].

For salts which electrostrict water, $\overline{K}$ is usually appreciably negative. This arises because the electrostricted water, being more closely packed, has a lower compressibility than water (or the solvent) in bulk. Negative $\overline{K}$, however, is not uniquely indicative of electrostricted solvent since tetraalkylammonium salts in the series Me_4NBr to $(n\text{-amyl})_4NBr$ cause progressively increasing negative $\overline{K}$ while the salts NH_4Br to Me_3NHBr exhibit decreasing negative $\overline{K}$ as the electrostricting N^+ center is gradually blocked from interaction with the solvent by Me groups. In cases where $\overline{K}$ becomes more negative yet the ion, by virtue of its structure, cannot cause appreciable electrostriction, it is concluded [11,12] that the compressibility behavior indicates local structure preservation (increase of the solvent-lattice relaxation times in the solvent lattice about the ion; cf. the NMR results of Hertz and co-workers [39]). Examples relating to polyions will be referred to below.

D. Determination of Hydration from Dielectric Properties

Here, a useful method due to Haggis, Hasted, and Buchanan [40] has been developed and consists in the measurement of dielectric constant and loss at microwave frequencies (λ = 9.22, 3.175, and 1.264 cm). The loss is characterized by relaxation processes having rates determined by the binding of the water molecules. The dielectric relaxation time of H_2O is shortened by positive ions and lengthened by H-bond forming molecules (cf. the NMR spin-lattice relaxation times [39]). The relaxation times of water molecules in the vicinity of ions varies with concentration according to

$$\lambda_S = \lambda_S^0 + c(\delta\lambda_S) \qquad (20)$$

where c is the concentration and $\delta\lambda_S$ is the increment of relaxation time expressed as the equivalent wavelength of the dielectric absorption process. $\delta\lambda_S$ is related to the electrostriction ΔV_e as shown in Table 1.

Table 1

Relation between Increments of Relaxation Times
and Electrostriction at Ions

	ΔV_e (ml/mole)	$\delta \lambda_s$
NaCl	-16	-0.20
NaBr	-17	-0.25
KCl	-13	-0.20
NH_4Cl	-6	-0.15
CH_3CH_2COOH	0	$+0.20$
$CH_3(CH_2)_2NH_2$	$+13$	$+0.20$
$NH_3^+(CH_2)_2COO^-$	$+13$	0

After corrections for conductivity, the results are analyzed in terms of a low frequency dielectric constant ϵ_s (falling to the high frequency value ϵ_∞). The experimental quantities are ϵ' and ϵ'', the real and imaginary components of the dielectric constant at frequency w:

$$\epsilon' = n^2 - x^2 = \frac{\epsilon_s - \epsilon_0}{1 + w^2 \tau^2} + \epsilon_\infty \tag{21}$$

$$\epsilon'' = 2nK = \frac{(\epsilon_0 - \epsilon_\infty) w \tau}{1 + w^2 \tau^2} \tag{22}$$

and $w\tau = \lambda_s/\lambda$. ϵ_s represents the low frequency dielectric constant of water in the solution and may be used to deduce the extent to which water molecules near ionic or polar centers are prevented from becoming oriented by the external field and thus contributing to the polarization produced by the test signal. This is a relative effect since H_2O molecules are also restricted by other solvent molecules in the bulk. The effects observed are hence due to hydration. Various situations (Fig. 4) of water molecules are possible [40] and contribute differently to the dielectric polarization. A number n_{irr}, the effective number of water molecules "irrotationally bound," is defined [40] as the number which have lost freedom to contribute to the dielectric polarization by virtue of already being strongly oriented by the ion or other center to which they are attached. In terms of the static dielectric behavior, these molecules are in a region of electric saturation (dielectric saturation effect). The n_{irr} is calculated from the relation

$$\epsilon = \epsilon_{H_2O} - \delta c \tag{23}$$

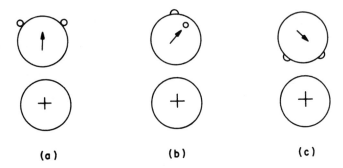

Fig. 4. Situations of water molecules near an ion in relation to dielectric relaxation (after Haggis, Hasted, and Buchanan [40]).

where c is in mole/liter, and

$$\delta = 1.5v \; \frac{\epsilon_{H_2O} - \epsilon_{\infty,solute}}{1000} + v_{H_2O} \; \frac{\epsilon_{H_2O} - \epsilon_{\infty,H_2O}}{1000} \; n_{irr}$$

where v is the actual molar volume of the solute and v_{H_2O} that of water. Some typical values for n_{irr} are summarized in Table 2.

Table 2

Values of n_{irr} for Selected Solutes in Water at 25°C [40]

Substance	δ (±0.5)	Volume (cc/mole)	n_{irr}
NaF	10	16	4 ± 1
NaCl	16	33	6 ± 1
NaBr	17	40	6 ± 1
NaI	17	53	6 ± 1
KCl	14	40	5 ± 1
Na propinate	14	55	4 ± 1
$EtNH_3^+Cl^-$	11	79	1 ± 1
$Et_2NH_2^+Cl^-$	19	111	3 ± 2
$Et_3NH^+Cl^-$	20	144	2 ± 1
$Et_4N^+Cl^-$	22	176	1 ± 1
Dioxane	8	69	0 ± 0.05
α-Alanine	12 ± 1	60	2 ± 1
β-Alanine	11 ± 1	60	2 ± 1

Positive ions are regarded as making the larger contribution (in most salts) to n_{irr}. The n_{irr} values approximate to the values of primary hydration numbers evaluated by other methods [1,4].

III. INDIVIDUAL IONIC CONTRIBUTIONS IN POLYELECTROLYTE SOLVATION

Early theories of, and work on, electrolyte solutions (Debye and Hückel, [41]) tended to emphasize the generality of the ionic strength principle at the expense of the specificity of ionic properties in solution although Bjerrum had noted the possibility of specific interactions of ions early in the development of the subject. The specific properties of ions are exhibited, of course, mainly in their short range interactions particularly in (a) their solvation and (b) ion pair formation. Both these aspects of ionic specificity are important in considering the properties of polyelectrolyte solutions in relation to solvation.

In the first place, the high charge density on polyion chains, for say $\alpha > 0.5$, causes appreciable counter-ion association at mono-mole concentrations at which, in the monomer salt solutions of the same concentration, little association would be found. The individual solvation properties of the counter-ions in relation to those of the polymer charge centers are thus of great importance. Second, the individual hydration behavior of the ionized centers on the polymer chain will determine the thermodynamics of ionization and interactions with other segments of the polymer chain, as well as interactions with other polymeric electrolytes, a matter of great interest in the biophysics of naturally occurring macromolecules. Evaluation of individual ionic solvation properties is therefore of great practical and theoretical significance and, for example, in the polysalt case it enables the polyion contribution to a given property to be separated from that due to its counter-ion atmosphere. In a polysalt, the properties of the polycation (or polyanion) will be expected to be substantially different from those of its counter-anions (or counter-cations, respectively) in distinction to the situation with ordinary simple 1:1 salts where the cation/anion differences, although significant, are of course not so marked as in the case of a polysalt. Hence, derivation of individual ionic properties in solution is of particular importance in the evaluation of solvation of polyions and its relation to the polymer structure and degree of polymerization.

In regard to the thermodynamic properties of salts it is, of course, not possible in principle to make a thermodynamic division of a measured partial molal property $\overline{X}_{\pm}$ for the salt into the individual ionic contributions $\overline{X}_+$ and $\overline{X}_-$, although such a division is possible in the case of kinetic properties such as the ionic mobility and the transference numbers. Nevertheless, a number of nonthermodynamic methods [1] based on the applicability of some theory or theoretical principle have been proposed, and they enable such ionic properties as the individual heat of solvation, the entropy of solvation, the partial gram ionic volume $\overline{V}_i$ and compressibility $\overline{K}_i$, and the H_2O/D_2O solvent isotope effect in $\overline{V}_i$ to be evaluated with some precision and reliability.

In the case of heats of solvation, Bernal and Fowler [27] proposed that the salt value for $K^+ F^-$ be divided almost equally except for a correction for the effect of the noncentral situation of the electric dipole in water. This method is, in fact, not now regarded as satisfactory due to the nonidentical ion-quadrupole contributions at the cation and the anion and the probable nonmirror-image orientations of H_2O at K^+ and F^-. A more satisfactory method, based on recognition of the ion-quadrupole effects, was proposed by Halliwell and Nyburg [42] and consisted in extrapolating the thermodynamically known differences of conventional heats of hydration of salts with a common cation or common anion with respect to $1/r_i^3$. The individual value of the heat of solvation of the proton (−260.7 kcal/mole) is then evaluated. Corrections for different orientations of water about cations and anions brings this figure to ca. −267 kcal/mole. A related method developed by Morris [43] involves extrapolation of the electrical component, $\Delta H_{e,\,solv}$ of the heat of solvation of a series of salts with a common cation or anion with respect to r_i^{-1} of the noncommon ion, i.e., after correction of the total heat of solvation for nonelectrostatic contributions which would not be dependent on a simple function of r. A summary of values of some individual heats of solvation and other ionic contributions to thermodynamic properties of salts is given in Table 3.

In the case of ionic entropies, individual values can be obtained from thermocell measurements [44-46] and a scale of individual partial gram ionic entropies and entropies of solvation can be drawn up on the basis of $\overline{S}_{H^+}^\circ$ (abs) = -5.5 ± 0.8 cal $^\circ C^{-1}$ g ion^{-1}.

In the case of ionic volume contributions, $\overline{V}_i$, which can lead to the evaluation of individual ionic electrostrictions, $\overline{V}_i - V_{i,\mathrm{intrinsic}}$, a procedure [10] to obtain the individual value for the $\overline{V}_i$ for the anion in a series of symmetrical tetraalkylammonium salts by extrapolation of $\overline{V}_{salt}$ to zero cation molecular weight has been proposed.*

---

*The modifications of this method by Panckhurst [5] have been shown [49] to be incorrect and extrapolations based on functions other than the molecular weight can be shown to give intercepts [10] which differ in expected ways from the individual anionic $\overline{V}^0$.

Table 3[a]

Standard Thermodynamic Functions for Hydration of Individual Ions at 25°C

Ion	$-\Delta G_h^o$ (kcal g/ion)	$\bar{S}_i^o$ (Gbs)	$-\Delta S_h^o$ (Gbs)	$-\Delta H_h^o$ (kcal g/ion)	$\bar{V}_i^o = \phi_V^o$ (dens) (ml/mole)	$\bar{V}_i^o$ (uvp) (ml/mole)
H$^+$	260.5	−5.3	31.3	269.8	−5.5	−5.4
Li$^+$	122.1	−1.9	33.7	132.1	−6.6	−11.2
Na$^+$	98.2	9.1	26.2	106.0	−7.0	−7.4
K$^+$	80.6	19.2	17.7	85.8	3.3	3.4
Rb$^+$	75.5	24.4	14.8	79.8	8.3	9.0
Cs$^+$	67.5	26.5	14.1	72.0	15.6	15.5
F$^-$	103.8	3.0	31.8	113.3	5.8	10.5
Cl$^-$	75.8	18.5	18.2	81.3	23.6	23.7
Br$^-$	72.5	24.6	14.5	77.9	30.9	30.2
I$^-$	61.4	31.4	9.0	64.1	42.2	41.4
OH$^-$	−	2.8	−	101.0	−	−

[a]Based on the survey of Desnoyers and Jolicoeur [1]. Data in the last two columns are based on density ("dens") and ultrasonic vibration potentials ("uvp").

The result for Br$^-$ agrees within ca. 0.5 ml g/ion with that obtained by a completely different procedure based on measurements of ultrasonic potentials [47] by Zana and Yeager [48]. Some results are shown in Table 3. Again, such data enable individual polyion volumes to be deduced* from measured values for the corresponding polymeric salts after appropriate allowance (see below) for any ion-pairing. These methods for evaluation of individual ionic properties in solution have been reviewed in more detail elsewhere [1].

IV. ELECTROSTATIC TREATMENTS OF POLYIONS FOR SOLVATION CALCULATIONS

The solvation of polyions is a relatively short-range phenomenon and so will be little affected by the longer range configurational changes which arise [30] from changing degree of ionization α or ionic strength μ of added simple electrolyte. The solvation is, however, indirectly affected by the two factors α and μ on account of counter-ion association with the charge-bearing centers.

The electric potential and field near polyions is required in order to formulate the solvation effects in terms of (a) dielectric saturation in the solvent, (b) counter-ion distribution, (c) electrostriction

*
This method has been employed for various polysalts, and the data are discussed and tabulated in Sect. V.B.3.

about the ion, and (d) distribution of other nonelectrolyte species (in relation to solvent molecules) that may be present in the solution (salting-out effect). Several models are available:

A. Rigid Infinite Rod without Ionic Atmosphere

Here the electric field at r from the polyion axis is simply

$$\frac{d\psi}{dr} = E = \frac{-2\alpha e}{\lambda \epsilon r} \tag{25}$$

a relation which may be employed (see below) to evaluate the profile of dielectric constant near the polyion and the corresponding limit of the primary solvation envelope within which (cf. the case of simple ions) in the case of water $\epsilon \leq 5$ [32,50], and for which figure primary hydration can be defined [51] in terms of the limiting radius at which ϵ relatively suddenly increases toward the normal value (ϵ_0) of 78. In Eq. (25), λ is the distance between charges on the chain.

B. Rigid Finite Rod without Ionic Atmosphere

From the point of view of the short-range interactions involved in polyion solvation, the infinite rod model is qualitatively as satisfactory as a model based on a charged rod of finite length. However, the forms of the potential and field functions for the latter case are different, and since shorter chain elements may be of interest in branched chain structures or with oligomeric ions, the finite rod case is of some interest.

The model can be examined in terms of the electrostatic treatment of a charged wire or prolate ellipsoid of high aspect ratio [52]. The potential at a field point distant r from the charged rod of length 2c (Fig. 5) is

$$\psi = \frac{q}{2c} \int_{-c}^{+c} d\xi / r \tag{26}$$

where ξ is a parameter for the length along the z axis taken along the rod. q is the total charge so $q/2c$ is the line density of charge. Taking the origin at the midpoint of the rod enables r to be written as

$$r = [(z - \xi)^2 + x^2 + y^2]^{1/2} \tag{27}$$

so that

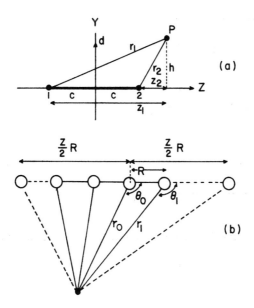

Fig. 5. Models for electrostatic calculations on polarization by a rigid charged rod.

$$\phi = -\frac{e}{2c} \left| \log (z - \xi + r) \right|_{\xi=-c}^{\xi=c}$$

$$= \frac{e}{2c} \log \left[\frac{z + c + r_1}{z - c + r_2} \right] \tag{28}$$

where r_1 and r_2 are the distances of the field point from the ends of the rod ($= c$) at which $\xi = +c$ and $-c$, respectively. Introducing elliptic coordinates α and β in the zh plane (Fig. 5)

$$\alpha = (r_1 + r_2)/2 \tag{29a}$$

$$\beta = (r_1 - r_2)/2 \tag{29b}$$

and from Fig. 5

$$r_1^2 = h^2 + (z + c)^2 \tag{30a}$$

$$r_2^2 = h^2 + (z - c)^2 \tag{30b}$$

so that

$$r_1 = \alpha + \beta; \ r_2 = \alpha - \beta \tag{31}$$

and

$$z = \alpha\beta/c \tag{32}$$

$$h = \frac{1}{c} \sqrt{(\alpha^2 - c^2)(c^2 - \beta^2)}$$

The potential ψ is then independent of β and is expressed by

$$\psi = \frac{q}{2c} \log \left[\frac{\alpha + c}{\alpha - c}\right] \tag{33}$$

noting that since

$$\frac{\alpha}{z} = \frac{c}{\beta} = \frac{\alpha + c}{z + \beta} = \frac{\alpha - c}{z - \beta}, \qquad \frac{\alpha + c}{\alpha - c} = \frac{\alpha + c + z + \beta}{\alpha - c + z - \beta}$$

along the median $(\xi = 0)$, $r_1 = r_2 = r$ $(\alpha = r)$,

$$\psi = \frac{q}{2c} \log \left[\frac{r + c}{r - c}\right]$$

and the field vector $d\psi/dr$ along each r is given by

$$\frac{d\psi}{dr} = \frac{q}{2c}\left(\frac{r - c}{r + c}\right)\frac{2c}{(r - c)^2} = \left(\frac{q}{2c}\right)\frac{(-2c)}{r^2 - c^2}$$

$$= -\rho 2c/(r^2 - c^2)$$

$$= -\rho 2c/d^2$$

when ρ represents the line density of charge and d is the distance along the median line normal to the rod at the origin. In the general case, equipotentials are over α = constant, i.e., on ellipsoids of revolution with the ends of the charged rod as foci. The potential along the median line is also represented in terms of distance d from the origin by

$$\psi = \frac{q}{2c} \log \left[\frac{(d^2 + c^2)^{1/2} + c}{(d^2 + c^2)^{1/2} - c} \right] \tag{34}$$

The field along this direction is $d\psi/dd$ and is obtained, after differentiating Eq. (34) and making simple but extensive algebraic rearrangements, as

$$\frac{d\psi}{dd} = \frac{-q(d^2 + c^2)^{-1/2}}{d} = -\frac{q}{dr} \tag{35}$$

In the case of the finite charged rod, Eq. (34) for the potential can be applied to the case of the equipotential ellipsoids regarded now as conductors having α for their surfaces equal to "a", their semi-major axes. Then, on such ellipsoids, the potential is

$$\psi^1 = \frac{q}{2c} \log \frac{a + c}{a - c} \tag{36}$$

and the capacity C is

$$\frac{1}{C} = \frac{\psi^1}{q} = \frac{1}{2c} \log \frac{a + c}{a - c} \tag{37}$$

Also, for the case of a very long rodlike ellipsoid, i.e., for a small value of the axial ratio b/a, $1/c = (1/a) \log (2a/b)$. In terms of the capacity, the Born charging energy is $-\frac{1}{2} C\psi^2$ as is seen for the case of a spherical ion ($c = r$; $\psi = q/r$, hence, $G_e = (1/2)(q^2/r^2)$. $r = (1/2)(q^2/r)$. In the case of the long ellipsoid, application of this principle gives

$$G_e = \left(\frac{1}{2} \right) 2c \left(\log \frac{a + c}{a - c} \right)^{-1} \frac{q^2}{4c^2} \left(\log \frac{a + c}{a - c} \right)^2 \tag{38}$$

$$= \frac{q^2}{4c} \log \frac{a + c}{a - c}$$

For the limiting case of a thin rod ($b \ll a$),

$$\psi \doteq \frac{q}{a} \log \frac{2a}{b} \qquad \text{so that} \qquad G_e \doteq \frac{q^2}{2a} \log \frac{2a}{b} \tag{39}$$

and the charge on the ellipsoid perpendicularly projected on its axis of symmetry can be shown to be equivalent to uniform line density on the axis. In terms of the line density ρ , now written as q/a ,

$$G_e = a\rho^2 \log 2a/b = a\rho^2(\log 2a - \log b) \tag{40}$$

whence the charging energy becomes more negative with decreasing log b rather than increasing $1/r$ as in the case of spherical ions. Obviously, the Born electrostatic energy of the rodlike ellipsoid having a given length varies much less rapidly with its "cylindrical" radius than does the energy of spherical ions with respect to their radii. The charging energy in the solvent of dielectric constant ϵ is simply $1/\epsilon$ times the value of G_e deduced above and the solvation energy is $[(1/\epsilon) - 1]$ times these values (cf. Eq. 6).

C. Rodlike Particle with Ionic Atmosphere

Here the Poisson-Boltzmann equation is solved [15] for long rods lying parallel due to mutual orientation and occupying a co-volume of the solution $2\pi R^2 L$ ($L \rightarrow \infty$) where 2R is the distance of their separation. The solution to the problem of evaluation of field and electrostatic potential was given by Alfrey, Berg, and Morawetz [15] and by Fuoss, Katchalsky, and Lifson [53]. This case may also be used for evaluation of electrostriction and solvation but the expressions for ψ or $d\psi/dR$ are not explicit. This representation is more realistic than that in the isolated charged rod model since the ionic atmosphere is taken into account. The result for $\psi(r)$ at distance r from the polyion of radius a having distance b between ionizable groups (line density $\pm \alpha e/b$) is

$$\psi(r) = \frac{1}{L} \left(\ln \frac{2\delta'^2}{LM} - 2 \ln r - 2 \ln \cos (\delta'[\ln r + \beta]) \right) \tag{41}$$

where δ' and β are constants determined by the boundary conditions and

$$L = \frac{4\pi}{\epsilon_0} \frac{Nc\alpha e}{1000} ; \quad M = e/kT$$

The other parameters follow from the boundary conditions:
1. The total charge due to counter-ions is equal and opposite to that due to the polyion rod, viz.

$$-\alpha e/b = \int_a^R 2\pi r \rho(r) \, dr \tag{42}$$

with $\rho_{(r)} = \rho_0 \exp e\psi_r/kT$, the space-charge density.

2. The electric field vanishes at the boundary of the co-cylinder volume containing the counter ions due to the (assumed) cylindrical symmetry of neighboring polyions and their atmospheres (this condition would not be applicable to shorter polyions whose orientation would be more random)

$$(d\psi/dr)_{r=R} = 0$$

Then if $\delta'(\ln R + \beta)$ is set equal to η, the boundary conditions lead to $\delta' = \cot \eta$ and

$$\eta = \tan^{-1}\left[\frac{1 - \alpha e^2/b\epsilon_0 kT}{\delta'}\right] + \delta' \ln R/a \qquad (43)$$

These equations enable the field to be evaluated for various conditions and hence the electrostriction and the polyion-solvent polarization can be calculated.

An analytical approximation to the solution of the Poisson-Boltzmann equation for a charged linear cylindrical particle of radius r_0 was also developed by Philip and Wooding [54]. The Poisson-Boltzmann equation for their treatment was written

$$\frac{1}{r}\frac{d}{dr}\left(r\frac{d\psi}{dr}\right) = -\frac{4\pi e}{\epsilon_0}\sum n_i z_i \exp\left(\frac{z_i e\psi}{kT}\right) \qquad (44)$$

subject to the boundary conditions

$$r = r_0, \quad \psi = \psi_0 \quad \text{or} \quad \frac{d\psi}{dr} = -4\pi\rho/\epsilon \qquad (45)$$

and $r \to \infty$, $\psi \to 0$, where r is a radial space coordinate about the cylinder, ϵ the dielectric constant, and ψ the electric potential. The first boundary condition applies when the surface potential ψ_0 is given while the second applies if the surface charge density ρ is known. A symmetrical electrolyte is considered, $i = 1,2$, $z_1 = -z_2$ $(=z)$; $n_1 = n_2 = n$. Then

$$r^{-1}\frac{d}{dr}\left(\frac{r\,d\psi}{dr}\right) = \frac{8\pi nze}{\epsilon}\sinh\frac{ze\psi}{kT} \qquad (46)$$

The substitutions

$$\frac{R}{r} = \frac{R_o}{r_o} = [\,8\pi nz^2e^2/\epsilon kT\,]^{1/2} \tag{47}$$

$$\Psi/\psi = \Psi_0/\psi_0 = ze/kT \tag{48}$$

$$(d\Psi/dR)_0/\tau = -(2\pi/\epsilon nkT)^{1/2} \tag{49}$$

then reduce the initial set of equations to

$$R^{-1}(d/dR)(R\,d\Psi/dR) = \sinh\Psi \tag{50}$$

$$R = R_0\;;\;\Psi = \Psi_0 \quad \text{or} \quad \frac{d\Psi}{dR} = (d\Psi/dR) \tag{51}$$

$$R \to \infty \qquad \Psi \to 0 \tag{52}$$

An analytical approximation for the sinh function is made which enables solutions to be obtained in elementary functions:

$0 \le \Psi \le 1 \quad \sinh\Psi \doteqdot \Psi$ (Debye-Hückel type approximation)

$\Psi \gg 1 \qquad \sinh\Psi \doteqdot \frac{1}{2}\exp\Psi$

Five cases were considered for the solution of the problem which give various limiting analytical expressions. Comparison with the exact solution by computer calculation was made and values of Ψ as a function of R were tabulated for various conditions.

D. Field and Electrostriction at a Linear Array of Charges

For a linear array of discrete charges separated by a distance 2λ, the field vector can be calculated [18] at a distance r from the chain. For the case of two charges on a chain (or at the midpoint of an array of charges), the field at points along a line normal to the chain midway between the charges will also be directed normally (and radially) to the chain and will have the magnitude

$$E = 2er/(r^2 + \lambda^2)^{3/2}\epsilon \tag{53}$$

In the general case of an array of like charges, the field at a point midway along the chain will be

$$E = \sum_{o}^{n} 2er/[\,r^2 + (2n-1)^2\lambda^2\,]^{3/2}\epsilon \tag{54}$$

where $(2n - 1)\lambda$ is the distance of the nth charge from the midpoint of the chain. At other points, the field vector will not be normal to the chain but can be evaluated numerically by trigonometric procedures.

For the ion with two charges at various separations (cf. the limiting case of bolaform electrolytes) it is of interest to evaluate the variation of E with λ and r.

Differentiating Eq. (53) gives

$$dE = (2e(\lambda^2 - 2r^2)/\epsilon(r^2 + \lambda^2)^{2.5}) \, dr - \frac{6er\lambda \, d\lambda}{(r^2 + \lambda^2)^{2.5}\epsilon} \qquad (55)$$

so that for the variation of field radially

$$(\partial E/\partial r)_\lambda = 2e(\lambda^2 - 2r^2)/(r^2 + \lambda^2)^{2.5}\epsilon \qquad (56)$$

and for the dependence on separation λ

$$(\partial E/\partial \lambda)_r = -6er\lambda/(r^2 + \lambda^2)^{2.5}\epsilon \qquad (57)$$

The field at r hence continuously diminishes as λ increases, as may be expected; however, it is of interest to note that the radial variation of field for a given charge separation evidently exhibits a maximum at $\lambda = \sqrt{2r}$ as may be seen from Eq. (55). At this point,

$$E_m = 4e/3^{1.5}\lambda^2\epsilon \qquad (58)$$

is the maximum field; alternatively, in terms of r,

$$E_m = 2e/3^{1.5}r^2\epsilon \qquad (59)$$

Introduction of dielectric saturation effects (cf. Refs. 32 and 51) increases the field at short ranges but the general trend of the relations shown above will be maintained. Detailed numerical calculations for the rigid polyion model have been given previously [51] taking into account dielectric saturation effects [32].

In terms of the integral electrostriction caused by the charges, either the low field or high field cases of previously published equations [36] may be used (they have the same form but different constants). Thus, in a cylindrical element of solution, length Δl, about the charged rod the relative electrostriction v/v_0 is given by

$$\frac{v}{v_0} = \frac{\int_0^r 2\pi r \Delta l \,(\rho_0/\rho_r) \, dr}{\int_0^r 2\pi r \Delta l \, dr} \tag{60}$$

where ρ_r/ρ_0 is the density ratio function

$$\frac{\rho_r}{\rho_0} = \left[\frac{A(1-A)\epsilon_0 E_r^2}{8\pi\beta D} + 1 \right]^{D/1-A} \tag{61}$$

dependent on field E_r at r. A numerical solution is possible using E_r given by Eq. (53) and the high or low field forms of Eq. (61). The constants A and D define (for water) the known variation of compressibility and dielectric constant, respectively, with pressure, and ϵ_0 is, as usual, the static dielectric constant.

E. Relation to Electrode Interfaces

The charged linear rod is, in one dimension, analogous to the two-dimensional charged colloid interface or to an electrode interface except that in the latter case the charge on one side of the double-layer is delocalized. A charged polyion carries a one-dimensional (but cylindrical) double-layer and can be treated in principle like an electrode. The application of the Poisson-Boltzmann equation for the double-layer for such a case was first made by Chapman in 1915 [55] based on Gouy's model of a diffuse ionic atmosphere. Only in the case of hydrogen bonded polyions such as polymethacrylate or polyacrylate at $\alpha = 0.5$ can any "quasi-delocalization" of (negative) charge arise on the chain and this would arise by proton migration among COO^- and $COOH$ groups, a relatively "slow" process in comparison with electron delocalization in a metal. The electrostatic treatments for cylindrical ions with an ionic atmosphere are similar to those for the ionic atmosphere at an electrode except that cylindrical symmetry is involved. At electrodes, the solvation of the interface can be treated [56,57] in terms of a progressive orientation of dipoles of the solvent, dependent on electrode surface charge.

F. Dielectric Saturation Effects

1. **Method of Treatment.** In any continuum treatment of the solvent in ionic solutions it is necessary to recognize that the dielectric constant of the solvent will usually be a function of local field due to electric saturation orientation effects, and hence of distance from the polarizing ion. In fact, since the dielectric constant is a sensitive

function of the field at critically high fields of ca. 10^6-10^7 V/cm and the field itself is dependent on $1/\epsilon$, the variation of ϵ with distance from an ion is usually a sharp one corresponding approximately to the limit of primary hydration. Dielectric saturation effects are, of course, particularly large in associated solvents due to the large value of ϵ_0 at zero field and the saturation effect depends in a complex way on correlation effects in the orientation process. The treatment of Booth [32], based on Kirkwood's theory [58], is usually employed [36,51]. Since the saturation effect, particularly in water, must arise very near the ion, the significance of a macroscopic property such as dielectric constant becomes somewhat uncertain. In fact, a step function in dielectric constant from a low value near 2 (or 5-6 [50]) for $r \leq r_h$, the primary hydration radius, to a value $\epsilon = 80$ for $r > r_h$ may be almost as satisfactory as a detailed evaluation of ϵ as $f(r)$, the distance from the ion. In the case of polyion hydration, appreciable fields persist to longer distances out from the ion than they do in the case of simple spherical ions so that evaluation of the dielectric saturation profiles of ϵ as $f(r)$ are necessary. They are also required for the evaluation of the salting-out of nonelectrolytes caused by polyions (see below).

Theoretical treatment of dielectric saturation at simple ions was first given by Webb in 1929 [59] but the theory of Booth [32], based on the Kirkwood theory for the dielectric constant of associated liquids, is to be preferred. Applications of the latter approach were made by Laidler [60] for monatomic uni- and polyvalent ions. Conway, Desnoyers, and Smith [51] developed a treatment for the case of polyions and obtained numerical solutions for the dependence of ϵ on field and distance near polyions. In particular, they were able to evaluate the critical distances r_d (analogous to r_h) at which ϵ started to vary rapidly with distance r from the polyion and approach the zero-field value. These values of r_d were found to be similar (for various polyion sizes and degrees of ionization) to the r_h values deduced (see below) from partial molal volume measurements and evaluations of electrostriction.

For the polyion case, the model of Alfrey, Berg, and Morawetz [15] is employed (see p. 138) and the Poisson equation is written as

$$\nabla^2(\psi) = \frac{1}{r}\frac{d}{dr}\left(\epsilon_i r \frac{d\psi}{dr}\right) = -4\pi\rho \qquad (62)$$

In the region between a and R, the charge density is associated with the counter-ions and, if these are univalent anions, the space charge density is

$$\rho = -\frac{\alpha emN}{1000} \exp\left(\frac{e\psi}{kT}\right) \tag{63}$$

where α, as usual, is the degree of ionization and m the concentration (mole/liter) of the counter-ions.

Combining Eqs. (62) and (63) gives

$$\frac{d^2\psi}{dr^2} = \frac{1}{\epsilon_d} \left\{ \frac{4\pi e\alpha mN}{1000} \exp\left(\frac{e\psi}{kT}\right) - \frac{\epsilon_i}{r}\frac{d\psi}{dr} \right\} \tag{64}$$

where ϵ_i is the integral and ϵ_d the differential dielectric constant. To obtain a solution for $d\psi/dr$, the field, and ϵ as $f(d\psi/dr)$ two boundary conditions are considered. The first is that the field at R is equal to zero, as in the simple ion case, where R is defined in terms of the co-volume for the parallel cylindrical system as

$$R = (1000/\pi mN\lambda)^{1/2} \tag{65}$$

and λ is the distance between ionizable groups on the polymer chain. The second boundary condition is defined by the space charge between a and R which is equal to $-\alpha e/\lambda$, i.e.,

$$\int_a^r 2\pi r\rho\,dr = -\alpha e/\lambda \tag{66}$$

which, with ρ obtained from Poisson's Eq. (62), gives as a second boundary condition

$$\left(\epsilon_i \frac{d\psi}{dr}\right)_a = \frac{2\alpha e}{a\lambda} \tag{67}$$

The starting conditions for numerical integration are

$$\left(\frac{d\psi}{dr}\right)_R = 0 \tag{68a}$$

$$\left(\frac{d^2\psi}{dr^2}\right)_R = \frac{4\pi emN\alpha}{1000\epsilon_0} \exp\left[e\psi_R/kT\right] \tag{68b}$$

and

$$\left(\frac{d^3\psi}{dr^3}\right)_R = -\frac{1}{R}\left(\frac{d^2\psi}{dr^2}\right)_R \tag{68c}$$

2. **Results for the Charged Rod Model.** The variables in the problem for rod-shaped particles are the concentration m, the degree of ionization α, and the radius a of the polyion. The distance between ionizable groups, λ, was taken as 2.5 Å in the series of calculations (the value used by Alfrey et al. [15]) and is the approximate effective value for vinyl polyions. The temperature was taken as 298°K and ϵ_0 as 78.5.

The calculated values for the integral and differential dielectric constants, ϵ_i and ϵ_d, and the field $d\psi/dr$ are shown as a function of r for selected conditions in Figures 6, 7, and 8. As in the case

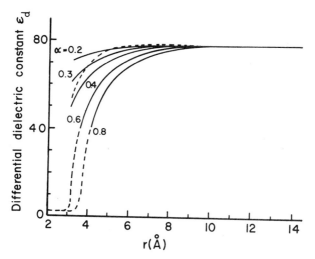

Fig. 6. Differential dielectric constant ϵ_d as a function of distance from a polyion of radius 3.2 Å for various degrees of ionization, α = 0.2, 0.3, 0.4, 0.6, and 0.8. Upper dotted line is for corresponding monomeric ion.

of simple ions, the distance at which the differential dielectric constant is equal to 55* can be conveniently defined as r_d for the purposes of comparing degrees of dielectric saturation and the relative extents of the primary hydration layer for monomeric and corresponding polymeric ions. The calculations were performed for 1 monomolar solutions but the results for r_d are not very sensitive to concentration. They depend, however, appreciably on the degree of neutralization (Fig. 9) as expected. The degree of dielectric

*This is the approximate value where the curve of ϵ_d rises most steeply towards the static value of 78 when ϵ_d is plotted as $f(r)$ or $f(d\psi/dr)$.

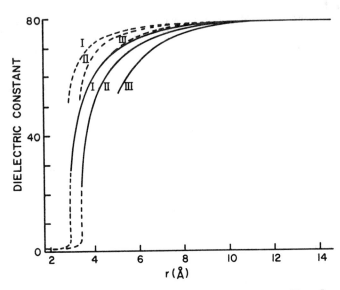

Fig. 7. Dielectric saturation effects at polyions of various radii a: I, a = 2.2 Å; II, a = 3.2 Å; III, a = 5.0 Å. α = 0.6, concentration 1.0 monomolar. (Solid lines represent differential dielectric constant ϵ_d, and dashed lines integral dielectric constant ϵ_i.)

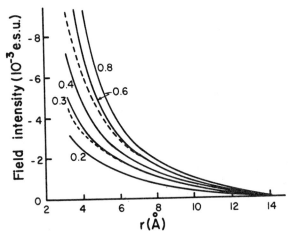

Fig. 8. Field intensity at polyions of radius 2.2 Å for the indicated values of α.

saturation near a polyion is quantitatively similar to that at a simple
univalent monomer ion of the same radius only when α = ca. 0.35.
This is consistent with the salting-out and electrostriction behavior
found experimentally [51] (see below).

The effect of dielectric saturation on the field function is shown
in Fig. 10 from which it can be seen that neglect of dielectric
saturation effects can lead to rather serious errors in these functions under some conditions.

The effect of the radius of a "time-average" cylindrical element
of the polyion on the degree of dielectric saturation in terms of ϵ_d
and ϵ_i, as displayed in Fig. 7, shows that a significant increase in
the "saturation" hydration radius of the polyion may be anticipated
with increasing intrinsic radius.

At quite low degrees of ionization (α < 0.1) most polyions adopt
the configuration of a random coil. The electrostatics of this case
have been considered by Wall and Berkowitz [61] for constant dielectric constant. Computational runs for field-dependent dielectric
constant were also made for this case [51] and it was found that the
results for reduced field and potential [61] as a function of r are
almost unaffected by taking into account the field dependence of the
dielectric constant, and the latter has values near that of ϵ_0 at the
periphery of the random coil where the over-all field is highest.
However, local effects inside the coil must still be significant but
are best considered in terms of a solution of localized ion sites at a
concentration determined by α and the volume density of the random
coil. As the coil becomes more open (α < 0.25), the linear rod
model becomes more and more applicable for evaluation of the short-
range effects such as are involved in primary hydration.

From the dielectric constant profiles calculated for the above
models it seems unlikely that there are any very long range hydration effects of the type proposed by Jacobson [62,63], at least not
due to electrostrictive effects. This matter will be examined further below.

V. THERMODYNAMICS OF POLYELECTROLYTE HYDRATION

A. Problems and Methods of Approach

The thermodynamic methods generally available for derivation of
standard free energies, entropies, and enthalpies of hydration of simple salts [1,3], e.g., from emf measurements, heats of solution, etc.
are often not applicable to polysalts because they rarely form ions
which behave reversibly in a cell and do not form well-defined crystalline solids, the lattice energies of which are known or could be
calculated, e.g., by Madelung's method. The thermodynamic methods

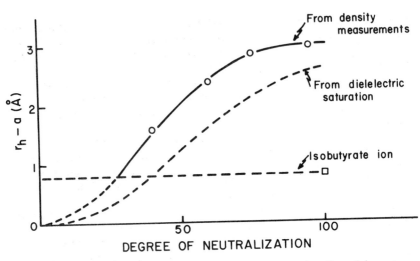

Fig. 9. Thickness of primary hydration shell r_h - a as a function of degree of neutralization of a polyacid deduced from dielectric saturation calculations and density measurements (electrostriction).

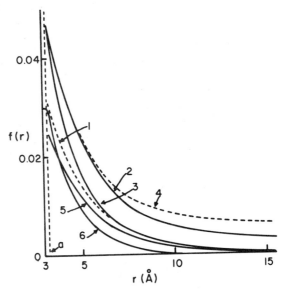

Fig. 10. Effects of dielectric saturation on the field function $f(r)$ at polyions for various conditions.

give $\mu_\pm^o$, $\overline{H}_\pm^o$, and $\overline{S}_\pm^o$, the standard chemical potential, the partial molal heat content, and entropy, respectively, the chemical potential being the primary quantity. If heats of solution are measured by direct calorimetry, and if the heat of sublimation of the salt to form gaseous ions is known, then the heat of hydration of the gaseous ions can easily be derived. It is readily seen that this procedure will not generally be applicable to the usually amorphous polysalts.

Other thermodynamic properties such as the activity and osmotic coefficients can, however, be derived from isopiestic vapor pressure measurements, freezing point depression, and osmotic pressure determinations. Unlike simple salts where the mean thermodynamic property is determined approximately equally by cations and anions, e.g., in 1:1 salts, in the case of polysalts the colligative properties are largely determined by the counter-ions, though the activity coefficients of these ions are strongly influenced by the presence of the polyion chain of low osmotic activity on account of the high local charge density. In some cases, the activity coefficients can be determined by emf measurements on cells with transference, e.g. [64],

$$\text{Ag/AgCl polyimine-HCl} \mid \text{polyimine-HCl AgCl/Ag}$$

$$\qquad\qquad 2 \qquad\qquad\qquad\qquad 1$$

the emf of which is

$$E_1 = \frac{(1 + \alpha)RT}{F} \int_{a_2}^{a_1} t_p \, d \ln a \tag{69}$$

where a_1 and a_2 are the mean activities of the hydrochloride in the two solutions 1 and 2, and α is the fraction of counter-ions dissociated from each macroion. The "single ion" activity coefficient of the gegen-ions was estimated using the cell

$$\text{Hg/Hg}_2\text{Cl}_2 \quad \begin{array}{c} \text{polysalt} \\ \text{solution} \end{array} \quad \text{AgCl/Ag}$$

the emf of which was written [64] as

$$E_2 = E_2^o - \frac{RT}{F} \ln a_{Cl^-} \tag{70}$$

In the case of simple electrolytes, activity coefficient information at high ionic strengths can lead to information concerning hydration, e.g., as in the theory of Stokes and Robinson [65] where "thermodynamic" hydration numbers for ions of the salt are derived.

With polysalts, however, an equivalent interpretation would be difficult due to (a) the counter-ion binding, (b) inapplicability of the Debye-Hückel theory to polyions,* and (c) the locally higher concentrations above the mean stoichiometric value of ions near the polyion. Hence the direct determination of hydration numbers or energies for polysalts presents serious difficulties in comparison with the situation for simple salts.

These difficulties are not, however, involved with the determination of other properties such as partial molal volume, compressibility, salting-out constant, etc. since they are not experimentally dependent on a direct chemical potential or energy measurement. Accordingly, these functions can be determined without any experimental ambiguities or difficulties of theoretical principle (e.g., significance of single counter-ion activity coefficients).

Conway, Desnoyers, and Smith [51] made some of the first thermodynamic measurements on polyelectrolyte hydration in a comprehensive study of theoretical dielectric saturation effects (cf. Ref. 66 and Sect. IV,F), partial molal volumes, and salting-out coefficients for solubility of simple nonelectrolytes in the polyelectrolyte solutions (polyphosphates, polyacrylates, and polyvinylpyridine-N-n butylbromide). Later work by Ise and Okubo [19] and by Lawrence and Conway [18] extended the volume studies to polyethyleneimine-hydrohalides, and adiabatic compressibility studies were reported in another paper by Lawrence and Conway [18]. As remarked earlier, the polyethylene-imines are of especial interest as polyionogenic molecules since the charges resulting from ionization reside on the polymer backbone rather than in side chains so that the geometrical distribution of the charges is well defined and approximates most closely to that considered in the theoretical models (Sect. IV).

B. Partial Molal Volumes $\overline{V}$ and Electrostriction

With polyions having varying degrees of ionization, the possibility exists of being able to change the relative contributions to $\overline{V}$ from electrostriction at the charge centers and from structure promotion changes caused by the un-ionized parts of the molecule. Also, with polyimines, the transition from simple electrolyte to polyelectrolyte behavior can be followed with regard to hydration (cf. the ion association effects at polyethyleneimine oligomers studied by Rice et al. [67]).

1. Polyphosphates. The first polyion volume studies in aqueous solution were made on polyphosphates of various molecular weights [51]. As with the polyimines, the higher molecular weight materials may have branched-chain or cyclic structures but for the short-range

*But compare the early treatment of Linderstrøm-Lang for proteins [65].

effects arising in hydration this should not introduce too serious a complication in the interpretation of the results, e.g., in terms of electrostriction.

The apparent molal volumes of a series of polyphosphates are shown as a function of molecular weight in Fig. 11 from the results of Conway, Desnoyers, and Smith [51]. The data for NaH_2PO_2, NaH_2PO_3, and NaH_2PO_4 are shown for comparison. The relation between ϕ_V for the polyphosphates and the monomer analog NaH_2PO_4 is anomalous insofar as the volumes of the polysalts are larger than that of the "monomer" salt [with potassium PMA and $PV\overline{PBuBr}$ the volumes of the polysalts are smaller when $\alpha > 0.4$ (on a monomole basis) than the volume of the monomer due to the relatively greater electrostriction by the charged chain].

This anomaly arises because of the abnormally high degree of hydration and electrostriction of NaH_2PO_4 (cf. Ref. 68). In order to clarify this matter, reference must also be made to the ϕ_V for sodium hydrogen phosphite and of sodium hypophosphite. It may be suggested that the anomalous results arise because the salt $Na^+HO-P{\overset{\displaystyle O}{\underset{\displaystyle O^-}{\diagdown}}}OH$

was compared with NaPP in which the repeating group is, in fact,

$-\overset{\displaystyle O}{\underset{\displaystyle O^-Na^+}{\overset{\|}{P}}}-O-$. Hence, $Na^+H-\overset{\displaystyle O}{\underset{\displaystyle O^-}{\overset{\|}{P}}}-OH$ and $Na^+H-\overset{\displaystyle O}{\underset{\displaystyle O^-}{\overset{\|}{P}}}-H$ may be a preferable

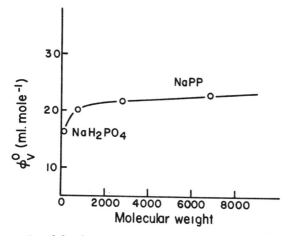

Fig. 11. Apparent molal volumes ϕ_V for a series of polyphosphates as a function of molecular weight.

basis for reference as "monomeric" salts. As expected by comparison with the case of KPMA and theoretically [51], the apparent
molal volumes of these two salts are larger than that of the polymeric
salt NaPP. The result which is anomalous is therefore that for
NaH_2PO_4 rather than that for the polymer; this is probably a result
of hydrogen bonding which also plays an important role in the hydration of the polyphosphates of low molecular weight through end-group
effects. The change of volume behavior with increasing molecular
weight is consistent with the trend of salting-out constants for these
polyions.

    2. Polyimines. *a. Concentration dependence of* ϕ_V: The hydro-
halide salts of various polyethyleneimines (PEI) and the oligomers ethylene diamine (ED), diethylene triamine (DT), triethylene tetramine (TT),
and tetraethylene pentamine (TP) were investigated by Conway and
Lawrence [18] using a differential density balance technique with dil-
atometry for the solutions of lowest concentrations and by Ise and
Okubo [19] by pyknometry. The latter technique is insufficiently
sensitive to provide density measurements of high enough accuracy
on solutions down to low enough concentrations for reliable extrapo-
lations of ϕ_V to be made towards infinite dilution to evaluate $\overline{V}^\circ$, the
quantity characterizing the effective volume of the isolated individual
polysalt. (It is to be noted, however, that even at the lowest limits of
practicably attainable dilutions, the cations and anions of polysalts
will not be uniformly distributed in the solvent due to the counter-
ion atmosphere carried by each macroion and the tendency for minimization of finite space-charge in regions of the solution.)

    With the oligomeric polyimine hydrochlorides, Ise and Okubo [19]
found that ϕ_V increased with (monomole) concentration in the range
0.1-1.3 M while a polyimine of degree of polymerization (DP) = 100
showed no concentration dependence of ϕ_V. Similar behavior was
found with tetraalkylammonium, K^+, Na^+, and Li^+ acrylates. Independence of ϕ_V on c was attributed to the balancing of electrostric-
tional effects which tend to make $d\phi_V/dc$ positive and "structure-
promoting" effects which lead to an opposite dependence of ϕ_V on c.
Conway and Lawrence [18] evaluated the dependence of ϕ_V on c for
a similar series of polyimine oligomers as hydrobromides and found
B positive and C negative in the empirical relation

$$\phi_V = A + Bc + Cc^2 \tag{71}$$

B was also positive and not zero for polysalts having molecular
weights of 600, 1200, and 1800. Values of the coefficients are given

in Table 4. For higher polymers with molecular weights of 50,000 and 75,000 and containing some branched chain structure, B was appreciably negative and C positive. For these salts with $\alpha = 0.7$

Table 4

Coefficients of Molar Concentration Dependence of ϕ_V Data
Expressed as $\phi_V = A + Bc + Cc^2$ ml/mole

Solute[a]	A	B	C
HBr	25.99	3.15	−5.24
ED(2HBr)	94.84	15.90	−32.94
DT(2HBr)	143.57	19.92	−36.85
DT(3HBr)	149.43	20.09	−26.47
TT(2HBr)	185.86	10.39	−8.88
TT(3HBr)	205.34	23.50	−24.74
TT(4HBr)	214.70	18.86	−20.83
TP(2HBr)	215.54	13.20	−17.38
TP(3HBr)	230.14	34.35	−64.04
TP(4HBr)	243.24	46.37	−87.62
PEI 6(2HBr)	577.50	15.57	−40.35
PEI 6(7HBr)	481.45	287.88	−1,791.1
PEI 6(HBr)$_{0.8}$	749.51	95.39	−6.09
PEI 12(HBr)$_{0.77}$	1,486.26	256.77	−82.55
PEI 18(HBr)$_{0.7}$	2,171.37	1,405.75	−13,789.6
PEI 600(HBr)$_{0.7}$	65,627.2	−1,190.51	880.99
PEI 1000(HBr)$_{0.7}$	90,498.3	−994.40	177.45
ED	63.08	−0.72	1.18
DT	101.20	1.05	−3.05
TT	137.59	2.12	−2.83
TP	175.96	−0.235	−3.72
PEI 6	537.95	−8.39	−7.09
PEI 12	1,061.47	−53.81	67.20
PEI 18	1,582.38	−62.10	62.98
PEI 600	43,133.3	57.45	−23.17
PEI 1000	65,171.7	−108.01	−6.47

[a]The numerical subscripts used in the nomenclature for the solute salts represent the apparent degree of ionization, α. The numbers in parentheses for the second to the twelfth entries in Column 1 for the polyimine oligomers refer to the stoichiometry of the hydrobromide salts prepared from the corresponding bases by controlled additions of HBr. The last 9 entries in the table refer to the neutral bases.

a minimum in part of the ϕ_V vs. $c^{1/2}$ curve was observed. The neutral un-ionized polymer of molecular weight 1200 also showed a decrease of ϕ_V with c. The independence of ϕ_V on c for polysalts is therefore not a general phenomenon and probably depends on (a) the degree of association of counter-ions and hence on the radius and type of counter-ion (anion or cation) that is involved; and (b) the molecular weight and entanglement factor, i.e., the co-sphere or co-cylinder volume for the polyion (dependent upon whether it is randomly coiled or more like the rigid rod model). However, for Na polyacrylates, Ise and Okubo [19] found ϕ_V was independent of c from $\alpha = 0$ to $\alpha = 1$.

The variation of B (Table 4) with the DP, z, is shown in Fig. 12 from Lawrence and Conway's results [18] while the concentration dependence of ϕ_V is shown in Figs. 13 and 14 for several salts

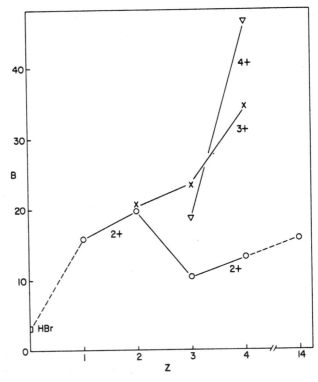

Fig. 12. Variation of coefficient B in Eq. (71) with z for oligomeric imines of various charges [18].

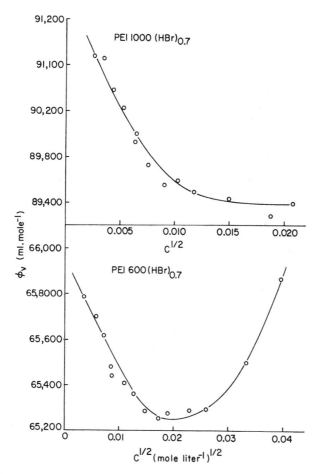

Fig. 13. Concentration dependence of ϕ_V for two PEI hydrobromides at 25°C [18].

including those investigated by Ise and Okubo. All values of B are positive for the oligomer cations and polyions of low DP up to PEI 12 (Table 4) and in this respect the direction of the concentration dependence of ϕ_V is the same as that for simple electrolytes. The sign of B at low concentration for the higher molecular weight cations, however, becomes rapidly negative (Table 4) and it is to be

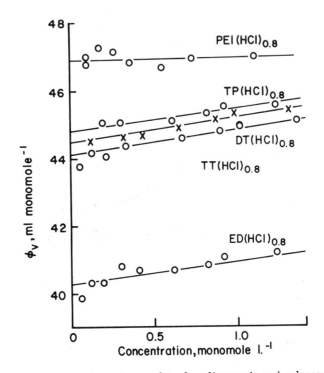

Fig. 14. Concentration dependence of ϕ_V for oligomeric and polymeric imine hydrochlorides at 25°C (after Ise and Ikubo [19]).

presumed that this arises from the appreciable degree of ion association by site binding and looser association [67] within the polycation random coil which occurs when the molecular weight becomes sufficiently high for random coil configurations* to be increasingly adopted (polymers PEI 600 and PEI 1000; see Table 4). Also, significant chain branching arises with the higher molecular weight polyimines.

Corrections for counter-ion association were made in the experiments of Lawrence and Conway by radio-tracer measurements of the apparent binding [72]. The changes which this makes to the electrostriction were estimated on the basis of the known volume

*At these relatively low degrees of polymerization, it is doubtful if the polymer is long enough for the statistics of the random coil representation to apply strictly.

changes for analogous ion-pair formation with simple ions. This correction may, in fact, be too large since an appreciable fraction of the ions associated with the polyion chain may not be present as solvent-shared or contact pairs where loss of hydration has occurred.

Plots of ϕ_V against $c^{1/2}$ for the polyimine hydrobromides (or c for the neutral bases) show some linearity* with positive slopes for the salts and negative or near zero slopes for the bases. Zero slopes for the polyimine salts were not found for the bromides (contrast Ise and Okubo's results for the hydrochlorides). The plots for DT(3HBr) and the neutral polybase PEI 12 are shown in Fig. 15 as two typical examples. Exceptions to this behavior are exhibited by the salts PEI 600 $(HBr)_{0.7}$ (where the fractional subscripts denote the apparent degree of ionization) and PEI 1000 $(HBr)_{0.7}$ and the results for these materials are shown in Fig. 13. The distinct minimum at $c^{1/2} = 0.018$ for PEI 600 $(HBr)_{0.7}$ and that which appears to exist at some higher concentration for PEI 1000 $(HBr)_{0.7}$ could be due to a change in configuration of the polymeric chain or to chain branching in the higher molecular weight preparations. Alternatively, at infinite dilution, the cations will tend more to assume a "stretched rodlike" configuration as a result of the usual electrostatic repulsion between the charged N centers, but as the concentration is increased the anions tend to come into closer proximity to the polyions and partially screen the positive charges. As a result, the intramolecular repulsion will decrease in the usual way, allowing the polyion to become more loosely coiled with interpolyion attraction [71]. An apparent insensitivity of ϕ_V to changes of c with PEI $(HCl)_{0.8}$ (z = 770) was reported by Ise and Okubo [19] (Fig. 2 of Ref. 19) but on closer examination the results also exhibit a definite minimum at ca. c = 0.5 monomole/liter which corresponds with the minimum found in the results of Lawrence and Conway at c = 0.00032 mole/liter (0.38 monomole/liter). Extrapolation of the ϕ_V against $c^{1/2}$ or c plots to zero c gives values for the apparent molar volume at infinite dilution ϕ_V^o (A in Table 4). While these empirical extrapolations raise the same problems as arise in the case of R_4N^+ salts, owing to persistence of nonideality to very low concentrations, the additivity of the extrapolated ϕ_V data (Fig. 16) is nevertheless quite satisfactory.

---

*For oligomeric or polymeric salts a simple $c^{1/2}$ relation will not be expected with the normal Debye–Hückel slopes since the charged ions do not have the charges localized at a single geometric center, e.g., as in the case of simple 1:1, 1:2, 1:3, and 1:4 salts.

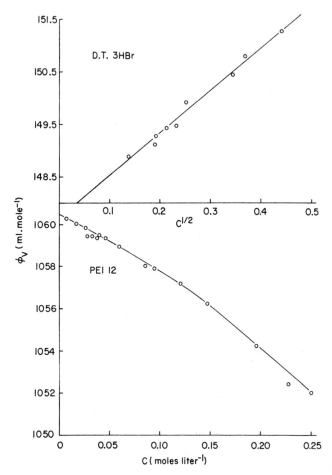

Fig. 15. Concentration dependence of ϕ_V for DT(3HBr) and a neutral polyimine base PEI 12 [18].

b. Additivity of volumes and the individual polycation volumes:
The infinite dilution volume, $\overline{V}^{\circ}_{-C_2H_4NH-}$, per monomer group in neutral polyimines, $(-C_2H_4NH-)$, can be calculated from $\overline{V}^{\circ}_{base}$ by subtracting 23.5 ml/mole for the volume of one of the terminal $-NH_2$ groups and dividing by z. Results are shown in Fig. 17 as a function of z, and it can be seen that except for the slight increase for $z \leq 4$, $\overline{V}^{\circ}_{-C_2H_4NH-}$ is almost independent of chain length, a result

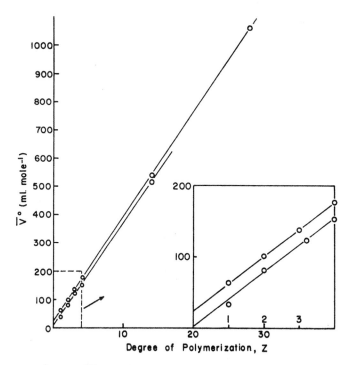

Fig. 16. Additivity of $\bar{V}^\circ$ data for polyimines as a function of degree of polymerization z. Lower curve for divalent ions; upper curve for neutral bases.

which indicates reasonable additivity of $\bar{V}^\circ$ contributions per monomer. The small increase in $\bar{V}^\circ$ indicated in Curve (a) of Fig. 17 is presumably the result of a structure-forming interaction of the remaining terminal N being greater than that associated with the intermediate N atoms in the chain, an effect which must become relatively negligible on a $\bar{V}^\circ$ monomole^{-1} basis for the higher polymers.

The $\bar{V}^\circ_{-C_2H_4NH-}$ value derived by Ise and Okubo [19] for the neutral base PEI with z = 770 was 10% lower than that obtained in the work of Lawrence and Conway [18] but this is probably because the former authors did not suppress the hydrolysis of the weak base, e.g., by using 0.1 N aqueous KOH as "solvent." The results are illustrated in another way in Fig. 16 (upper line) where $\bar{V}^\circ$ for the bases are plotted against z. Good linearity is observed with a slope of 36.8 which is consistent with the approximately constant value of $\bar{V}^\circ_{-C_2H_4NH-}$ of

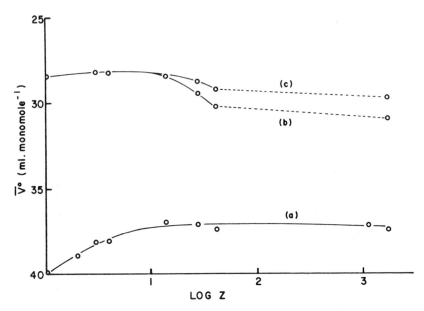

Fig. 17. $\overline{V}^{\circ}$ per monomer group for polyimines in aq solution at 25°C.
(a) Volume for monomer group of neutral bases as a function of log z.
(b) Estimated volume of monomer group of polycations (α taken as 0.7-0.8).
(c) Corrected volumes per monomer group of polycations allowing for ion association.

Fig. 17, Line (a). Extrapolation to $z = 0$ gives a value of 24 ml/mole for the volume of the terminal $-NH_2$ group and this agrees well with the value of 23.5 referred to earlier. The constancy of $\overline{V}^{\circ}_{-C_2H_4NH-}$ indicates that the volumes of the bases are directly proportional to the lengths of the polymer chains and therefore suggests that those systems, when ionized, can be adequately represented with regard to short-range interactions involved in hydration by the uniform linear rod model of Alfrey, Berg, and Morawetz [15] employed previously [51] for other ionized polymeric species (polyphosphates and K salts of polymethacrylic acid).

$\overline{V}^{\circ}_{Br^-}$ can be estimated from the apparent molar volume of aq HBr taking $\overline{V}^{\circ}_{H^+}$ as -5.7 ml/(g ion) [10,49]. The resulting value of 31.6 ml/(g ion) may then be used to calculate the individual partial gram ionic volumes of the polymeric cations. The volumes of the divalent cations are shown in Fig. 16 (lower line). The same linear relationship is observed as was found for the neutral bases and the two lines are virtually parallel since the slopes have the same significance because the repeating group within the chain $-CH_2-CH_2-NH-$ is the same. Extrapolation to zero z leads to a value of $\overline{V}^{\circ}_{NH_3^+}$ of 2 ml/mole for the end group on the polyion chain.

The approximate volume per monomer for the polycations with apparent degree of ionization $\alpha = 0.7$ to 0.8 (i.e., $-\overset{0.8+}{NH_2}-C_2H_4-$) can be calculated from:

$$\overline{V}^{\circ}_{(BH_n)^{n+}} = (\overline{V}^{\circ}_{salt} - n\overline{V}^{\circ}_{Br^-} - \overline{V}^{\circ}_{NH_3^+})/z \qquad (72)$$

The results show that, unlike the behavior of the neutral bases, there is a substantial increase in volume as z increases in the case of the higher molecular weight polymers, i.e., there is a relative decrease in electrostriction per N^+ center for the longer chain molecules, an effect which probably arises from ion association. Some data for a PEI hydrochloride and oligomer hydrochlorides obtained by Ise and Okubo [19] are shown in Table 5.

Table 5

Individual Partial Molal Volumes of Macroions in
Weak Polyelectrolytes at 25° in ml/monomole[19]

Weak polyelec-trolytes (α)	$\overline{V}^{\circ}_p$	$V_{int,p}$	V_s	V_e
NaPAA (1.0)	38.7	65.3	−17.5	−9.1
(0.8)	40.6			−7.2
(0.6)	42.0			−5.8
(0.4)	44.0			−3.8
(0.2)	46.0			−1.8
KPMA (0.95)	43.5 [a]	81.6	−9.1	−29.0
(0.75)	46.6 [a]			−25.9
(0.6)	51.3 [a]			−21.2
(0.4)	60.0 [a]			−12.5
PEI (HCl) (0.8)	29.1	54.7	−21.5	−4.1
TP (HCl) (0.8)	24.9	54.0	−20.3	−8.8
TT (HCl) (0.8)	24.9	53.3	−19.6	−8.8
DT (HCl) (0.8)	24.5	52.0	−18.4	−9.1
ED (HCl) (0.8)	20.3	50.6	−19.2	−11.1

[a] From Ref. 51.

c. Ion binding and electrostriction at polyimine cations: Complete evaluation of $\overline{V}^{\circ}_{(BH_n)^{n+}}$ must take into account the ion-binding associated with the larger ions. Hamann, Pearce, and Strauss [73] obtained a value for the volume change ΔV_d which occurs when ion pairs of $Mg^{2+}SO_4^{2-}$ and $La^{3+}Fe(CN)_6^{3-}$ dissociate: ΔV_d was evaluated from the pressure dependence of the (over-all) ion-pair dissociation constant (cf. Eigen and Tamm [74]), and these measurements together with the known individual ionic volumes (e.g., 1) suggest that most ($>85\%$) of the electrostriction associated with hydration is maintained when ion association occurs, i.e., the ion pairs are hydrated-ion pairs and not contact pairs. The electrostriction associated with the salt $TP(HBr)_{0.8}$ was calculated by Lawrence and Conway [18] from the experimental volume of the TP base and that of its salt by considering $\overline{V}^{\circ}$ to be composed of the three contributions (compare Eq. 18):

$$\overline{V}^{\circ} = \overline{V}_i + \overline{V}_s + \overline{V}_e \qquad (73)$$

where $\overline{V}_i$ is the intrinsic volume of the compound, $\overline{V}_s$ is the volume due to a change in structure of the surrounding water (i.e., the cavity volume and any hydrophobic or structure-breaking term), and $\overline{V}_e$ is the volume change due to electrostriction of the surrounding water [36]. $\overline{V}_e$ for the neutral bases is taken equal to zero and therefore $\overline{V}^{\circ}_{base} = \overline{V}_i + \overline{V}_s$. A difficulty arises with the quantity $\overline{V}_s$ for the base and the conjugate cation; if $\overline{V}_s$ were assumed to be the same for the cation as for the base, then $\overline{V}_e$ could be simply expressed as:

$$\overline{V}_e = \overline{V}^{\circ}_{(BH_n)^{n+}} - \overline{V}^{\circ}_{base} \qquad (74)$$

The validity of the above assumption for $\overline{V}_s$ (also made by Ise and Okubo [19]) receives some justification from studies [13] on the ionization of 2,6-lutidine in water which indicate specific structural effects in the apparent molar volume ϕ_V which are largely independent of whether lutidine is in the form of a neutral molecule or the protonated base.

By using Eq. (73) a value of $\overline{V}_e$ for the salt $TP(HBr)_{0.8}$ can be derived from the experimental results [18] as -8.8 ml/monomole. This value can then be used to calculate first the apparent volume change ΔV_d resulting from dissociation of ions bound to a monomole of polycation at a degree of ionization α, for the polysalt PEI $6(HBr)_{0.8}$, viz.,

$$\Delta V_d = \overline{V}^{\circ}_{(PEI 6)^{n+}} - \overline{V}^{\circ}_{(PEI 6)} + 8.8 \qquad (75)$$

Then, taking account of the apparent degree of ionization α and the
fraction $1 - f$ of counter-ions bound (determined with radio-tracers
[73]), the true volume change ΔV_d° arising from the dissociation of
a monomole ion pair can be written

$$\Delta V_d^{\circ} = V_d/(1 - f)\alpha \tag{76}$$

which, upon introducing appropriate values for α and f and noting
the individual $\overline{V}_{Br^-}^{\circ}$ value [10,48], gives $\Delta V_d^{\circ} = 2.5$ ml/monomole
for the PEI 6 salt. In Eqs. (74) and (75), it is convenient to express
all volume terms per monomole in order to allow comparison between
the various data. If this value for ΔV_d° (per monomole) is assumed
to be independent of z, then a corrected volume (i.e., for the fully
dissociated polysalts) for the other polymeric cations can be calculated by means of the relation

$$\overline{V}_{(BH_n)^{n+}_{corr}}^{\circ} = \overline{V}_{(BH_n)^{n+}_{expt}}^{\circ} - V_d^{\circ}\alpha(1 - f) \tag{77}$$

The corrected volumes (Curve c in Fig. 17) still show a significant
increase with increasing z and this could be explained, within the
limitation of the correction described above, by a decrease in $\overline{V}_e$
resulting from a decrease in E, the electric field at a point near the
axis of the ion, with increasing z. Thus, it has been shown in Ref.
51 that for the "linear charged rod" model of a polyion, the average
field at a distance r from the polyion axis is given approximately by
$E = -2\alpha e/\lambda\epsilon r$ (from the logarithmic potential function) where λ is
the distance between the ionizable groups on the chain and ϵ_0 is the
dielectric constant, whereas the field at a distance r from a simple
ion is $E = -ze/\epsilon_0 r^2$. Consequently, as z increases, the field and
therefore the electrostriction tends to change its functional dependence from r^{-2} to r^{-1} (see Sects. IV.A and IV.B).

The increase of electrostriction about the charged nitrogen centers in polyiminium cations which arises with increasing charge is
illustrated in Fig. 18 where $\overline{V}_{(BH_n)^{n+}}^{\circ}$ (written as $\overline{V}_{cation}^{\circ}$) is plotted
against the net charge for each of the oligomeric imine salts and
against the apparent charge for PEI 6. In this plot, the results have
been expressed in milliliter/gram ion to illustrate the progressive
change of $\overline{V}^{\circ}$. The nonlinear decrease of volume with net charge is
presumably mainly the result of interaction of primary hydration
shells as more and more "adjacent" N atoms become ionized, although a small contribution to the curvature might be expected to
arise from the fact that the terminal (primary) N atoms are more
accessible for hydration than are the inner (secondary) N atoms.

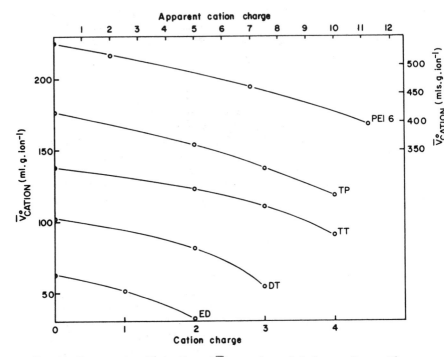

Fig. 18. Progressive diminution of $\overline{V}^\circ_{cation}$ for polyimines cations with increasing charge due to electrostriction. Upper curve and scales are for PEI 6 polymer salt.

Such steric effects have already been examined [11-13] with simpler N-containing molecules, e.g., pyridine and its homologs. The end-group effects will, of course, only be significant for the polyions of low DP.

    d. Volume of ionization of polyimines: The volume change $\Delta\overline{V}^\circ_{ioniz}$ (associated with hydration) accompanying the ionization process can be examined directly for lower molecular weight imines by calculating the volume change occurring in the reaction:

$$(BH_n)^{n+} \; nBr^- \; \rightleftharpoons \; B + n(H^+Br^-) \qquad (78)$$

Therefore, without any thermodynamic ambiguity, $\Delta\overline{V}^\circ_{ioniz}$ can be expressed as

$$\Delta \overline{V}^{\circ}_{ioniz} = \overline{V}^{\circ}_{base} + n\overline{V}^{\circ}_{H^+ Br^-} - \overline{V}^{\circ}_{(BH_n)^{n+} nBr^-} \tag{79}$$

It might be expected that $\Delta \overline{V}^{\circ}_{ioniz}$ for the doubly charged (bolaform) ions would be independent of z since the only hydration changes that occur would tend to arise at the terminal N atoms. However, it can be seen from Fig. 19 that this is evidently not the case for $z \leq 4$. The minimum at $z = 3$ suggests that the hydration sheaths have least interaction in the case of the triethylene-tetramine salts and only the longer chain divalent ions tend to behave as bolaform electrolytes and thus possess sufficient flexibility to allow the N^+ center at one end of the chain to interact with the counter-ion atmosphere and solvent-influenced region surrounding the ionized center at the further end. Above $z = 4$, the addition of extra uncharged monomer units to the chain evidently has little effect on the $\Delta \overline{V}^{\circ}_{ioniz}$. Fig. 19 also shows the data for singly and multiply charged ions.

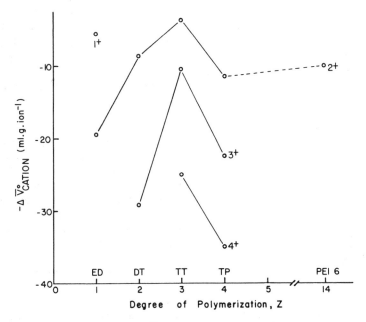

Fig. 19. Volume of ionization $\Delta \overline{V}^{\circ}_{cation}$ of polyimines of various apparent charges as a function of degree of polymerization [18].

Lawrence and Conway [18] compared $\Delta \overline{V}^\circ_{ioniz}$ for the various
oligomer ions with the values for the $(CH_3)_n H_{3-n} N^+ H$ series ($n \le 3$)
investigated previously [11-13] with regard to steric effects in hydration at N centers. The data are given in Table 6.

Table 6

$\overline{V}^\circ_{ioniz}$ (ml/mole)		$\overline{V}^\circ_{ioniz}$ (ml/mole)	
$CH_3NH_3^+$	$+4.1 = 0.4$	ED^+	$+5.5$
$(CH_3)_2NH_2^+$	$+4.0 = 0.4$	ED^{2+}	$+11.5$
$(CH_3)_3NH^+$	$+5.2 = 0.4$	DT^{2+}	$+8.7$
$(C_2H_5)_3NH^+$	$-1 = 0.4$	TT^{2+}	$+3.7$
		TP^{2+}	$+11.5$

The $\overline{V}^\circ_{ioniz}$ for the first ionization (ED^+) is a little larger than
that for the primary aminium ion $CH_3NH_3^+$ and the second ionization
(ED^{2+}) contributes a further 6 ml/mole. The contributions per +
charge in the TP series increase in the order 5.8, 7.5, and 8.8
ml/mole, respectively, in going from the 2+ to the 4+ ion (Fig. 19),
as they do in the TT series (from 1.9 to 3.5 to 6.3 ml/mole). This
is the effect predicted [51] when a linear array of charges is accu-
mulated on a chain. Also, with the longest chain divalent ion derived
from PEI 6, $\frac{1}{2}\Delta \overline{V}^\circ_{ioniz} = 5.0$ while the value for ED^+ is 5.5 ml/mole;
hence intercharge effects are almost attenuated to zero in a chain of
this length (cf. Ref. 67) and also to a large extent already at z = 4
(TP, Fig. 19).

The apparent electrostriction for various types of charge situation on the chains may also be estimated from the data of Table 4
using the absolute value for $\overline{V}^\circ_{H^+} = -5.7$ ml g/ion (cf. Ref. 48) and
the volumes of the un-ionized bases, if it is assumed that the V_s
contribution per monomole in the un-ionized part of a partly ionized
polymer ($0.1 < \alpha < 0.9$) is the same as that in the neutral base
($\alpha = 0$). For appreciable α, there is no reason why this should
be the case, and this places a limitation on the evaluation of V_e for
polyions (cf. the work of Ise and Okubo [19]).

3. Vinyl Polyions. *a. Volume behavior of polymethacrylate
salts:* The effect of degree of ionization in PMA potassium salts
was investigated by Conway, Desnoyers, and Smith [51] with regard
to the salting-out coefficients (see below) and the apparent molal
volumes. The dependence of ϕ°_V on degree of neutralization is shown
in Fig. 20. The pure "monomer salt" was taken as potassium isobutyrate. For $\alpha > 0.4$, the ϕ_V values for the polysalts were less

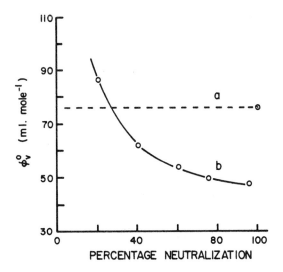

Fig. 20. $\phi°$ for KPMA salts as a function of degree of neutralization (after Conway, Desnoyers, and Smith [51]). Curve (a), potassium isobutyrate "monomer" salt; curve (b), KPMA salts.

than that for the monomer but for $\alpha = 0.2$, ϕ_V values were greater than those for the monomer salt and the concentration dependence of ϕ_V was also larger. The polysalts having high α exhibited the lowest slopes $d\phi_V/dc^{1/2}$ as also found (Fig. 21) for the polysalts studied by Ise and Okubo [19] (but contrast the behavior of polyimine hydrobromides investigated by Lawrence and Conway [18]).

In the case of KPMA and other polysalts, the apparent molal volume of the neutralized monomer unit on the chain must be evaluated by assuming additivity of contributions from the neutralized and unneutralized acid monomer units with respect to change of density resulting from the presence of the polysalt in solution, i.e., the total change in density $d - d_0$ due to introduction of polysalt into the solvent water must be corrected for contributions associated with the presence of <u>neutral</u> groups in the polymer chain in the evaluation of the ϕ_V contribution for the ionic groups in the chains. The densities of the corresponding simple salt solutions must also be evaluated in order to compare the electrostriction effects (in terms of ϕ_V° values) of the polysalts with those of corresponding monomeric salts.

The change of ϕ_V with α, caused by increasing electrostriction, is closely paralleled by the salting-out behavior (see below) as also

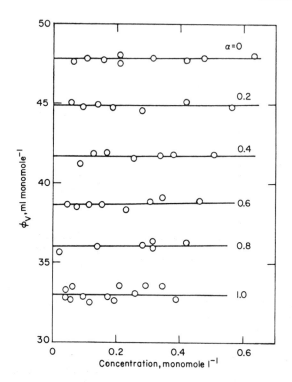

Fig. 21. ϕ_V for NaPAA salts as a function of concentration (after Ise and Okubo [19]).

found in the case of the polyphosphates (see above). The trend of ϕ_V with percent neutralization is shown in Fig. 20 and it is evident that as $\alpha \to 1$, ϕ_V varies less rapidly with α. This is presumably due to (a) the less rapid change of overlapping solvation regions as $\alpha > 0.5$ (cf. Ref. 67), and (b) the increasing screening effect of the associated counter-ions. For $\alpha > 0.25$, ϕ_V for KPMA polysalts is lower than the value for the corresponding monomer, illustrating the cooperative effects of the chain charges in increasing the electrostriction.

   b. Individual polyion volumes: The partial molal volumes $\overline{V}°$ at "infinite" dilution of a series of R_4N^+ salts of polyvinylacids were plotted by Ise and Okubo [19] as a function of molecular weight to obtain the polyanion co-volume by the extrapolation procedure of Conway, Desnoyers, and Verrall [10]. (These values could also be directly obtained from the $\overline{V}^\circ$ for the polysalt by subtracting the appropriate absolute volume of the counter-ion, also derived by taking into account the value of α).

The individual partial volume of the polyions $\overline{V}_p^\circ$ can be expressed ([18,19]; cf. Eqs. 18 and 73) as[*]

$$\overline{V}_p^\circ = \overline{V}_i + \overline{V}_s' + \overline{V}_c + \overline{V}_e \qquad (80)$$

where $\overline{V}_i$ is the intrinsic volume of the polyion including the dead space between polyion and solvent molecules, $\overline{V}_s' + \overline{V}_c$ are the structural volume terms (cavity effect and structure promotion) and $\overline{V}_e$ is again the volume change due to electrostriction. The intrinsic volume for polyions can be calculated from the equation of Conway, Desnoyers, and Smith [51] for polyions, viz.,

$$V_{int,p} = \pi \lambda N_A \left\{ 1 + \left(\frac{4}{\pi} - 1 \right) r_w / a \right\} a^2 \qquad (81)$$

where λ is the intercharge separation, a is the radius of the polyion, and r_w is that of solvent molecules. For weakly dissociated salts or in the presence of acid or base to inhibit ionization of the polyacid or polybase, respectively, the sum $V_{int,p} + V_s + V_c$ can be measured experimentally from $\overline{V}^\circ$ at $\alpha = 0$. Hence V_s can be also evaluated. V_c is usually negative due to occupation of cavity space in the solvent, an effect usually not outweighed by any volume increases due to hydrophobic structure promotion [69]. For example, Masterton [70] found that the $\overline{V}$ for CH_4, C_2H_6, and C_3H_8 were smaller in water than in nonpolar liquids by ca. 20 ml/mole.

Some values of $\overline{V}_p^\circ$, $V_{int,p}$, V_s, and V_e are listed in Tables 5 and 7 for a series of polyions including the polyimine salts discussed earlier. The electrostrictions V_e were evaluated by Ise and Okubo [19] assuming V_{int} and V_s are not dependent on α. The latter assumption is dubious since as soon as α becomes appreciable ($>$ ca. 0.3), charge centers become relatively close, and reversal of any structure formation effects at un-ionized centers is probable, particularly for polyimine salts. The apparent electrostrictions are shown in Fig. 22 for PEI salts in relation to those derived by Ise and Okubo [19] for other polysalts using their own data and the earlier results of Conway et al. for polyphosphates [51] and polymethacrylates [51]. The number η of electrostricted water molecules per

[*]This equation is similar to Eqn. (73) except that $\overline{V}_S$ has been further subdivided.

Table 7

Individual Partial Molal Volumes of Macroions from
Strong Polyelectrolytes at 25° in ml/monomole (α = 1) [19]

Strong polyelectrolytes (DP)	V_p^o	$V_{int,p}$	V_S	V_e
NaPSt	116.0	125.0	−6.0	−3.0
NaPES	−4.9	61.5	−20.0	−46.4
NaPP (6800)	28.5[a]	55.0	0	−26.5
NaPP (2800)	27.5[a]	55.0	0	−27.5
NaPP (800)	25.9[a]	55.0	0	−29.1

[a] From Ref. 51.

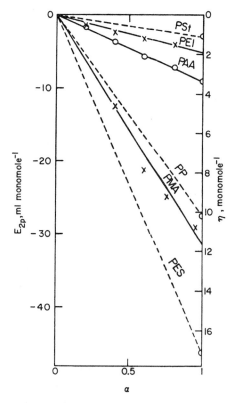

Fig. 22. Apparent electrostriction of various polysalts as a function of α (based on data of Ise and Okubo [19], and Conway, Desnoyers, and Smith [51]).

monomole, based on the figure of -2.7 ml/mole H_2O derived by
Conway et al. [36], is also shown on the right-hand ordinate of Fig.
22. (Compare also Fig. 18.)

By considering the order of increasing osmotic coefficients ϕ for
various polysalts, a relation to electrostriction is apparent [19].
For sodium salts of a series of polyacids, ϕ increases in the order

$$PES = PAA < PMA < PP < PSt$$

while the electrostriction increases in the order

$$PSt < PEI < PAA < PP < PMA < PES$$

This inequality would be expected to coincide with that for ϕ
since the higher the electrostriction the lower is the solvent activity.
However, the order of decreasing V_s is

$$PES > PAA > PMA > PST > PP$$

which is approximately consistent with the order for ϕ. Thus, from
these data, ϕ for the anionic polyelectrolytes is apparently [19] determined mainly by V_s. This is a surprising result and is not found
with simple salts. It may arise on account of lack of consideration
([19]; cf. Ref. 18) of ion association in evaluation of the $\overline{V}$ contributions and from the assumption of independence of the V_s and V_e
changes which was remarked upon above.

C. Compressibility Behavior of Polysalts

The use of compressibility measurements for evaluation of hydration effects at simple salts was referred to in Sect. II.C. The method
provides information complementary to that obtained from density
measurements.

Using a differential ultrasonic velocity apparatus [11,12] for determining the difference of velocities of ultrasound at 5.2 MHz in
water and in polyimine hydrobromide solutions, Lawrence and Conway [18] related the partial molal adiabatic compressibilities to the
degree of ionization, the behavior of lower molecular weight oligomer
salts, and the partial molal volumes determined from the density
measurements referred to above.

Plots of the apparent adiabatic compressibility against $c^{1/2}$ for
the polyimine salts, or c for the neutral bases, showed good linearity with positive slopes for all the compounds studied except PEI
$600(HBr)_{0.7}$ for which the results exhibited a maximum at

$c^{1/2}$ = 0.016 and PEI 1000(HBr)$_{0.7}$ for which ϕ_K exhibited a constant negative slope with respect to $c^{1/2}$ over the entire concentration range examined (Fig. 23). As in the case of the data for ϕ_v, the ϕ_K values for all polysalts can be plotted empirically as a function of $c^{1/2}$ although, for polyions, there is no a priori basis for the $c^{1/2}$ plot as there is for monomeric ions.

The ϕ_K^o values derived by empirical extrapolation of the ϕ_K values as a function of $c^{1/2}$ must be regarded as apparent quantities owing to the difficulties of obtaining accurate results for ϕ_K below 0.01 monomole/liter concentration, even by the differential technique [18], and on account of the persistence of appreciable nonideality of

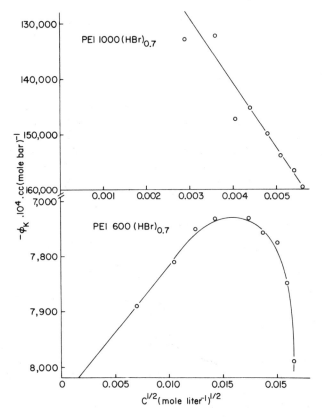

Fig. 23. Plots of apparent molar adiabatic compressibility ϕ for some polyimine hydrobromides at 25°C (after Lawrence and Conway [18]).

organic salt solutions down to very low concentrations for nonelectrostatic reasons.

An unexpected result of the studies on the polyimine salts is that
the compressibilities [$\phi_K^0 = -25 \times 10^{-4}$ cc/(monomole bar)], are
higher (less negative) in comparison with the values for 1:1 inorganic electrolytes such as KBr for which $\phi_K^0 = -30.5 \times 10^{-4}$ cc/
(mole bar). This result implies that the polymeric cations must be
apparently more compressible (per monomole) than a potassium
ion. A similar effect was observed with the tetraalkylammonium
cations but the compressibility becomes more negative with increasing length of the alkyl chains. Analogous effects are also observed
with the neutral polybases with increasing z. Since the intrinsic
compressibility of an ion is normally only a relatively small part of
the over-all apparent compressibility, the above effect was explained
[11,12] in terms of water having limitingly different types of compressibility behavior in the hydration layers around "hydrophilic"
[e.g., $(Me)_3NH^+$, $(Me)_2NH_2^+$, etc.] and "hydrophobic" (e.g., R_4N^+)
types of ions. Although the polybases have progressively negative
ϕ_K values with increasing z, ionization causes relatively large
changes to more negative values (Table 8) consistent with electrostriction as in the case of the protonated ions derived from secondary bases [e.g., $(Me)_2NH_2^+$, Refs. 11 and 12, i.e., with secondary
structures similar to that at N atoms within the polymer chain].
For example, the change of compressibility upon ionization of intra-
chain N atoms at z = 4 (Fig. 24) may be estimated as -24 cc/(g
ion bar) noting that as $z > 4$, $\Delta\phi_K^0$ (Fig. 24) becomes independent
of z, while the corresponding value for ionization of Me_2NH is -19.4
cc/(g ion bar). In the polymer, the over-all $\Delta\phi_K^0$ will be determined
by the balance between this type of electrostriction effect and any
structure promotion effect (change to a relaxationally less mobile
situation) in the water brought about by the un-ionized parts of the
partially ionized chain.

The neutral polymer bases have, as expected, higher ϕ_K values
due to lack of electrostriction and their smaller tendency (e.g., in
relation to R_4N^+ ions) to cause structure promotion with resulting
negative ϕ_K contributions. For the neutral bases, the ϕ_K is additive
in chain length but the behavior is quite different for the ionized
polymers.

A value for ϕ_K^0 of the iodide ion has been derived by Conway and
Laliberte [69] by an extrapolation procedure. They obtained
$\phi_{K_{I^-}}^0 = +6.9 \times 10^{-4}$ cc/(g ion bar) and this, combined with the known
difference $\Delta\phi_{K_{(Br-I^-)}}^0$, leads to $\phi_{K_{Br^-}}^0 = 3.4 \times 10^{-4}$ cc/(g ion bar).
The ϕ_K^0 for the polyethylene imine cations can then be estimated

Table 8

Adiabatic Compressibility Data for Imine Polymers and Oligomers and Their Hydrobromide Salts: Slopes and Intercepts of the Linear Plots of ϕ_K against $c^{1/2}$ or c and ϕ_K° per Monomer Unit for the Neutral Bases

Salt	$-10^4 \phi_K^\circ$ [cc/(mole bar)][a]	$d\phi_K/dc^{1/2}$	Base	$-10^4 \phi_K^\circ$ [cc/(mole bar)]	$d\phi_K/dc$	$-10^4 \phi_K^\circ$/monomer
ED 2HBr	49.3	22.6	ED	-0.36	0.80	-0.36
DT 2HBr	32.1	26.0	DT	4.86	2.4	2.43
DT 3HBr	74.5	37.5	TT	11.08	3.7	3.67
TT 2HBr	30.3	22.5	TP	14.6	4.7	3.66
TT 4HBr	78.3	28.0	PEI 6	48.8	12.5	3.13
TP 2HBr	41.1	27.5	PEI 12	93.5	46.0	3.35
TP 4HBr	88.0	54.0	PEI 18	135.3	15.0	3.24
PEI 6 2HBr	70.5	45.5	PEI 600	3559	1.28	3.26
PEI 6 (HBr)$_{0.8}$	203.9	133	PEI 1000	6268	2.5	3.60
PEI 12 (HBr)$_{0.77}$	341.4	349				
PEI 18 (HBr)$_{0.7}$	388.3	484				
PEI 600 (HBr)$_{0.7}$	8540	Graph not linear				
PEI 1000 (HBr)$_{0.7}$	89400	-1.09×10^6				

[a]The ϕ_K° values for the salts must be regarded only as apparent values owing to the difficulty of obtaining measurements of ϕ_K below ca. 0.01 monomole/liter at low concentrations comparable with those that can be reached with the ϕ_V measurements.

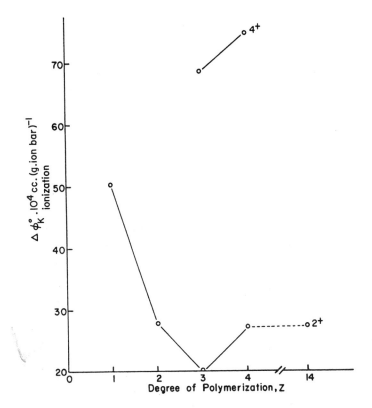

Fig. 24. Change of ϕ_K for polyimines upon ionization in aq HBr (after Lawrence and Conway [18].

from the salt compressibilities assuming additivity of the ionic contributions at infinite dilution. The plot of $\phi^0_{K\,cation}$ against z at constant cation charge shows a distinct maximum at z = 3 (compare Fig. 24). This is satisfactorily consistent with the minimum volume of ionization observed at this chain length because once interaction of the hydration sheaths between neighboring N^+ centers occurs, a greater and more cylindrical region of solvation about the oligomeric ion tends to arise and lead to an over-all decrease in compressibility. The overlap of hydration sheaths (cf. Ref. 66) about adjacent charged centers evidently prevents the compressibility of the partially ionized cations from being estimated simply from an additivity expression of the type:

$$\phi_{K_{\text{cation}}} = \alpha \phi_{K_+} + (1 - \alpha)\phi_{K_{\text{base}}} \qquad (82)$$

involving the compressibility of the corresponding neutral base and the compressibility ϕ_{K_+} of the fully ionized cation.

The compressibility changes $\Delta\phi_{K,\text{ioniz}}^{\circ}$ occurring in the ionization process can be calculated by a method analogous to that used for the evaluation of $\Delta\overline{V}_{K,\text{ioniz}}^{\circ}$, i.e., by considering the change in compressibility associated with the following type of reaction

$$(BH_n)^{n+} \; nBr^- \longrightarrow B + nHBr$$

i.e., $\Delta\phi_{K,\text{ioniz}}^{\circ}$ can be evaluated from an equation in ϕ_K° terms analogous to Eq. (79). The resulting values of $\Delta\phi_{K,\text{ioniz}}^{\circ}$ are plotted in Fig. 24 as a function of z. The sharp minimum at z = 3 is consistent again with the maximum of $\Delta\overline{V}^{\circ}$ in Fig. 19 at the same z, and the fact that the compressibility of the bases is directly proportional to z should result in a maximum in $\phi_{K,\text{cation}}^{\circ}$

Density and compressibility of a number of simple electrolytes were studied by Goto [75,76] in relation to the state of water around clathrates and the conformational arrangements in protein structures, but these papers give, however, mainly the background information on the hydration behavior of simple salts.

For comparative purposes, we refer finally, in this section, to the studies of Nomura and Miyahara [77] on hydration of some neutral polymers (cf. the comparison of neutral and ionized polyimines referred to above). In this work, hydration of a number of neutral polymers was investigated by ultrasonic velocity measurements. Polyethylene glycol, polyacrylamide, poly(vinyl alcohol), and methyl cellulose were studied in the range 5-55° C. For neutral macromolecules the interpretation of ultrasonic compressibility measurements in terms of hydration is not so unambiguous as it is in aqueous solutions of simple salts and polyelectrolytes where a region of relatively incompressible solvent exists in the primary hydration layers around the ionic centers where electrostatic forces predominate.

VI. SALTING-OUT BY POLYIONS

The hydration of polyions, like that of simple ions, can usefully be studied by examining what partitioning effects the ions bring about in the solvent with respect to the distribution of a nonelectrolyte. Salts which preferentially interact with the solvent molecules at the expense of a nonelectrolyte solute usually cause salting-out but the relative sizes and molar polarizations of the solute and solvent species must be considered. Salting-out by linear polysalts was studied by Conway, Desnoyers, and Smith [51], who also related their observations to the results of partial molal volume determinations and dielectric saturation calculations. Distribution effects associated with salting-out of sucrose by a cross-linked, ion exchange polyelectrolyte were investigated by Konyushko [78].

A. Theory of Salting-Out by Simple and Polyions

The general theory of salting-out was first given by Debye and MacAulay [79] and by Butler [80]. Conway et al. [51], in developing the theory for polysalts, improved the treatment for simple ions and introduced the same ideas in the analysis of salting-out by polyions. We briefly show the principal equations.

The relative change of solubility $\Delta S/S_0$ is evaluated, where S_0 is the solubility in the pure solvent, S is that in the simple or polysalt solution, and $\Delta S = S_0 - S$. The solubility S differs from S_0 by electrostatic distribution effects associated with the difference of energy of solute and solvent molecules near the ion.

The energy U stored in an element of volume dV of a medium of dielectric constant ϵ, subject to the action of an electrical field E, is given by

$$dU = (\epsilon E^2/8\pi)\, dV \tag{83}$$

The distribution of solute and solvent about the ion may be calculated by means of the distribution equation

$$dn_2 = S_0 \exp - (\Delta U/kT)4\pi r^2\, dr \tag{84}$$

where n_2 is the number of nonelectrolyte molecules in a spherical volume element of thickness dr at a distance r from the ion; the energy ΔU arises from the difference of the energy of the ion when the dielectric constant is changed from ϵ_0 in the absence of nonelectrolyte to ϵ when it is present. From electrostatic theory, ΔU is obtained as

$$\Delta U = \frac{1000z^2e^2}{8\pi r^4}\left(\frac{1}{\epsilon} - \frac{1}{\epsilon_0}\right)\frac{1}{NS} \text{ ergs/molecule} \tag{85}$$

Integration of Eq. (83) over spherical volume elements from r = a, the ionic radius, to r = R, a critical radius corresponding to the volume available per ion in the solution and defined by

$$R = (3000/4\pi Nm)^{1/3} \tag{86}$$

(where m is the gram ionic concentration), then gives the relative change of solubility $(S_0 - S)/S_0$ as

$$\frac{S_0 - S}{S_0} = \frac{4\pi Nm}{1000} \int_a^R (1 - \exp(-\Delta U/kT))r^2\, dr \tag{87}$$

Usually the exponential in ΔU is expanded to its linear term and a simple result is obtained for the salting-out ratio defined as $(S_0 - S)/S_0 m$. This procedure is, however, quite unjustified since with small ions in water ΔU is usually not small in comparison with kT near the ions where relatively the biggest salting-out effect is to be expected. The linear expansion causes the calculated value of the salting-out ratio to be seriously in error.

Equation (85) may be written in terms of the ionic field $E (= -ze/\epsilon_0 r^2)$ as

$$\Delta U/kT = \frac{1000E^2}{8\pi kT}(\epsilon_0 - \epsilon)\frac{1}{NS} \tag{88}$$

assuming $\epsilon_0 \epsilon = \epsilon_0^2$.

When the dielectric constant ϵ of a solution is high compared with the optical dielectric constant of the solvent ϵ_∞, it may be shown, by using a limiting case of Kirkwood's theory of dielectrics, that

$$1000(\epsilon_0 - \epsilon)/S = V_2\epsilon_0 - \frac{9}{2}P_2 \tag{89}$$

where V_2 is the molar or partial molar volume of the nonelectrolyte and P_2 is the total molar polarization of the nonelectrolyte, defined by

$$P_2 = \frac{4}{3}\pi N(\alpha_0 + \mu\bar{\mu}/3kT) \tag{90}$$

where α_0 is the polarizability and μ the moment of the individual nonelectrolyte molecules in solution, and $\bar{\mu}$ the vector sum of the moment of the central molecule plus that of all the neighbors which may affect its orientation. For nonassociated polar molecules $\mu\bar{\mu}$ may be related to μ_0, the moment of the molecule in the gaseous state, by Onsager's theory as

$$\mu\overline{\mu} = \frac{1}{9}(n^2 + 2)^2 \mu_0^2 \qquad (91)$$

where n is the refractive index of the molecule.
The energy function is then

$$\Delta U/kT = (E^2/8\pi kTN)\left(V_2\epsilon_0 - \frac{9}{2}P_2\right) \qquad (92)$$

The salting-out of a nonelectrolyte by an ion may hence be calculated if the size of the ion, the molar volume and the polarization of
the nonelectrolyte are known.

The above equations represent fairly well the situation existing
at intermediate distances and far from the ion but cannot be at all
reliable in the immediate vicinity of most ions for the following
reasons:

1. The dielectric constant near the ion is usually much lower
than that of the pure solvent, owing to electric saturation effects.

2. Equation (89) is not valid in the region near the ion where the
field intensity is very high.

3. Important interactions in the vicinity of the ion (ion-dipole,
ion-quadrupole, dipole-dipole) are not considered in detail, i.e., the
molecular details of the primary hydration of the ion by the solvent
should preferably be taken into account near the ion. Primary solvation effects may be introduced in one way by correcting the field in
the salting-out equation for the effect of dielectric saturation.

In the first case, if $\Delta U/kT$ is small compared with unity, then,
as in Butler's treatment [80], the salting-out ratio is obtained approximately as

$$\frac{S_0 - S}{S_0 m} = \frac{4\pi N}{1000} \int_a^R (\Delta U/kT)r^2\, dr \qquad (93)$$

and substituting for E in Eq. (92) gives

$$\frac{S_0 - S}{S_0 m} = \frac{4\pi N}{1000} \int_a^R \frac{z^2e^2}{8\pi kTN\epsilon^2}\left(V_2\epsilon_0 - \frac{9}{2}P_2\right)\frac{1}{r^2}\, dr \qquad (94)$$

If a graphical solution is required (e.g., when a field-dependent dielectric constant is considered), it is necessary to plot $f(r)$ against r, where

$$f(r) = \frac{z^2 e^2}{2000\,\epsilon^2 kT} \left(V_2\epsilon_0 - \tfrac{9}{2}P_2\right)\frac{1}{r^2} \text{ liter mole}^{-1} \text{ cm}^{-1} \tag{95}$$

If the "exp" in the salting-out equation is not expanded, then $f(r)$ is given directly by

$$f(r) = \frac{4\pi N}{1000}\,(1 - \exp - \Delta U/kT)r^2 \tag{96}$$

and $f(r)$ tends then to zero instead of ∞ as $r \to 0$. This removes the main objection to the earlier treatments involving unrealistic linearization of the "exp." The salting-out equation can be further improved by taking into account two regions near the ion where (a) $\Delta U \gg kT$ so that $1 - \exp(-\Delta U/kT) \to 1$, and (b) $\Delta U < kT$ and $\exp - \Delta U/kT \to 1 - \Delta U/kT$, as discussed above. The condition $\Delta U \gg kT$ will apply in the primary hydration region where the ionic field is high and E is low (dielectric saturation effect; see Sect. IV.F).

Then the integration of the salting-out equation may be carried out over two integrands; from a to r_h where $\epsilon \ll \epsilon_0$ and from r_h to R where $\epsilon \approx \epsilon_0$ or to $r = \infty$ when $m \to 0$); Eq. (96) then becomes

$$f(r) = \frac{4\pi N}{1000}\left[\left(r^2\right)_a^{r_h} + \left(\frac{\Delta U}{kT}\,r^2\right)_{r_h}^{R}\right] \tag{97}$$

from which it can be seen that the limit r_h of the primary hydration shell is one of the critical factors determining k_s, and a close relation should hence exist between the geometry of the primary hydration shell and the degree of salting-out caused by the ions.

The salting-out equation corresponding to Eq. (97) is

$$\frac{S_0 - S}{S_0 m} = \frac{4\pi N}{1000}\left(\int_a^{r_h} r^2\,dr + \int_{r_h}^{R}(\Delta U/kT)r^2\,dr\right) \tag{98}$$

The field term in ΔU may be taken as $-ze/\epsilon_0 r^2$ for $r > r_h$ $(\epsilon \to \epsilon_0)$ and, after integration, Eq. (98) becomes

$$\frac{S_0 - S}{S_0 m} = \frac{4\pi N}{3000}\,(r_h^3 - a^3) + \frac{z^2 e^2}{2000 kT\epsilon_0^2}\left(V_2\epsilon_0 - \tfrac{9}{2}P_2\right)\left(\frac{1}{r_h} - \frac{1}{R}\right) \tag{99}$$

This relation at once eliminates the difficulty of using Kirkwood's

relation for the polarization energy in a high field region and allows
the salting-out also to be expressed, in part, in terms of the primary
hydration behavior of the ion, i.e., through the term r_h, the primary
hydration radius. Secondary concentration effects are also taken
account of through the R term.

More empirically, in terms of the primary hydration effect only,
S/S_0 can be written

$$\frac{S}{S_0} = \frac{55.5 - nm}{55.5} \tag{100}$$

where n is a primary hydration number and m the molarity. If the
concentration is expressed in terms of molarities, then the salting-
out equation, corresponding to solvent removal in the primary hydration shell only, becomes

$$\frac{S_0 - S}{S_0} = \frac{18nm}{1000d - mW} \tag{101}$$

where d is the density of the salt solution and W the molecular weight
of the dissolved salt. The term on the right-hand side of this equation
is equivalent to the first term of Eq. (99) but has the advantage of not
involving any assumption about the particular extent (in terms of r_h)
of the primary hydration shell. The over-all salting-out equation
may then be rewritten in the form

$$\frac{S_0 - S}{S_0 m} = \frac{18n}{1000d - mW} + \frac{z^2 e^2 (V_2 \epsilon_0 - \frac{9}{2} P_2)}{2000kT \epsilon_0^2} \left(\frac{1}{r_h} - \frac{1}{R} \right) \tag{102}$$

which gives k_s as $m \rightarrow 0$, $R \rightarrow \infty$, and $d \rightarrow d_0$ the density of pure solvent.

We now show how the treatment may be applied to the case of the
rigid polyion (charged rod model).

For cylindrical symmetry, Eq. (87) becomes

$$\frac{S_0 - S}{S_0} = \frac{\bar{C}N}{1000} \int_a^R (1 - \exp(-\Delta U/kT)) 2\pi l r \, dr \tag{103}$$

where $\bar{C}$ is the molar concentration of the polyion of length l and the
terms a and R have been defined previously. Now $l\bar{C} = \lambda \bar{m}$, where
$\bar{m}$ is the molar concentration of ionizable groups and λ is the distance between the ionizable groups on the polymer chain; also,
$\alpha \bar{m} = m$, where m is the monomer mole concentration of free
charges on the polyion chain when the degree of dissociation is α.

The energy term ΔU can be obtained from Eq. (92) but the choice of a suitable field function for this equation is more difficult. Normally, the field obtained from the solution of the Poisson-Boltzmann equation, e.g., as derived by Alfrey, Berg, and Morawetz [15], should be used since the central polyion cannot be separated from its atmosphere of gegen-ions even at high dilution. Unfortunately, owing to the complexity of the field function derived by Alfrey et al. [15], such calculations are very tedious. It is easier to evaluate field intensities numerically on a computer and solve the salting-out equation graphically. Alternatively, the field function for an isolated charged rod can be used in the salting-out equation. It is found that the value of k_s predicted for this case is not too different from the solutions where the ionic atmosphere is taken into consideration.

The field intensity at a distance r from an infinitely long charged rod is given by (cf. Eq. 25)

$$E = -2\alpha e/\epsilon\lambda r \tag{104}$$

so that the energy term hence becomes

$$\frac{\Delta U}{kT} = \frac{\alpha^2 e^2}{2\pi\lambda^2\epsilon^2 NkT} \frac{1}{r^2} (V_2\epsilon_0 - \tfrac{9}{2}P_2) \tag{105}$$

Then substituting Eq. (105) into Eq. (103) and otherwise treating the polyion case in the same manner as the simple ion case (see Eqs. 98 and 99), the result

$$\frac{S_0 - S}{S_0 m} = \frac{18n}{1000d - mW} + \frac{\alpha e^2}{1000\lambda\epsilon^2 kT} (V_2\epsilon_0 - \tfrac{9}{2}P_2) \ln\frac{R}{r_h} \tag{106}$$

is obtained where R is defined by an equation analogous to Eq. (86) (cf. Eq. 65), W is the molecular weight per ionized group, r_h the radius of the cylindrical primary hydration shell, and n is the hydration number per charged unit on the polymer chain. For the cylindrical polyion case, the equation corresponding to Eq. (99) simply has the term $(\pi\lambda N/1000\alpha)(r_h^2 - a^2)$ instead of the first term on the right-hand side of Eq. (99).

The unknown parameters in Eq. (106) are r_h and n. The parameter r_h can either be evaluated (as r_d) from calculated dielectric saturation curves (see Section IV.F) or r_h and n can be calculated from the apparent molal volume of the polyion.

Figure 25 shows the theoretical salting-out function f(r) calculated

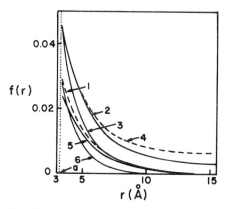

Fig. 25. Theoretical salting-out functions for change of solubility of benzene in water for simple and polyions of radius 3.2 Å. 1: $\epsilon = \epsilon_0$ (other conditions as for Curve 3). 2: $\alpha = 0.6$, m = 0.1 M, a = 3.2 Å. 3: $\alpha = 0.6$, M = 1.0 M,
a = 3.2 Å. 4: $\alpha = 0.6$, a = 3.2 Å., field taken as $-2\alpha e/\lambda\epsilon r$. 5: $\alpha = 0.3$, m = 1.0 M,
a = 3.2 Å. 6: Simple ion, a = 3.2 Å, m = 1.0 M.

for the nonelectrolyte benzene in water for a simple ion of radius 3.2 Å
and for polyion cylinders of the same radius but for various α and
concentration values. The effect of taking into account dielectric
saturation is also shown. It is evident that for polyions of appreciable degree of ionization, the salting-out distribution function $f(r)$
will lead (a) to a greater degree of salting-out at a given equivalent
concentration and (b) to a greater penetration of appreciable salting-
out effects from the ion into the bulk of the solution due to the different properties of the cylindrical field function from those of the
spherical ion function. The effect of increasing α is also clearly
illustrated.

The salting-out ratio $\Delta S/S_0 m$ is also found to increase quite significantly with dilution, and from Eq. (106), $(S_0 - S)/S_0 m$ is proportional to log R, and hence depends on dilution. The same situation
arises with the more exact field function of Alfrey et al. [15] since
all these equations result in a logarithmic dependence of $(S_0 - S)/S_0 m$
on R; this causes a mathematical difficulty in evaluation of an infinite dilution value for k_S which arises from the fact that the models
used all assume the polyions to be infinite in length. The theoretical
salting-out Eq. (103) can, of course, be satisfactorily used to calculate $(S_0 - S)/S_0 m$ for polyions in the range of finite concentrations
(0.1-1 M) used experimentally.

B. Relation to Polyion Volumes

The hydration data calculated from measurements of density and apparent molal volume can be used to evaluate the salting-out. The hydration number n is given by

$$n = \frac{V_a - \phi_V^0}{V_0 - V_{0,h}} \tag{107}$$

where v_a, the effective intrinsic ionic volume, is used in conjunction with the volume v_h of the hydration envelope (in terms of electrostricted water) given by

$$V_h = \frac{V_a V_0 - \phi_V^0 V_{0,h}}{V_0 - V_{0,h}} \tag{108}$$

In Eqs. (107) and (108) $V_0 - V_{0,h}$ is the difference in molar volume of normal water (V_0) and electrostricted water $(V_{0,h})$ in the hydration envelope. The affective volume V_a must allow for dead space around the ion, and for polyions

$$V_a = \pi\lambda N \left[1 + \left(\frac{4}{\pi} - 1\right) \frac{r_{H_2O}}{a} \right] a^2 \tag{109}$$

where r_{H_2O} is the radius of a water molecule. The values of v_h and n and the corresponding r_h (Eq. 106) are shown in Table 8 in relation to the values of r_h estimated from the distance from the polyion at which ϵ changes rather rapidly from a small saturation value to its normal bulk value. The saturation value for ϵ is probably near 5-6 according to Rampolla, Miller, and Smyth [50] rather than ca. 2 as assumed in earlier calculations. A comparison of $r_h - a$, the "thickness" of the annular hydration envelope, derived from density measurements and dielectric constant calculations has been shown in Fig. 9. In terms of experimental density measurements, $r_h - a$ for polymethacrylate becomes equal to $r_h - a$ for the simple monomer ion (isobutyrate) at $\alpha = 0.25$ while the theoretical calculations predict this identity at $\alpha \doteq 0.35$.

Using the r_h and n values discussed above (see Table 9), the k_S values can be calculated for salting out, e.g., of argon by KPMA and the monomer salt, and the results are shown in Fig. 26. In this case, for $\alpha > 0.4$, the k_S is larger for the polyion than the monomer ion, as found experimentally (Fig. 27), but k_S shows a maximum with increasing α, presumably due to K^+ association, which becomes appre-

Table 9

Effective Ionic and Hydration Radii of Polymethacrylate[a]
and Isobutyrate Ions [b]

α	ϕ_v^0 (ml)	V_h (ml)	n	r_h (density) (Å)	r_h (dielectric saturation) (Å)
0.95	43.3	217.8	9.1	6.6(0)	5.9(0)
0.80	–	–	–	–	–
0.75	45.5	210.1	9.2	6.4(9)	–
0.60	69.5	182.6	7.4	6.0(3)	5.35
0.40	57.3	138.2	4.5	5.2(2)	4.45
0.30	–	–	–	–	4.00
0.20	81.0	–	–	–	3.84

[a]Polymethacrylate ion (molecular weight = 43,000): V_a = 69.4 ml,
a = 3.65 Å (using Eq. 109).
[b]Isobutyrate ion: V_a = 85.9 ml, a = 2.88 Å (obtained from V_a); ϕ_v^0 = 71.5
ml (for a value of ϕ_v^0 for K^+ of 4.5 ml, Mukerjee 1961); V_h = 167.0 ml,
r_h = 3.68 Å (from Eqs. 108 and 109); n = 5.3.

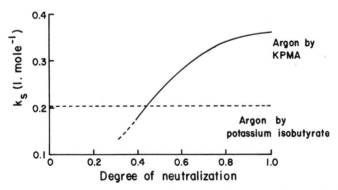

Fig. 26. Theoretically calculated k_S values for salting-out of argon by KPMA.

ciable for $\alpha > 0.5$. The ion association affects principally the long-
range salting-out of the polyion (second term of Eq. 106) since in the
binding, primary water of hydration is mainly retained so that the
short-range salting-out due to electrostriction and dielectric saturation near the ions would not be greatly changed on account of ion
association.

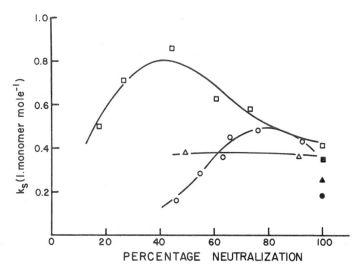

Fig. 27. Experimental k_S values for salting-out of argon by KPMA ($\square$), and PVPBuBr ($\triangle$) and benzamide by KPMA ($\bigcirc$). ■, ▲, and ● are the points for the corresponding monomer salts.

When Eq. (106) is used for the estimation of k_S, any effects of ion association on the primary hydration are, in fact, empirically allowed for since the first term of Eq. (106) is effectively corrected for any ion association effects insofar as it is based on experimental ϕ_V measurements.

An interesting development of salting-out studies in polyion hydration was pursued by Konyushko [78] who studied the distribution of a dissolved nonelectrolyte between an ion-exchange resin (see following section) containing sorbed water and an external solution. These measurements give an estimate of the bound water of hydration and the radii of the hydrated ions, e.g., in cation forms of the exchange resin. The system M-Dowex 50 (8% divinylbenzene cross-linkage)/sucrose/water was studied where $M \equiv Li^+$, Na^+, or K^+. The choice of sucrose as the nonelectrolyte solute was not, however, a good one owing to the electrically complex nature of this molecule with many dipolar hydrophilic groups. The theoretical interpretation of salting-out of such molecules is impossibly complex in the present state of knowledge of the properties of aqueous ionic solutions.

VII. HYDRATION OF CROSS-LINKED POLYELECTROLYTES: ION EXCHANGE RESINS AND MEMBRANES

With cross-linked polyelectrolytes in the form of ion exchange resins, the opportunity is presented of studying the progressive hydration of ionic centers at low water content of the system without the limitation [85] of crystallization that occurs with all simple salts.

Some of the first systematic studies of hydration of cross-linked polyelectrolytes were made by Gregor et al. [81] on polystyrenesulfonate salts cross-linked by divinylbenzene. Cation specificity is exhibited in the water uptake at various isopiestic relative humidities. At a given relative humidity the order of sorption was $H^+ > Li^+ > Na^+ > K^+$ for monovalent cation salts and $Mg^{2+} > Ca^{2+} > Ba^{2+}$ ($> K^+$). At high relative humidity the extent of sorption of water increased, as expected, with decreasing density of cross-linking.

The partial molal volumes of water in the resin matrix can also be derived and the resulting values are of course characteristic of the electrostriction and types of sites at which the water molecules are bound. The $\overline{V}$ data are obtained by graphical differentiation of the changes in volume of the resin with increasing sorption or relative humidity. Some values are shown in Table 10.

Table 10

Partial Molar Volume of Water in Cation Exchange Resins[a]

Cation	$\overline{V}_{H_2O}$ (ml/mole)	Cation	$\overline{V}_{H_2O}$ (ml/mole)
H^+	16.85	K^+	17.25
Li^+	17.55	Ag^+	17.00
Na^+	17.35	Mg^{++}	16.85
$(CH_3)_4N^+$	17.15	Ca^{++}	16.90
NH_4^+	17.16	Ba^{++}	16.25

[a] $\overline{V}_{H_2O}$ in polystyrene-10% divinylbenzene resin as a function of the counter-ion (in the relative humidity range 45-100%).

The electrostrictions which these figures imply, on a reference basis of 18 ml/mole for $V^0_{H_2O}$ at 4° C, are all smaller than the values for the same ions free in bulk water. From the isotherms, these relative humidity figures correspond to a ratio R of H_2O molecules to cation or anionic sites in the lattice between 4 and 8. At free ions with hydration numbers in the range 4-6 (e.g., Li^+, Na^+, NH_4^+), the electrostriction per water molecule is ca. 2.7-4 ml/mole and becomes larger at bivalent cations which have primary hydration numbers of 12-14 (6 octahedrally coordinated water molecules plus 8 in the octahedral faces 15-20% further away from the cation). These figures for $\overline{V}_{H_2O}$ hence suggest significant loss of the electrostriction of the corresponding free ions due to association with the anionic centers in the polymer matrix. In cases where conductivity data for the mobility of small ions in ion-exchange matrices [82,83] are available, interpretation of changes of counter-ion mobility in terms of ion association are obscured by other factors such as the internal viscosity and swelling of the resin phase. In the fully neutralized resin, ion association is indicated by the concentration dependence of the mobility but the effect is not that found for simple salt solutions. In polymethacrylate resin membranes the counter-ion association becomes appreciable once a substantial fraction of adjacent pairs of COO^- groups are present, i.e., as the charge distribution approaches that of a rodlike particle (cf. Ref. 67).

Glueckauf and Kitt [84] measured the sorption of water into a polystyrene sulfonate ion-exchange system by an isopiestic approach at various temperatures which enabled the adsorption equilibria and free energy relations to be determined, as well as the differential entropy and enthalpy of the progressive adsorption to be investigated. Concentrated electrolyte solutions were examined in a related way by Stokes and Robinson [65] in terms of "adsorption" of water at ions.

The general trend of the sorption isotherms ($R = H_2O/ion$ vs. a_{H_2O}, the isopiestic water activity) for various cation salts were similar (the NH_4^+ salt being the most different in behavior from other Li^+, Na^+, and Et_4N^+ salts) but the differential enthalpy $\Delta\overline{H}$ and entropy $\Delta\overline{S}$ behavior was rather more specific (Figs. 28, 29a, and 29b). In particular, the $\Delta\overline{S}$ dependence on R showed maxima near $R = 1$ and another step near $R = 2$. The $\Delta\overline{H}$ quantities are cation specific at low R in the series Li^+, Na^+, K^+, Cs^+, NH_4^+, Ag^+ and more particularly for the divalent ion series Hg^{2+}, Ba^{2+}, Sr^{2+}, Ca^{2+}, Mg^{2+}, Be^{2+}. Irreversible sorption effects were observed at very low humidities.

A primary hydration step of the form $C^+A^- + W \rightarrow C^+WA^-$ or C^+A^-W, where $W = H_2O$, $C = $ cation, and $A = $ anionic site, was first considered. This mechanism, corresponding to undissociated C^+A^-, is equivalent to Langmuir adsorption and leads to an initial extent of sorption proportional to A_W. A square-root dependence is actually observed [84,85].

A mechanism

$$C^+A^- + W \rightarrow 2 \text{ dissociated ions}$$

gives an initial water uptake proportional to $(a_W)^{1/2}$ in agreement

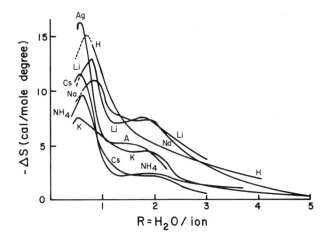

Fig. 28. Contributions of individual adsorption steps (1-5) toward total
H_2O sorption for NH_4^+ cation exchange resin at 0°C (after Glueckauf and Kitt
[84]) as a function of water activity a_W.

with experiment. The water may initially be preferentially associated with C^+ or A^-, i.e.,

$$C^+A^- + W \rightarrow CW^+ + A^-$$

or

$$C^+A^- + W \rightarrow C^+ + AW^-$$

(cf. the spectroscopic infrared observations of Zundel et al. [86-88]).
Since in the NMe_4^+ and NEt_4^+ resins the first water is bound strongly,
it is concluded that the sulfonate anion centers bind the initially
sorbed water (cf. the mechanism of Boyd and Soldano [89] and the
fact that dehydration of $CuSO_4 \cdot 5H_2O$ proceeds initially to form
$Cu^{2+}SO_4^{2-} \cdot H_2O$ where the last H_2O molecule is preferentially associated with the SO_4^{2-} group. Presumably H-bonding provides a substantial enhancement of interaction energy with 2 O-centers over
that arising for purely electrostatic reasons).

In the case of the bivalent salts, the $-\Delta\bar{H}$ are larger but this is
compensated by a larger $-\Delta\bar{S}$ so that the water affinities are not so
different from those of the monovalent salt resins. Appreciable heat
is evolved even for continuing sorption up to R = 6.

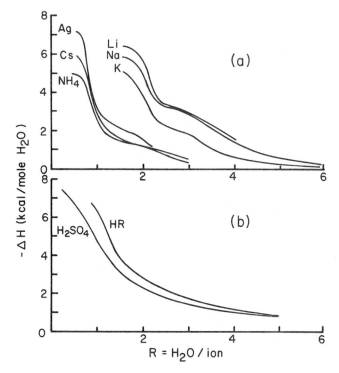

Fig. 29. Differential heats and entropies of sorption of water into univalent salt and acid forms of a cation exchange resin as a function of water sorbed [R = (H$_2$O)/(ion site)] (after Glueckauf and Kitt [84]).

That the second sorbed water molecule is also attached to the sulfonate group is ruled out directly as substantially the same $\Delta \bar{H}$ values would be involved for all counter-ions and this is not experimentally the case; indeed there is substantial cation specificity. The sorption of second water molecules follows the scheme

$$C^+ + AW^- + W \rightarrow CW^+ + AW^-$$

with successive additions of water to give CW_2^+, CW_3^+, etc. Gregor et al. [81] made a distinction between "free" swelling water and hydration water associated with cations in the structure.

The differential $\Delta \bar{H}$ and $\Delta \bar{S}$ for the sorption of the distinguishable first and second water molecules can be evaluated (Figs. 29a and 29b)

Table 11

Standard Enthalpies and Entropies of Water Sorption in the
Polystyrene Sulfonate Series [84]

Counter cation	$r_i \times 10^8$ (cm)[a]	$-\Delta \bar{H}_1$ (kcal/mole)	$-\Delta \bar{S}_1$ (Gbs)	$-\Delta \bar{H}_2$ (kcal/mole)	$-\Delta \bar{S}_2$ (Gbs)
H^+	0	8.15	18.3	4.71	10.3
Li^+	0.6	6.78	14.4	3.75	9.8
Na^+	0.95	6.21	12.8	3.18	8.2
Ag^+	1.13	7.14	18.5	1.80	2.8
K^+	1.33	5.50	11.6	2.19	5.5
NH_4^+	1.48	4.83	10.8	1.38	3.1 (5)
H_3O^+	1.48	4.51	9.5	(1.28)	(1.7)
Cs^+	1.65	6.32	15.1	0.65	0.05

[a]Based on the Pauling scale of ionic radii.

and both $(\Delta \bar{H}_1 + \Delta \bar{H}_2)$ and $(\Delta \bar{S}_1 + \Delta \bar{S}_2)$ vary linearly with the radius of the cationic counter-ions (Fig. 30). The usual (e.g., Ref. 25) compensation effect between the $\Delta \bar{S}$ and $\Delta \bar{H}$ quantities is also observed as in the hydration of free ions in the aqueous solvent.

The contributions of individual successive absorption steps (1 to 5) to the total water sorption can be evaluated [84] approximately (Fig. 28) for the NH_4^+ resin.

Extrapolation studies on dinonylnaphthalene-sulfonic acid and divinylbenzene resins in the Ag salt form also gave evidence of various specific stoichiometric hydrates [91].

The heats of swelling of various (presumably Russian) ion-exchange resins in H_2O and D_2O were measured by Myagkoi and Meleshko [92] and related to the total sorption of water by the resin. Greater degree of cross-linkage gave increased heats of hydration per unit volume, presumably due to the greater ion-exchange capacity and density of ionic groups. Increase in D_2O concentration caused, in all cases, a decrease in the heat of hydration (cf. Friedman [93]).

Rates of sorption of water on various cation salts of ion exchangers were measured by Westermark [90] using the (initially) almost dry materials (cf. again the spectroscopic work of Zundel [86-88]). The solvent-ion-dipole interactions with the exchangeable cation were considered.

A phosphonate resin (Duolite GG3) was examined by Persoz and Rosset [94] with regard to volume changes accompanying hydration. In comparison with the Na^+ form, volume changes are 70% for

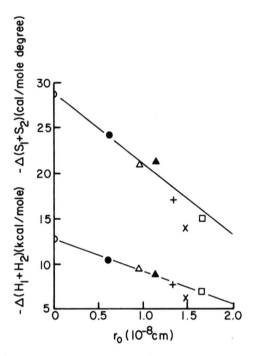

Fig. 30. Heat and entropy changes for sorption of first two water molecules per ion site in cation exchange resins as a function of cation ionic radius (after Glueckauf and Kitt [84]).

exchange with bivalent cations and 57% with H^+. The Na^+ form of the structure is a matrix of $RPO_3^{2-} 2Na^+$ where R is a cross-linked polystyrenedivinylbenzene structure. Alkali metal cations are not strongly associated with the resin and retain their water of hydration. The reverse behavior is found with heavy metal cations. The order of affinity of a number of cations for association with the resin was as follows: $UO_2^{2+} > Be^{2+} > Pb^{2+} > Cu^{2+} > Zn^{2+} > Cd^{2+} > Mn^{2+} > Co^{2+} > Ni^{2+} > Ca^{2+} > Mg^{2+} > Sr^{2+} > Ba^{2+}$.

A theoretical basis was given by Konyushko and Konyushko [95] for the possible use of an indicator method for determining bound water in salt forms of ion-exchange resins. The water which causes swelling is the bound water since water in the cation exchange phase is regarded [95] as having a higher (sic) thermodynamic activity than in the solution. As the chemical potentials of the components in the phases equalize, water becomes released.

Dielectric constant studies on a number of ion-exchange resins were made by Dickel and Bunzl [96] in relation to the state of water of hydration sorbed in the matrix. The resins examined contained SO_3H, SO_3Na, PO_3H_2, and PO_3K_2 groups; H and K forms of m-phenol-sulfonic acid; an H form of disulfonated rings; and the Cl⁻ form of anion exchange groups. The dielectric constant when plotted against a sorption function for the amount of H_2O present showed abrupt changes of slope. The dielectric loss angle of the PO_2H_2 resin also showed a sharp break when plotted against the amount of sorbed water. The H forms absorb 2, the Cl⁻ form of anionic exchange groups 3, and both Na and K forms, 4 molecules of H_2O per group. Hysteresis in terms of the measured dielectric constant was found in the absorption and desorption isotherms.

On the basis of the idea of the existence of a limiting temperature above which an ion exhibiting negative (hydrophobic) hydration becomes normally hydrated, and below which the reverse is true, it was shown [97] that a characteristic feature of ion-exchange processes is the fact that the temperature dependence of the selectivity often passes through a minimum. The temperature which corresponds to the minimum in the selectivity coefficient changes in accord with the values of the entropy associated with structural changes in the water which influence the hydration of the ions.

The selectivity of anion exchange resins in contact with very dilute external solutions (i.e., with negligible resin invasion by non-exchange electrolyte) was considered by Chu, Whitney, and Diamond [98] to be mainly due to changes in the solvation of the ions resulting from differences in the properties of the resin phase solution in comparison with the external solution. The resin phase is in effect a concentrated solution having three principal differences from the external solution: (a) the cation charges are fixed on the resin matrix, (b) electrostatic forces are stronger (cf., the electrical situation at a linear polyion), and (c) the water molecules in the resin may have a less ordered structure. The tendency for large univalent ions to be forced out of the dilute solution into the resin phase is considered to be due to their small degree of hydration and considerable water structure-breaking ability. The analogy to specific adsorption of ions at electrode interfaces is clear here and similar effects evidently operate, except that at electrode interfaces the surface charge is delocalized.

VIII. SOLVENT SELF-DIFFUSION STUDIES
ON MACROION HYDRATION

Early work on the complex question of protein hydration has been reviewed by Edsall [99]. In most previous measurements the results can only be expressed as a function of both the axial ratio and the hydration of the polymer, and either of these quantities can only be estimated individually with some ambiguity. The dielectric method gives a less ambiguous interpretation of relaxation behavior in terms of shape of the molecule, but polarization due to proton migration may introduce difficulties in the interpretation of the relaxation time spectrum [100]. A method developed by Wang [101] avoids some of the ambiguities, and the hydration determined is independent of the value of the molecular weight and, for prolate ellipsoids, is also almost independent of the shape of the macroions.

A macroion solute modifies the self-diffusion behavior of the solvent in three ways: (a) by a blocking effect, since in a cell of given dimensions, the path length for a given net linear translation of the diffusing particle down the cell is greater than that in the absence of a macromolecular solute. This effect is determined by the size and volume fraction of the macroion solute and constitutes a decrease in the self-diffusion constant of the solvent; (b) the second effect (of interest here) arises because the macroion binds a fraction of water molecules which are therefore impeded (in the time average) in their transport across the cell. Various degrees of binding will arise depending on site distribution and temperature, and a loosely bound solvent molecule which is attached to the macroion only during some fraction of the latter's own diffusional progress in the solution will be counted as a fraction of a solvating solvent molecule. (c) Most solutes change the fluidity and hence self-diffusion constant of the solvent due to structure-promotion or structure-breaking effects. For protein solutions, such effects have been regarded as small.

We shall proceed directly to a statement of the theoretical results for the diffusion effect, the derivations having been given in the original publication by Wang [101].

1. The obstruction effect is expressed as a function of ϕ, the volume fraction of hydrated macroions, and the effective diffusion coefficient D_i' is related to D_0, the self-diffusion coefficient of the solvent at infinite dilution, by

$$D_i' = (1 - \beta_i \phi)D_0 \qquad\qquad (110)$$

where i refers to a particular limiting orientation of the obstructing ellipsoids equivalent to the macroion. The parameter β_i is

$$\beta_i = 2/(2 - abcw_i) \tag{111}$$

and

$$w_i = \int_0^\infty d\lambda/(i^2 + \lambda)(a^2 + \lambda)^{1/2}(b^2 + \lambda)^{1/2}(c^2 + \lambda)^{1/2} \tag{112}$$

with i = a, b, c in turn and λ is defined as one of the ellipsoidal coordinates. The direction down the diffusion tube is taken as the x axis with the origin located at the center of the ellipsoid. An ellipsoidal solute molecule of ellipsoidal semiaxes a, b, c is considered with "a" along the x axis. In Cartesian coordinates

$$dx/d\lambda = x/2(a^2 + \lambda) \tag{113}$$

For the case of ellipsoids of revolution having two of their axes equal, e.g., a prolate ellipsoid with a = ρb = ρc with $\rho > 1$,

$$w_a = \int_0^\infty d\lambda/(a^2 + \lambda)^{3/2}(b^2 + \lambda)$$

$$= \frac{1}{a^2 - b^2} \left[\frac{1}{(a^2 - b^2)^{1/2}} \ln \frac{a + (a^2 - b^2)^{1/2}}{a - (a^2 - b^2)^{1/2}} - \frac{2}{a} \right] \tag{114}$$

so that

$$\beta_a = \left[\frac{\rho^2}{\rho^2 - 1} - \frac{\rho}{2(\rho^2 - 1)^{3/2}} \ln \frac{\rho + (\rho^2 - 1)^{1/2}}{\rho - (\rho^2 - 1)^{1/2}} \right]^{-1} \tag{115}$$

[When a = b = c (sphere), $\beta_a = \beta_b = \beta_c = 1.5$.]

Similarly

$$\beta_b = 2/\left[\frac{\rho^2 - 2}{\rho^2 - 1} + \frac{\rho}{2(\rho^2 - 1)^{3/2}} \ln \frac{\rho + (\rho^2 - 1)^{1/2}}{\rho - (\rho^2 - 1)^{1/2}} \right] \tag{116}$$

For oblate ellipsoids, a = b = a with $\rho < 1$; then

$$\beta_a = \left(1 - \frac{\rho}{1 - \rho^2} \left\{ \frac{1}{(1 - \rho^2)^{1/2}} \left[\tan^{-1} \frac{\rho}{(1 - \rho^2)^{1/2}} - \frac{\pi}{2} \right] + 1/\rho \right\} \right)^{-1} \tag{117}$$

and

$$\beta_b = 2 / \left\{ \frac{2 - \rho^2}{1 - \rho^2} - \frac{\rho}{(1 - \rho^2)^{3/2}} \left[\frac{\pi}{2} - \tan^{-1} \frac{\rho}{(1 - \rho^2)^{1/2}} \right] \right\} \quad (118)$$

Since all orientations of the obstructing ellipsoids are possible in a real solution, the orientations must be averaged with respect to the cosines of the orientations to the x axis. This gives

$$D' = \frac{1}{3}(D_a + D_b + D_c) \tag{119}$$

and the corresponding β to be used in Eq. (110) is hence

$$\overline{\beta} = \frac{1}{3}(\beta_a + \beta_b + \beta_c) \tag{120}$$

Values of $\overline{\beta}$ are shown in Table 12. The limiting cases of rod and disc differ physically in their obstructing effects since solvent molecules can freely diffuse among a network of rods but are blocked by a system of randomly oriented discs.

Table 12

Values of β for Ellipsoids of Revolution with
Different Axial Ratios ρ

$\rho = a/b$	$\overline{\beta}$	$1/\rho = b/a$	$\overline{\beta}$
1.0	1.500	1.0	1.500
1.5	1.516	1.5	1.525
2.0	1.539	2.0	1.577
2.5	1.561	2.5	1.649
3.0	1.576	3.0	1.730
4.0	1.601	4.0	1.909
5.0	1.616	5.0	2.101
6.0	1.627	6.0	2.295
7.0	1.634	7.0	2.489
8.0	1.640	8.0	2.694
9.0	1.644	9.0	2.916
10.0	1.647	10.0	3.107
∞ (rod)	1.667	∞ (disc)	∞

2. The direct solvent binding effect is derived by employing Fick's second law with concentrations of c_0 and c_k of total water and total bound water, and c_0^* and c_k^* as the respective concentrations for labelled solvent, H_2O^{18}, in the case of hydration studies, used for the self-diffusion measurement (cf. Orr and Butler [101a]). In terms of the experimentally measured diffusion constant D in the presence of macroion solutes,

$$D = D'(1 - c_k/c_0) \qquad (121)$$

(the self-diffusion constant of water $\gg$ the diffusion constant of macroion solutes such as proteins; also the rate of exchange between bound and free isotopically labeled water molecules is fast).

3. The complete theoretical equation for hydration in terms of the diffusion effects can now be written. Let H be defined as the hydration of the macroion protein (in grams bound water per gram anhydrous protein) and c_p = the (anhydrous) protein concentration in g/cm^3. Let w = weight fraction of anhydrous protein in solution, i.e., 100w = wt % of dry protein in solution. Then

$$c_p/c_0 = w/(1 - w) \qquad (122)$$

and

$$c_p \overline{V}_p + c_0/d_0 = 1 \qquad (123)$$

where $\overline{V}_p$ is the apparent specific volume* of protein in aq. solution and d_0 is the density of pure water as solvent. The volume fraction of hydrated protein is hence

$$\phi = c_p(\overline{V}_p + H/d_0) = \frac{\overline{V}_p + H/d_0}{\overline{V}_p + 1/d_0 (1 - w)/w} = W \text{ (say) } (124)$$

Combining this result with that for the obstruction effect leads to

$$D = D_0 \left\{ 1 - \overline{\beta} \, W \, (1 - \frac{w}{1 - w} H) \right\} \qquad (125)$$

*The use of the apparent specific volume here avoids problems about the significance of electrostriction effects, selective adsorption, etc., in expressing the volume fraction.

where W is given by Eq. (124).
For numerical computations

$$\frac{D}{D_0} - \Delta_1 = 1 - [\bar{\beta}(\bar{V}_p d_0 + H) + H]w + \Delta_2 \tag{126}$$

where

$$\Delta_1 = \frac{\bar{\beta}\,\bar{V}_p d_0(\bar{V}_p d_0 - 1)w^2}{1 + (\bar{V}_p d_0 - 1)w} \tag{127}$$

and

$$\frac{\Delta_2}{w^2} = \frac{\bar{\beta}H(\bar{V}_p d_0 - 1)}{1 + (\bar{V}_p d_0 - 1)w} - \frac{H}{1 - w}$$

$$+ \frac{\bar{\beta}(V_p d_0 + H)H}{1 + (\bar{V}_p d_0 - 1)w(1 - w)} \tag{128}$$

so that H can be evaluated. The method was tested using the self-diffusion data of Wang, Anfinsen, and Polestra [102].

IX. ION ASSOCIATION AND ITS EFFECTS ON HYDRATION OF POLYIONS

The question of preferential hydration of polyions is intimately connected with the ion-association behavior of the given polyion and its counter-ions. Ion binding is usually treated in terms of a distribution of specific binding sites [103]. Various equations have been developed for the preferential hydration [104] in terms of the number of salt ions and water molecules bound. Ion binding and preferential hydration effects are, in fact, difficult to separate in the analysis of experimental results on ion binding, e.g., by emf, equilibrium dialysis, or conductivity experiments. The factors are similar to those for the case of simple electrolytes where various types of ion association can occur: (a) between completely hydrated ions (in the case of hydrophilic ions of large charge/radius ratio), (b) between cations and anions which share a primary hydration sheath, and (c) between relatively less hydrated ions (low charge/radius ratio) where "contact" association (e.g., Fuoss [105]) arises. In Cases (b) and (c), hydration water will to some extent be released upon ion-pair formation [73]. The corresponding volume change ΔV_a on association can be measured by determining the effect of pressure on the association equilibrium constant, K_a,

$$\left(\frac{d \ln K_a}{dp}\right)_T = (-\Delta V_a/RT)$$

It is important to note that ΔV_a does not usually correspond to complete loss of the volume of electrostriction of the unassociated ions and, in fact, is only a fraction of it. Association according to Case (b) (or sometimes Case C) is therefore indicated in most cases. Related conclusions follow from the recalculated data [106] for simple metal sulfates which show that the entropies of association of ions are not independent of their entropies of hydration. Hence the association is not simply between the completely hydrated ions, irrespective of the strength of their hydration.

For interaction of small molecules (or ions) with a macromolecule, the mass-action law for the distribution may be written, according to the treatment of Klotz [103],

$$n_{ij} = \lambda_i K_{ij} m_i/(1 + K_{ij} m_j) \tag{129}$$

where K_{ij} is the association constant for binding of j species at sites of type i, m_j is the molality of free (unbound) ions in the solution, and n_{ij} is the number of moles of j bound at sites i. The groups of sites i contain λ_i individual sites. For the composition of the solvent to remain the same at the sites λ_i (zero surface excess; cf. the Gibbs theory of adsorption) as it is in solution, there would have to be $n_{ij} 55.51/n_j$ water molecules present (but not necessarily chemically bound) at the λ_i sites. The difference between this number and the number n_{ij} of water actually bound, viz., $\lambda_i - n_{ij}$, will be termed the preferential hydration α_{ij}, i.e.,

$$\alpha_{ij} = (\lambda_i - n_{ij}) - n_{ij} 55.51/m_j \tag{130}$$

This quantity is regarded as equal to the number of water molecules at the sites i in excess or deficiency of that needed to "balance the bound ions of species j."* It may be positive or negative; if it is

*The significance of this description by the authors is unclear since water binding and ion binding are not exclusive functions. In the hydrate water, shared ion pair situation (Case b above), the ion and water binding are not competitive processes.

negative, the macromolecule is considered to bind ions preferentially at the sites i. Finally α_{ij} can be summed over all i sites to
give an over-all measure α_j of the preferential hydration of the
whole macromolecule:

$$\alpha_j = \sum_j \alpha_{ij} \tag{131}$$

The relation of these deductions to the results of ion binding studies were also explored by Schumaker and Cox [109,111].

In ion binding studies the molality m_j of the free ion is measured
in a solution containing g kilograms of water, n_j^o moles of ions of
type j, and n_p moles of polyion (e.g., protein). The number r_{obs}
is then calculated [107] from

$$r_{obs} = \frac{1}{n_p} (n_j^o - m_j g) \tag{132}$$

The experimental results may be interpreted, on the other hand, in
terms of preferential hydration α_j. Upon addition of n_p moles of
polyion, let $r_j n_p$ be the number of moles of salt ions that are actually bound. Then $(\lambda - r_j)n_p$ moles of water which do not contain
charges of species i are present at the remainder of the sites. The
complete expression for m_j is hence

$$m_j = \frac{n_k^o - n_p r_j}{g - n_p \dfrac{(\lambda - r_j)}{55.51}} \tag{133}$$

which is equivalent to

$$n_j^o - m_j g = \frac{-m_j}{55.51} \left[\lambda - r_j(1 + \frac{55.51}{m_j}) \right] n_p \tag{134}$$

But, from above, the left-hand side of Eq. (134) is equal to $n_p r_{obs}$
and the expression on the right-hand side of Eq. (134) is α_j. This
is seen by summing the equation for α_{ij} over the sites i. Thus

$$r_{obs} = \frac{-m_j}{55.51} \alpha_j \tag{135}$$

which is simply related to the preferential hydration. This result

is of some importance since Eqs. (130) and (131) show that α_j can refer to several groups of sites including those which exclude ions strongly.
By considering a macromolecule having λ_e sites at which ions are completely excluded and λ_b at which they are firmly bound* with an association constant K_0, Eqs. (130) and (131) give

$$\alpha_j = \lambda_e + \lambda_b \left(\frac{1 - K_0 55.51}{1 + K_0 m_j} \right) \tag{136}$$

If $\lambda_e \gg \lambda_b$, appreciable errors can result if r_{obs} and α_j are interpreted in terms of λ_b only.

In the case of equilibrium dialysis experiments in a three-component system (e.g., water, sucrose, and protein), the quantity measured is the specific adsorption coefficient which can be defined thermodynamically and interpreted in terms of preferential hydration [108]. The expression for a solution containing isoionic protein and univalent electrolyte is

$$\left(g - \frac{n_p \alpha_+}{55.51} \right) \left(g - \frac{n_p \alpha_-}{55.51} \right) = \left(\frac{n}{m'} \right)^2 \tag{137}$$

where α_+, α_- are the preferential hydration values for the cation and the anion, g the number of kilograms of water inside the dialysis bag, n_p the number of moles of polyion, n the total number of moles of salt inside the sack, and m' the molality of salt outside the sack.

The magnitude of the hydration is shown by the appreciable amounts of bound water associated with ribonuclease, bovine serum albumin, etc. found in various studies [109]. The question arises if a monolayer of bound water distributed over the surface† (e.g., of a protein) could account for the relatively large values observed. The minimum surface areas of the above two proteins may be estimated as 3000 $Å^2$ for RNase and 9000 $Å^2$ for BSA. For water, a 3.1 $Å^2$ cube may be assigned to each molecule so that the monolayer would correspond to 0.4 g H_2O/g protein for RNase and 0.25 g H_2O

---

*Specific ion binding may not only occur electrostatically at charge centers on the polyion. Complex formation by neutral functions may also be significant, e.g., in the binding of Zn^{2+} to imidazole residues in serum albumin.

†Hydration of ions was regarded as a type of adsorption process by Stokes and Robinson [65].

for BSA. These figures are in quite good agreement with the observed results.

In the case of proteins, for preferential hydration to be positive at all, it is seen from Eqs. (130) and (131) that K_{ij}° 55.51 < 1, i.e., the standard free energy of ion binding $-RT \ln 1/55.51$ ($= +2339$ cal at $20^{\circ}C$) must be positive. In order for a symmetrically hydrated free salt ion to become incorporated in the monolayer of hydrate water at the macromolecule, it is assumed [108] that some distortion of the hydrate shells will be required and it has been proposed that this is the reason for appreciable apparent preferential hydration at high salt concentrations. By comparison with the situation at simple ions, it would appear, however, that this state of affairs would only arise for binding of cations at a cationic polymer or of anions to an anionic polymer. When association of opposite charges occurs, hydrate layer sharing is more facile due to the mutually favorable orientation of solvent dipoles at each of the charge centers which can retain their original orientation after the association process has been completed. Finally, hydration due to specific macromolecule/solvent interaction must be distinguished from that, in a monolayer, which will always be present about a macroion for purely geometrical reasons. In terms of the adsorption model and the situation at electrode interfaces, the "surface excess" hydration is the quantity of physical and molecular significance.

Equilibrium isopiestic compositions of solutions which contain a volatile and a nonvolatile solvent component, and varying amounts of a macromolecular substance, can be used to determine directly the extent of preferential binding of either solvent component to the macromolecule. In a treatment by Hade and Tanford [110], it was shown how this method could be used to evaluate the preferential hydration of serum albumin in 2.5 m CsCl. Unfolded proteins in concentrated guanidine HCl, however, preferentially bind the guanidine to a small extent. Preferential hydration of proteins has also been treated theoretically by Shumaker and Cox [111] who showed that several hundred solvent molecules would be expected to come within the sphere of influence of the surface of most native proteins.

The linear rod model with discrete charge centers was treated by Lapanje, Haebig, Davis, and Rice [67] in their calculation of the activity coefficient γ of bound ions. A linear array of $Z + 1$ charges was considered, with $Z/2$ charges on each side of the charge labeled O. An arbitrary field point P is taken at a distance r_i from the various charges and the line of P to a typical charge i makes an angle θ with the linear array. The distance of the jth charge from P is then (see Fig. 5)

$$r_j^2 = r_0^2 + j^2 R^2 - Z j r_0 R \cos \theta_0 \tag{138}$$

where r_0 and θ_0 represent the position of charge O in relation to P. The distance between charges is constant ($= R$). The linearized Poisson-Boltzmann equation was solved for the region outside the ion and the Laplace equation $\nabla^2 \psi = 0$ inside the ion. Numerical values were calculated for $-\ln \gamma_{Cl^-}$ for Cl^- counter-ions at a linear trivalent ($Z + 1 = 3$) and pentavalent ion ($Z + 1 = 5$).

The transition from simple ion, through bolaform ion, to polyion behavior (with regard to counter-ion activity coefficients and binding) was found to occur at $Z + 1 > 5$ (cf. Ref. 18). Specific ion pair formation at individual sites was shown, on the basis of radiotracer experiments on counter-ion binding in polyethylene imine HCl, to be ruled out but the counter-ion distribution can be sharply peaked near the polyion. In fact, the associated ions can be regarded as forming a mobile monolayer on the polyion surface. When the charge density on the polyion skeleton has local peaks (e.g., with polyphosphates), the counter-ion distribution will have local maxima. This shell of ions (cf. the Bjerrum-Fuoss criterion [3] for ion association in monomeric salts) provides effective shielding of the polyion charges. Counter-ion "binding" and low counter-ion activity coefficients are regarded as alternative descriptions of the same phenomenon.

With regard to hydration, the implications of this work are that ion-binding at the polyion may not diminish the short-range hydration as much as true ion pair formation does in the case of simple salts. Longer range polarization effects (cf. Eq. 102 and the treatment of Conway, Desnoyers, and Smith [51]) depending on the line density of charge will, however, be attenuated by counter-ion association. These effects should be discernable in dilatometric studies on partial molal volumes of polyions at various ionic strengths of the monomeric salts [69].

The counter-ion binding at polyions was investigated by Ikegami [66] in relation to hydration, with special reference to the change in the structure of water in the neighborhood of the charged polymer skeleton induced by the bound ions [112]. The molar volume change due to changes in the properties of water as counter-ion binding increases was determined by a method employing refractivity measurements. Strictly, the volume change must be determined from the pressure coefficient of counter-ion association constants (cf. Hamann and Pearce [73]) but if the properties of the water about the ion are sufficiently changed by the ion binding, the volume change can be deduced approximately and the refractivity changes themselves can be directly related to the binding.

If two forms of water in the solution are distinguished with regard to the bulk and the hydrating water, then the refractive index difference between solution and water is

$$\Delta n = \frac{2\pi}{9 \times 10^3} \frac{(n_0^2 + 2)^2}{n_0^2} \left[\sum_1^i (C_a P_a + C_h P_h + C_0 P_0 - C_{00} P_0) \right] \tag{139}$$

where C_a and P_a are the concentration and molar polarizability of component a, C_h and P_h those of the hydrating water, C_0 and P_0 those for the usual water in the solution, and C_{00} is the concentration of H_2O in pure water. The above relation is based on

$$\frac{n^2 - 1}{n^2 + 2} = \frac{4\pi}{3 \times 10^3} \sum_1^i C_i P_i \tag{140}$$

for the refractive index n of a solution in terms of the polarizabilities P_i of its components at concentrations C_i. If the number of hydrating water molecules per solute molecule i is H_i, then

$$C_h = \sum_1^i H_i C_i \tag{141}$$

and the concentration difference of normal water in the pure solvent and in solution is

$$C_{00} - C_0 = v_h C_h + \sum_1^i v_i C_i \tag{142}$$

where v_i and v_h are the ratios of the volume of the solute component and of the hydration water to that of normal water, respectively. The increment of refractivity, Δn, in terms of hydration is hence

$$\Delta n = \frac{2\pi}{9 \times 10^3} \frac{(n_0^2 + 2)^2}{n_0}$$

$$\sum_1^i [(1 - v_h) H_i C_i P_0 - v_i C_i P_0 + H_i C_i (P_h - P_0) + C_i P_i] \tag{143}$$

Next, two solutions I and J are considered in a mixture with i and j solute species. Upon mixing, the refractive increment of the solution I + J is equal to the sum of those of I and J. When the

components i and j interact and make a complex ij, the difference
in the refractive index will be

$$\Delta n = \Delta n(A + B) - \Delta n_A - \Delta n_B$$

$$= \frac{2\pi}{9 \times 10^3} \frac{(n_0^2 + 2)^2}{n_0} \left[(H_{ij} - H_i - H_j)(1 - v_h)P_0 - (v_{ij} - v_i - v_j)P_0 \right.$$

$$\left. + (H_{i,j} - H_i - H_j)(P_h - P_0) + (P_{ij} - P_i - P_j) \right] C_{ij} \qquad (144)$$

because the polarizability P_{ij}, volume ratio v_{ij}, and the number of
hydrating water molecules H_{ij} of the complex ij must be different
from the individual quantities for either i or j. In the above equation, the first and second terms come from the volume change of
water and solute species due to the complex formation. The last two
terms come from the change of polarizability of the component and
are small relative to the first terms. Then the volume change associated with i + j − ij is directly related to the refractivity, density
ρ_0, and molecular weight M_0:

$$\Delta V \equiv \overline{V}_{ij} - \overline{V}_i - \overline{V}_j$$

$$= \frac{-M_0}{\rho_0} \left[(H_{ij} - H_i - H_j)(1 - v_h) - (V_{ij} - v_i - v_j) \right]$$

$$= \frac{-6n_0 10^3}{(n_0^2 + 2)(n_0^2 - 1)} \frac{d\Delta n}{dC_{ij}} \qquad (145)$$

where $\overline{V}$ is the partial molal volume of the indicated component. In
electrolyte solutions, the volume change in complex formation is
usually much smaller than that due to the change of hydration. Numerically, with $v_h = 0.89$, as estimated from ultrasonic measurements [66],

$$\Delta(H) = \frac{6}{11} \frac{n_0 10^5}{(n_0^2 + 2)(n_0^2 - 1)} \frac{d\Delta n}{dC_{ij}} \qquad (146)$$

This is a very useful relation as it enables hydration and volume
changes to be discussed simply in terms of refractivity, at least in
an approximate way.

For simple acids, the decrement of refractivity Δn varies linearly with degree of neutralization. For polyacrylic acid the relations

are less linear and also depend on the cation [Na^+ or $(n\text{-}Bu)_4N^+$]. The relation between the change of $\overline{V}$ accompanying binding of various other cations to the Bu_4N^+ salt of polyacrylic acid and α (the degree of neutralization or the quantity of cations bound expressed as a fraction of the total "COOH" groups) is linear. The slopes of these relations are the <u>same</u> indicating that they are determined only by hydration of $-COO^-$ groups.

Binding of Na^+, as NaCl added to various polyacids neutralized to different degrees by Bu_4NOH, gave the result shown in Fig. 31. Δn greatly increases with added NaCl up to a critical concentration depending on the degree of neutralization α (Fig. 32).

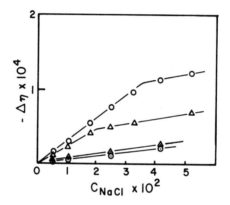

Fig. 31. Decrement of refraction $\Delta\eta$ accompanying binding of added Na^+ to PAA partially neutralized by $Bu_4N^+OH^-$ as a function of NaCl concentration. ($\bigcirc$) $\alpha = 1$; ($\triangle$) $\alpha = 0.69$; ($\triangle$) $\alpha = 0.4$; ($\odot$) $\alpha = 0.1$, neutralized by NaOH. (The Bu_4N^+ ion is assumed to remain unbound to the polyanion.)

With increasing α, hydrate shells of ionized groups will eventually overlap at $\alpha = 0.3$ and water is progressively oriented by the cooperative effect of neighboring charges. At high α, the rigid charged rod model becomes applicable.

For these conditions, Ikegami considered the field and dielectric saturation (cf. Conway et al. [51]) to be given in the simplest case by

$$E = \frac{-2\alpha e}{\epsilon_E \lambda r} \tag{147}$$

for distance r from the rod and line density of charge $= \alpha e/\lambda$. At

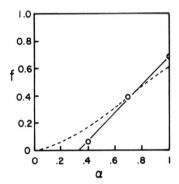

Fig. 32. Relation between function f of bound Na^+ and α.

α = 1, the condition for the boundary of hydration water affected by
the field to an extent kT in energy is calculated to be 4.3 Å. This
is similar to the cut-off region evaluated by the more rigorous numerical calculation of Conway et al. [51] for the variation of ϵ_E
with E at a polyion (see Sect. IV.F). Actually, the limit for defining the hydration region in terms of relative modification of the properties of water should probably be at least the H-bond energy of ca.
10 kT rather than simply the average thermal energy in two translational modes.

The binding of hydration water and hydrated counter-ions to a
linear charged chain bears some similarity to the question of the
binding of iodine and I_3^- to amylose. The latter problem was treated
by Rawlings and Schneider [113] in terms of competitive adsorption
on a linear chain, and an exact solution for the binding isotherm was
obtained by a matrix calculation under conditions where nearest
neighbor interactions were significant. The mathematical treatment
is applicable to competitive solvent substitution adsorption at linear
polyions.

The surface of a polyion resembles, in "one dimension," the situation in two dimensions at a colloidal electrolyte micelle where
similar ion association and hydration effects arise.

In the case of a colloidal electrolyte, the effects of various counter-
ions (Li^+, K^+, Cs^+, Me_4N^+, Et_4N^+, n-Pr_4N^+) on the critical micelle concentration of dodecyl sulfate were investigated by Mukerjee et al.
[114]. The ion association and the structure of the micellar double-
layer determines the stability of the micelle and hence the magnitude
of the critical micelle concentration. It is concluded that it is the
interaction of the hydrated counter-ion with the micelle that is the

critical factor, and ions with smaller hydration radii favor greater interaction, and produce lower degrees of dissociation and more compact double layers. In the case of R_4N^+ ions, hydrophobic bonding with the interface of the micelle is the dominant factor.

The preference of anionic ion exchangers for cations of small hydration radius (and larger valence) was also noted (cf. Mukerjee's conclusions on ion association with micelles, [114]) by Tombalakian, Yeh, and Graydon [115].

The hydration of micelles was also estimated by Mukerjee [116] from viscosity data by extrapolation of reduced viscosity to the critical micelle concentration; calculations based on the primary hydration of charged groups gave only fair agreement with experiment.

X. HYDRATION AND SEDIMENTATION BEHAVIOR OF POLYIONS

Ion binding and hydration are also important factors in determining the sedimentation and diffusion behavior of macroions [117]. Schachman and Katz [118] dealt with the general case of a sedimenting macromolecule which binds salt ions and water in some proportion to their relative concentrations in the solution. Usually an excess of salt ions and/or water is bound over and above that corresponding to proportional binding (zero surface excess).

The partial molar volume of the hydrodynamically significant unit is the weighted sum of the partial molar volumes of the components, viz.,

$$M_h \bar{v}_h = M_p \bar{v}_p + (\alpha + Kn_w)M_w \bar{v}_w + kn_s M_s \bar{v}_s \qquad (148)$$

where subscripts h, p, w, and s refer to the hydrodynamic units involved in the sedimentation process, the polyion or protein itself, water, and salt, respectively. n_w and n_s are the total number of moles of water and salt in the solution, $\bar{v}$'s are partial specific volumes, and M's are the molecular weights, i.e., $M\bar{v}$ are partial molar volume terms. k is a proportionality constant such that kn_s is equal to the number of bound moles of salt and α is the preferentially bound water (moles per mole protein). Upon introduction of the molecular weight M_h of the hydrodynamic unit, viz.,

$$M_h = M_p + (kn_w + \alpha)M_w \rho + k_{ns}M_s \qquad (149)$$

where ρ is the density of the medium determining the sedimentation force, Eq. (148) becomes, for low macroion concentration,

$$M_h(1 - \overline{v}_h\rho) = M(1 - \overline{v}_r\rho) + \alpha M_w(1 - \overline{v}_w\rho) \tag{150}$$

This equation formally expresses all the specific effects of solvent on the buoyancy of the protein; the preferential solvation of the particle by water in relation to the preferential binding of salt ions is equally well described by assigning a negative value to α.

The general expression for the sedimentation coefficient S of the hydrodynamic unit (macroion + bound water and ions) is given by

$$S\eta N_A(f/\eta) = M_p + \alpha M_w - (M_p\overline{v}_p + M_w\alpha\overline{v}_w)\rho \tag{151}$$

where f/η is the intrinsic frictional coefficient, N_A is Avogedro's number, and η is the viscosity of the medium.

S may be determined in a series of solutions of increasing density ρ. If f/η and other parameters are independent of ρ, a plot of $S\eta$ vs. ρ will be linear with an intercept on the ρ axis at

$$\rho_h = \frac{M_p + M_w\alpha}{M_p\overline{v}_p + \alpha M_w\overline{v}_w} \tag{152}$$

If M_r is not known, the numerator and denominator of the right-hand side of Eq. (152) may be divided by M_r giving

$$\rho_h = \frac{1 + A}{\overline{v}_p + A\overline{v}_w} \tag{153}$$

where

$$A = \alpha M_w/M_p \tag{154}$$

The quantity A is evidently the preferential hydration in terms of excess water per gram protein. If $S\eta$ is not linear in ρ, ultracentrifuge data alone cannot show which of the parameters in Eq. (151) are varying, e.g., change of axial ratio, M_p, or $\overline{v}_p$, or if preferential hydration of the macroion would cause curvature in the $S\eta$-ρ plot.

XI. VISCOSITY AND VISCOELASTIC BEHAVIOR

As in the case of simple ions, hydration determines the hydrodynamic properties of polymer molecules or ions so that the solvation of polyions influences their rheological behavior. As an example of such effects we refer briefly to the work of Nishida [119] who investigated mechanical relaxation effects in concentrated solutions of sodium carboxymethyl cellulose by means of measurements of the dynamic viscoelastic modulus at mainly 500 Hz over 0-50°C. The dependence of rigidity and energy absorption on temperature indicated two kinds of relaxation processes, each of which was affected individually by urea, ethanol, neutral salts, and dioxane. The behavior was interpreted in terms of interaction of the polyions, their hydration shells, and H-bonds. Two activation energies for static viscous flow were observed which support the binary relaxation behavior.

Viscosity studies were also conducted by Woodside and Eisenberg [120] on $(CH_2-CH_2SO_3H)_n$ with regard to polymer phase separation and hydration. The dependence of the viscosity on the relative hydration radius of the counter-ions was interpreted in terms of hydration and specific counter-ion binding.

XII. HYDRATION OF POLYELECTROLYTES OF BIOCHEMICAL SIGNIFICANCE

A. Introduction

The unique* properties of water, which at all times has presumably been closely associated with the molecular evolution of biopolymers, seems to be manifested to a greater or lesser degree in the structure and function of many biopolymers. For example, few proteins can reversibly be completely dehydrated without changes of structure (denaturation) or loss (partial or complete) of any biological activity they may possess. Large single crystals of proteins are intrinsically hydrated [121] and solid proteins, in general, not only bind water but do so in preference to other components of the solvent [109]. The point has been well put by Lauffer [122]: "One of the serious obstacles to the understanding of the physical properties of proteins and other biological materials is the absence of adequate means for assessing quantitatively the role of hydration." While this statement was made in 1946 and appreciable advances have been made since that time by the various approaches described in this review, its cogence in regard to the understanding of molecular biochemical processes is not diminished. Indeed the highly selective nature of many processes with regard to the nature of the ions or

*Contrast the interesting and curious title of Dorsey's book [123] "The Properties of Ordinary Water Substance" written at a time when the special properties of water were less clearly realized. (Author's emphasis.)

ionized centers (e.g., in cholineesterase activity) involved, calls for a still more detailed understanding of the competive hydration and ion association processes which take place.

Polyelectrolytes of biochemical significance are both anionic (DNA, RNA, hyaluronic acid) and cationic (myosin) while the large body of proteins and enzyme proteins are polyampholytes capable of existing as polycationically or polyanionically ionized macromolecules or, more generally, at neutral pH as polyzwitter-ions.

We shall consider now some of the work in which evaluation of the hydration of biopolyelectrolytes has been made. A useful monograph, edited by Kayushin [184], covers recent Russian work on the role and properties of water in macromolecular systems of biological interest. Further details are referred to elsewhere in this review.

B. Dielectric Studies with Polyions and Polyampholytes

For application of dielectric methods to the study of solvation of proteins either the axial ratio must be known independently (e.g., from flow birefringence in suitable cases, light scattering, sedimentation, or x-ray diffraction) of the frictional ratio, or the hydration must be known independently and a method found to decide if the molecules are in the form of oblate or prolate ellipsoids.*

The dielectric properties of proteins in aqueous electrolyte solutions were first investigated at radio frequencies in a number of important papers by Oncley [124]. In 1938 he showed that above 1 MHz the dielectric constant falls with frequency to a value characteristic of the free water present [125]. Horse oxy- and methaemoglobin, lysozyme, β-lactoglobulin, bovine serum albumin, and gelatin were examined.

The experimental data were treated in terms of two Debye relaxation processes. Limiting values of the dielectric constants were approached above 10 MHz and below 0.1 MHz, and the relaxation times corresponded to the behavior of an ellipsoid of revolution approximating to the shape of the macromolecules concerned. The relaxation time constants are in the ratio of the axial ratio of this ellipsoid. Oncley estimated the amounts of water which must be assumed to rotate with the protein and hence would be bound to its surface. Values agreed with data obtained by other methods (viz., 0.2-0.5 g

*These representations of protein shape are, in most cases, idealizations. Recent x-ray diffraction analyses coupled with analytical information on amino acid sequences give, in certain cases, e.g., lysozyme, better knowledge of the shapes and structure of proteins which are often more complex in form than would correspond to simple prolate or oblate ellipsoids. Also the hydration may be relatively localized at certain regions.

H_2O/g protein). In similar microwave studies at 1000 MHz another
relaxation effect was observed by Buchanan et al. [126] which gave
dielectric decrements greater than those observed at lower frequencies by Oncley.

As in the treatment for simple ions [40], Buchanan et al. [126]
considered the so-called irrotationally bound water. The protein
plus the bound water is regarded as a cavity of low dielectric constant and the bound water is considered not to contribute to the
dipole orientation polarization.

The case of a random distribution of cavities of low dielectric
constant (ϵ_{solute}) in a medium of high dielectric constant (ϵ_{H_2O})
gives for the dielectric constant ϵ of the mixture

$$\epsilon - \epsilon_{H_2O} = \frac{b\phi}{1 - \phi} (\epsilon_{solute} - \epsilon) \frac{\epsilon_{solute}}{\epsilon_{H_2O}} \ll 1 \qquad (155)$$

where ϕ is the volume fraction of solute. For low concentrations

$$\epsilon \doteq \epsilon_{H_2O} - b\phi(\epsilon_{H_2O} - \epsilon_{solute}) \qquad (156)$$

b depends on the axial ratio of the ellipsoidal particle; b was plotted
for various molecular axial ratios.

The dielectric decrement δ is given (cf. the case for simple ion
solutions) by

$$\epsilon_s = \epsilon_{H_2O} - \delta c \qquad (157)$$

and

$$\delta = \frac{b}{100} [v(\epsilon_{H_2O} - \epsilon_{\infty,protein}) + w_{irr}(\epsilon_{H_2O} - \epsilon_{\infty,H_2O})] \qquad (158)$$

where c is the concentration in gram %, v the partial specific volume
of the protein, and ϵ_∞ the high frequency value of the dielectric constant of the protein (= 2) or of water (5.5 ± 1), as indicated. From δ,
the value of w_{irr}, the irrotationally bound water, was calculated.

In order to derive the true hydration from the irrotationally bound
water, w_{irr}, the total water bound, but not irrotationally bound, must
be determined. Two types of water were considered [126]: that adjacent to charges and that associated with polar groups.

Water Adjacent to Charged Groups. Previous studies by Haggis,
Hasted, and Buchanan [40] on simpler inorganic and organic ions
suggest that water round protein groups would not be irrotationally
bound if these groups were in an aqueous environment (the bonds

between such charged groups and water molecules have energies of ca. 14 kcal/mole due to ion-dipole interactions). Thus if charged groups protrude from the protein structure so that they are in a water environment and other adjacent molecules form other bonds only to free water molecules, the adjacent water molecules will be bound but not irrotationally bound. Water at anionic centers will tend to be bound with less rotational freedom than at cationic sites due to the orientation of the two OH groups about the negative charge.

Water Adjacent to Uncharged Polar Groups. Protruding polar groups in the aqueous environment will neither bind nor irrotationally bind water molecules. If, however, water molecules are shared* between two polar groups, e.g., $\diagdown$NH, $\diagdown$CO, by hydrogen bonding, then they can be bound irrotationally. If charged or uncharged groups lie, however, within the protein molecule, adjacent water molecules will tend to be both bound and irrotationally bound [40].

Estimates of the irrotationally bound water may be lower than the true total hydration by an amount corresponding to the maximum number of water molecules adjacent to charged groups (Table 13). X-Ray scattering results also allow the hydration to be estimated if assumptions about the axial ratio (prolate or oblate ellipsoids) are made. The data of Ritland et al. [127] are shown in Table 14 for the same proteins as those discussed above.

For egg albumin and β-lactoglobulin, the dielectric measurements do not support the oblate ellipsoid structures for the molecules (axial ratios 1/4 and 1/5) so that these proteins are elongated as indicated by Oncley.

In the case of haemoglobin [128], the ionizable groups are mainly at the surface and since the irrotationally bound water shows little change over the pH range 2.1-11.7, while nonsolvent water decreases on each side of the isoelectric point, it appears that this water is associated with polar groups within the protein molecule set back from the surface exposed to the solvent. Restricted rotation of water molecules sorbed in native and partially dried collagen is indicated also by the NMR studies of Berendsen [129,182] who found water molecules oriented in chains along the fiber axis.

Similar dielectric measurements on albumin and some amino acids and peptides were reported by Grant [130]. The relaxation time and activation energy for the relaxation process were evaluated and discussed in terms of hydration by bound water. The rotation of other polar groups on the protein structure, which has 52 glutamic acid and 20 lysine residues, was also considered as an explanation of the relaxation behavior. It is difficult to interpret the dielectric

*This provides a basis for H-bond cross-linking in protein structures and is thus of great importance.

Table 13

Maximum Water Adjacent to Charged Groups in Some Proteins (pH 7)[a]

| Protein | Residues and coordination numbers (for H_2O) assumed | | | | Mol. wt. | g H_2O/g protein adjacent to charges[b] |
	COO⁻ (6)	NH_3^+ (3)	$NH \cdot C^+ (NH_2)_2$ (5) (arginine)	Histidine (50% dissociated)		
Horse met-haemoglobin	53	38	14	36	66,700	0.14
Bovine serum albumin	92	60	25	17	69,000	0.23
Egg albumin	51	20	15	7	45,000	0.18
β-Lacto-globulin	59	29	6	4	35,500	0.24
Lysozyme	17	6	13	1	14,700	0.23
Gelatin	49	12	20	2	38,700	0.20

[a]From Buchanan, Harris, Hasted, and Robinson [126].
[b]The limits of hydration of these proteins as a function of possible axial ratios in the range 4-0-1/4 were also evaluated.

Table 14

X-Ray Scattering Results of Ritland et al. [127]

Protein	Axial ratio ± 20%	Hydration, g H_2O/g protein ± 50%
Bovine haemoglobin	2.1	0.28
	1/2.4	0.20
Bovine serum albumin	2.7	0.42
	1/3.4	0.30
Egg albumin	2.9	0.15
	1/4	0
β-Lactoglobulin	3.6	0.20
	1/5.5	0
Lysozyme	2.3	0.32
	1/2.8	0.25

behavior uniquely in terms of hydration water. In the case of amino acids and peptides, the dielectric relaxation is governed by the rupture or distortion of one hydrogen bond linking the solute molecule to its neighboring water molecule. Since the energy needed to achieve this was found to decrease with the higher peptides, it was suggested that the whole peptide molecule undergoes a partial rotation involving the bending of a hydrogen bond rather than its complete rupture. The energetics of bending H-bonds were considered by Pople [131] and by Conway [132].

Li and Schwan [133] made measurements similar to those of Buchanan et al. [126] on haemoglobin from 0.5-1000 MHz. The dispersion of ϵ occurs in two regions, < 1 to 5 MHz and from 8 to 600 MHz. The dielectric decrement values are shown below for two concentrations:

	100 MHz	300 MHz	600 MHz	900 MHz
5%	0.79	0.97	1.23	1.29
20%	0.71	0.8	0.86	0.88

At low frequencies, the decrement values approach 0.8.

The bound water and protein substrate is considered as a joint dielectric entity with a dielectric constant ϵ_c. This quantity, the measured value ϵ for the suspension, and the value ϵ_s for the electrolyte solution are related (compare Eq. 158) by

$$\frac{\epsilon + \epsilon_s}{\epsilon + 2\epsilon_s} = \phi \frac{\epsilon_e - \epsilon_s}{\epsilon_e + 2\epsilon_s} \tag{159}$$

where ϕ is again the volume fraction occupied by the hydrated macro-molecules. The above equation is the equivalent in dielectric terms of an equation of Maxwell for the conductivity of a suspension of spheres; it is applicable at frequencies which are high enough that capacitative currents are greater than ohmic ones. The equation can be used to calculate ϵ_e for the macromolecule. Assumptions must be made, however, about the hydration of the protein in order to convert the known specific volume of the haemoglobin and its concentration into the appropriate value for ϕ. Calculated ϵ_e values were obtained for two values of the hydration 0.3 and 0.4 g/g Hb. ϵ_e undergoes a substantial change as frequency varies from 10 to 1000 MHz. The extent of apparent binding of the water depends on the frequency.

The frequency dependence of the dielectric constant of the hydrated molecule can reflect the following effects:

1. Polar subgroups are able to rotate at frequencies where the whole molecule is unable to respond due to its longer relaxation time (the subgroups would have to be 100 times smaller than the whole molecule).

2. The water bound to the protein surface undergoes a corresponding change in dielectric properties. This is supported by the observed concentration dependence of the relaxation behavior.

The dielectric constant of the hydration shell can be calculated from the ϵ_e and assumed values for the protein itself ϵ_p. Thus

$$\frac{\epsilon_e - \epsilon_s}{\epsilon_e + 2\epsilon_s} = \left(\frac{R}{R + d}\right)^3 \frac{\epsilon_p - \epsilon_s}{\epsilon_p + 2\epsilon_s}$$

where R is the "radius" of the protein and d the mean thickness of the hydrate shell (the equation is based on a spherical shape for the particle). (For other shapes, the factor 2 in the denominator is replaced by another factor [134]). The dispersion behavior for bound water is compared with that of free water and ice (Fig. 33). ϵ_s can be evaluated as $f(\epsilon_p)$ for various assumed hydration values using values of ϵ_e derived from the measurements.

The degree of hydration of several amino acids and of serum and ovalbumin was also determined by Kazanskii et al. [135] by means of dielectric permittivity measurements at 8930 MHz. The bound water was derived in terms of the axial ratio in the usual way [124-

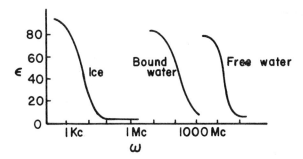

Fig. 33. Comparison of dielectric dispersion behavior for bound water with
that for free water and ice (schematic).

126]. With glycine, α-alanine, and β-alanine, however, the bound
water could be determined more definitely and approximately 4.6,
4.5, and 4.1 moles H_2O per mole of amino acid were found, respectively.

The above methods suffer the disadvantage that only the over-all
hydration of the protein can usually be evaluated. The high frequency
relaxation gives a little more information insofar as irrotationally
bound water must presumably be held at ionic sites but specific types
of sites for various kinds of binding of water are difficult to identify
unambiguously. Further work of a spectroscopic kind (see below for
the case of cross-linked polyelectrolytes) would be required to eluci-
date these problems further.

While macromolecular rotation and hydration can account for the
dielectric properties of proteins, linear polyelectrolytes such as
DNA, PVPBuBr, and hyaluronic acid exhibit large dielectric increments at low frequencies that cannot be accounted for in terms of
molecular rotation. If the increment for DNA were due to rotation
about the long axis (the relaxation time would actually be the wrong
order of magnitude), which is the only type of rotation which could
give a dispersion in the mega-Hertz region, the dielectric increment
should increase when the molecules are oriented in a direction perpendicular to the electric field. Jacobson [63] measured the streaming effect in the dielectric behavior of DNA but found no increase in
the low frequency increment (it, in fact, decreased slightly). For
such long polyelectrolytes, the molecular weight, axial ratios, and
hydration cannot therefore be derived from dielectric measurements
as they can in the case of compact proteins [126,133]. Other explanations of the polarization behavior therefore have to be considered.

Internal rotation of molecular groups (cf. Grant [130]) gives too small an effect and should not be much different in the polymer than in the corresponding monomer. Proton transfer polarization in H-bridges has also been considered [100]. The large dielectric effects observed with polyelectrolytes are more likely to be explicable in terms of Maxwell-Wagner dispersion [136] arising through the association of counter-ions near to the polyion which causes regions of high and low conductivity to be set up locally in the solution. The effect does not occur significantly with proteins, presumably because the charge density is never so high and a highly concentrated ionic atmosphere does not arise in that case.

Because some polyelectrolytes exhibit a streaming dielectric effect and others do not, Jacobson was led to postulate an alternative explanation of the high increment in the case of DNA in terms of a long range modification of the water lattice by the DNA ions. Specific coupling between the polyion structure and the water lattice was assumed to be the essential factor depending on the degree of geometrical similarity between the polyion structure and that of water. A substantial "lattice-ordering" hydration was considered, extending over quite long distances (500-1000 Å!) from the polyion chain. The effects were regarded as being supported by viscosity and osmotic observations on the effects of added salts on these properties in the case of DNA. This is not the case, however, since at infinite dilution there is little effect of added salts on the intrinsic dimensions of DNA and the large salt effects at finite concentrations were shown by Butler, Conway, and James [71] to be due to intersegment interactions through shared counter-ions (second electroviscous effect [137]).

Since ice has a dielectric dispersion in the range 10^2-10^4 Hz and water ca. 10^{10} Hz, it was supposed by Jacobson that the high increment for polyelectrolytes arose from the presence of relatively large regions of "icelike" water having a much longer relaxation time than that of free bulk water. The absence of a streaming effect on the dielectric behavior was held to be consistent with the model proposed since the lattice-ordered hydration region would itself exhibit dielectric properties to a large extent independent of the orientation of the main polyion chain [5].

Since, however, the thermodynamic solvation behavior of a number of polyions (discussed elsewhere in this review) indicates only a relatively thin shell of modified water, it appears that the dielectric effects are better treated in terms of Maxwell-Wagner dispersion than long-range hydration which would in any case imply unusually low entropies of solvation and large volume effects. However, the electrostatic theory, it must be recalled, allows rather longer range field-effects on the solvent by a rodlike polyion than are possible with isolated spherical ions, even when they are polyvalent (see Sects. IV.A-D).

Dielectric studies on DNA in the solid phase were carried out by Mesnard and Vasilescu [138] under various controlled humidities. The dispersion was characterized by an extended range of long relaxation times which were attributed to interfacial effects associated with ionic movements. The bound Na^+ counter-ions were regarded as being able to move from one site on a chain to another, causing large polarization. The influence of the sorbed water was attributed to modifications of the mobility and association of the counter-ions rather than to the hydrated water molecules themselves. In this respect the results support the view that Jacobson's observations are more likely to be due to Maxwell-Wagner effects than to hydration since the behavior discussed by Mesnard et al. is similar to a Maxwell-Wagner dispersion effect.

C. Thermodynamic Evaluation of Protein Hydration

A definition of protein hydration amenable to exact thermodynamic analysis was considered by Lauffer [139] and applications to association-dissociation processes in complex proteins were developed. It was shown how hydration can be measured by weighing, at equilibrium, a protein solution in an ideally semipermeable sack suspended in an appropriate multicomponent solution.

In principle, a number of other methods described in Sects. II.C, V.B, and V.C may also be used for evaluation of protein hydration, but the interpretation of results is more complex than in the case of linear polyions.

D. Hydrophobic and Structural Hydration Effects at Macroions

The role of "structured" water in the hydration of nonelectrolytes such as Ar and of hydrophobic ions such as R_4N^+ has been referred to earlier. Frank and Evans [35] called these regions "icebergs,"* but this description must not be taken too literally. They are characterized kinetically by enhanced NMR solvent-lattice relaxation times [39] and by decreases of molar fluidity of water by the solutes. However, at the small ions, these regions cannot exist over a sufficiently large distance for the ice-lattice structure to exist really significantly since such structures would require rings of at least

*These effects were first recognized by Everett and Wynne-Jones in 1941 [21] in their studies on ionization of alkylamines where unusual heat capacities and entropies of ionization were found.

six water molecules extending out from the ion. More extensive
lattice ordering hydration has, however, been proposed by Jacobson [62,63] for various biopolyions, as discussed above.

In a more recent and important paper, Klotz [140] provided interesting evidence for similar "iceberg" effects in protein hydration.
The ionization of the azomercurial group

$$-Hg-\langle O \rangle-N=N-\langle O \rangle-N(CH_3)_2$$

attached to mercaptyl groups in bovine serum albumin was studied.
The purpose of this experiment was to introduce a group, the ionization of which could be studied in an isolated manner (direct titration
of most other intrinsic groups on the protein structure cannot be
studied in this manner since their surface concentrations are too
great) but under the general influence of groups of other kinds. The
surprising result found by Klotz was that the slope of the titration
curve of the bound dye was the same as that of the dye attached to
a small SH-molecule, e.g., cysteine, and the titration curve was not
stretched out on the pH scale due to interaction effects as is usually
the case with other intrinsic ionizable groups or in the case of linear
polyions. However, the pK is lowered from ca. 3.4 to 1.7.

The effect is not due to masking by the protein macromolecular
structure since under denaturing conditions (strong aq. urea, which
unmasks other groups in proteins) the pK of the $-N-(CH_3)_2$ group
is indistinguishable from that for the same group when the compound
is bound to cysteine.

It was concluded that the azomercurial $-N(CH_3)_2$ group is in an
aqueous environment at the interface of the protein but not a normal
one. Thus the lowering of pK was attributed to the presence of hydrating water about the protein in an "ice-like" condition. Addition
of a proton to the N center in such an environment might be energetically more difficult than in ordinary water due to the necessity
for disruption of the lattice cage (but the entropy of ionization would
be less negative; cf. ΔH and ΔS compensation effects [25]).

Similar reasons may account for the volume behavior of proteins
in aqueous solutions. Thus, McMeekin and Marshall [141] showed
that volumes of nineteen proteins computed from the sum of the
specific volumes of constituent amino acids agreed well with the
experimental values. This is at first sight surprising since electrostriction at ionized groups is not allowed for [99,142]. For
human serum albumin, for example, electrostriction should cause
a decrease of volume of 1800 cm^3/mole protein; for ovalbumin

730 cm³, and for β-lactoglobulin 830 cm³. Since these decreases
are not observed, it was concluded that a structure-forming effect
compensated the electrostriction. Thus on freezing water the volume
change is ca. 2 cm³/mole. For serum albumin, this compensation
of 1800 cm³/mole amounts to a hydration of the protein of 20% by
weight, a figure in agreement with the experimentally determined
values (see above [101,102]), based on self-diffusion of water where
uncertainties about axial ratio effects are minimized.

These ideas of Klotz [140] have led to the recognition of important
interaction effects in proteins arising from so-called hydrophobic
bonds, i.e., binding of protein groups, chains, or subunits in a "pas-
sive" way on account of elimination of lattice ordered water of hydration which such groups would have in an unassociated state, with
assistance by van der Waals forces. The effects can be looked upon
as a diminution of the surface free energy (surface tension effects)
of water around hydrophobic groups as the total exposure in terms
of protein chain surface area is decreased.

Similar compensation effects between structural volume factors
occur with tetraalkylammonium ions which, from the point of view
of additivity of volumes, form ideal solutions in water [10,69]. The
structural increase in volume of the solvent about the ions just com-
pensates the cavity volume and any electrostriction (small in the
case of the R_4N^+ ions).

$\Delta H/\Delta S$ compensation effects associated with substitutional adsorption (with respect to bound water) of choline-esterase inhibitors at the
enzyme were found by Belleau [143]. The stronger the binding the
more positive was the entropy change, due presumably to release
of "iceberg" water from the enzyme interface. Similar effects occur
at the Hg electrode interface in water where competitive adsorption
between water and other solutes was studied by Conway and Gordon
[144] as a function of the electrode potential and surface charge
density of the metal.

Horowitz and Fenickel [145] considered the diffusion of amides,
alcohols, and ureas in cells in relation to the possible icelike regions
of hydration water about proteins and other biologically significant
structures. Solute specificities were found which could be related
to the nature of the polar group. The effects are obviously related
to Wang's treatment [101,102] for self-diffusion of water itself
(see Sect. VIII).

Water-protein interactions in relation to secondary protein structure and conformation were considered by Warner [146]. They will
also probably be of importance in conformational changes in allo-
steric enzymes.

Hydrophobic bonds also play a role in association of, and confor-

mational changes in, large macromolecules, e.g., in proteins and
their subunits. Even though many of the association reactions are
accompanied by increases of enthalpy (characteristic of hydrophobic
bond formation), they are nevertheless favored [147] by related large
increases of entropy (compensation effect commonly encountered for
various processes in the aqueous medium). An example of such association is the protein of tobacco mosaic virus [148,149].

Not only is the hydration of protein chains an important factor in
determining optimum conformations which are adopted, but hydration
can also determine energy transfer at protein interfaces. Rosen and
Ahnstrom [150], working with proteins conjugated with dye molecules,
showed that the energy transfer between photoexcited dye molecules
and the protein was substantially diminished with increasing uptake
of hydration water. The effect was of the same order as that expected from molecular expansion of the protein structure upon sorption of hydration water but was, however, far less drastic than the
change of biological radio-sensitivity caused by water associated
with biologically active proteins.

A further aspect of the role of hydrophobic bonds is [151,152]
the stabilization of conformations of biopolymers such as polypeptides (cf. Ref. 140). For example, formation of an hydrophobic bond
between two neighboring residues on an α-helix can stabilize the
helical structure. In the case of α-poly-L-alanine, the β-CH_3 group
of an ith residue can form an hydrophobic bond with the α-CH on
the (i + 3)th residue providing similar stabilization of the α-helix.
In the helix-coil transition, the possibility of hydrophobic bonding
has also been considered [153] in regard to poly-L-alanine.

Privalov et al. [154] made calorimetric estimations of heat capacities as a function of temperature for a number of hydrated biopolymers: DNA, procollagen, serum albumin, ovalbumin, and haemoglobin. The hydration, in all cases, was greater in the denatured
state than in the native materials. This result was considered to
be in agreement with the model of Kauzmann [155] but not with that
of Klotz [140] (see above), based on hydrophobic bonding.

A mathematical model for biopolymer hydration was considered
by Sedykh and Sedykh [156] in terms of pH dependence, macromolecular asymmetry, chemical composition, energy, and the number of
"bonds" participating in the hydration, together with the coordination
number for the water molecules bound at various centers. The values
calculated for an oriented monolayer and a less oriented, broader
region were in good agreement with the experimental estimates available for proteins, e.g., serum albumin, ovalbumin, and cytoplasmic
proteins. It is doubtful, however, if more than a broad estimate of

the hydration can be made by this approach owing to the rather specific nature of hydration around ionized organic structures which is already found with low molecular weight materials [11-13].

E. State of Hydration Water in Biochemical Systems

It has been suggested that the physical state of water near biologically significant structures, e.g., proteins, nucleic acids, and cell membranes, may be qualitatively different from that in normal water [63]. E.g., Forslind [157] has proposed that water near protein molecules may be in a state "between" that of liquid and solid, and Jacobson [63,158] supported this view by x-ray, dielectric, and NMR measurements on macromolecular solutions [158]. Szent-Gyorgyi [159] postulated icelike structures of water surrounding proteins, and Klotz et al. [140] supported and developed this concept. Further, the same ideas were envisaged by Jacobson with regard to hydration of polynucleotides including DNA. Icelike regions near proteins were deduced also by Grant [130] from dielectric measurements. These ideas are strangely prescient of the role of "anomalous" or "polywater" [160,161] in biological systems or at interfaces proposed in recent discussions of this topic. Other aspects of water in living cell and model systems were considered by Ling [162] who also pointed out the role of exclusion (distribution) of nonelectrolyte molecules between intra- and extracellular fluids. This effect may arise from salting-out by polyionic or polyampholytic substances in the cell as discussed earlier in this review. Analogous effects, reminiscent of salting-out, were noted by Beeman et al. [163] who concluded that serum albumin is surrounded by a layer of water which does not dissolve sucrose as normal water does.

Jacobson, Anderson, and Arnold [62] noted that the NMR lines for haemocyanin, egg albumin, and starch were almost identical with that for water, consistent with a relatively low degree of hydration also indicated by other methods (e.g., the dielectric dispersion). In the case of DNA, however, there is marked line broadening and a smaller peak area. Jacobson et al. concluded* that this was due to the lattice ordered hydration effect referred to above. Addition of salts causes the NMR line shape to revert to the more normal behavior usually found for water. It was supposed [164] that this was caused by a decrease of hydration caused by contraction and consequently less good fit in the water lattice (cf. Ref. 165). However, there is no evidence that salt effects are associated with short-range molecular contraction [71].

---

*Alternative explanations of these observations have been discussed by Berendsen [182].

Diminution of hydration may be due rather to cation association which diminishes the local field and leads to a change both in the over-all charge density and hence the longer range hydration effects and also the short-range hydration due to local neutralization of polyion charge at ion-binding sites.

Alkylation of DNA with N-mustard was found [166] to cause a reduction in buoyant density. The effect depends on the amount of mustard bound and not on the base composition. The decrease of relative density was attributed to increase of hydration due in part to the development of N^+ centers on the DNA arising from the bound N-mustard structure. The effects of pH support this interpretation. The major site of N-mustard attack is at the N-7 position of guanine [167].

The view that "cell hydration" [168] is determined by water adsorption on intracellular protein rather than by osmotic effects was examined by Cope [168] in relation to the Bradley isotherm for protein hydration. The possibility of control of cell hydration and water balance by conformational changes in protein structures requires further examination. The general question of the role of hydration in the structure of living matter, through ion-solvent interactions, was explored by Santamaria [169] in a qualitative way.

F. Calorimetric Studies

Few calorimetric studies on hydration of macroions have been performed and the existing enthalpy data is derived mainly from equilibrium sorption studies over a range of temperatures [84]. Mrevlishvili and Privalov [187] have carried out direct heat capacity measurements on collagen, procollagen, haemoglobin, and DNA, and they established that firmly bound water, associated with the macromolecules at low degrees of sorption, exhibited low heat capacity. Further sorption led to uptake of less firmly bound structural water giving a much higher heat capacity contribution which also increased with temperature, indicating a progressive local melting of the structural water. As in the case of simple ions in water, and with ionization of acids and bases, the partial molar heat capacity gives [21] a measure of the extent to which water around the ionic centers has become more or less "icelike." This term is used here in the sense that the greater is the degree of H-bonding in the structure around a molecule or ion, the larger is the amount of heat required per mole to break down or "melt" the structured regions. Correspondingly, centers that break down the local structure of water usually provide a negative contribution to the partial molar heat capacity. Further work is required on applications of heat capacity measurements to simpler macroions in water and other solvents. Extensions of the work on biological polymers were made by Andronikashvili, Mrevlishvili, and Privalov [188] to tissue material itself, and these authors made some indirect estimates of the heat and entropy changes associated with changes of the condition of intracellular water as the temperature was varied ($-22°$ to $-0.5°$ C). The derived entropy and enthalpy change with increasing temperature for water in the tissue material was much lower than that for fusion of ice. This was interpreted in terms of ordering of water adjacent to intracellular structures. Although the thermodynamics of the treatment employed in this work does not appear rigorous, the observations are of considerable interest in regard to the speculations which are now extant about a special role of water in macromolecular and biological systems.

XIII. INFRARED SPECTROSCOPIC STUDIES ON MACROION HYDRATION

For dilute aqueous solutions of simple salts, the interpretation of infrared spectroscopic information obtained in early work [170,171] is rendered difficult on account of uncertainties in assignment of infrared and Raman bands. In particular, the main question exists whether the "continuum" or the "mixture" model, with discrete states of H-bonding in the liquid water lattice, can be supported by spectroscopic evidence. Despite recent conflicting evidence [172-174] on this question (reviewed and discussed elsewhere [172,171]), it seems that the latest information obtained by laser-Raman spectroscopy [173] on water itself supports at least a "two-state" condition of water with a fraction of free O—H bonds dependent on the temperature. This fraction may be modified by the presence of ions which either diminish ("structure-breaking") or enhance ("structure-promoting," e.g., in the case of R_4N^+ ions) the time-average molecular cluster size [7] in water and cause related changes in the NMR spin-lattice relaxation time [39].

Although dilute solutions of polyions have not been studied in the infrared, important spectroscopic work on polyelectrolyte hydration has been carried out by Zundel and reported in a number of papers (e.g., see Refs. 86-88, 175, 176) and a monograph [177]. Since, in the latter, a description of the work and conclusions is given in great detail, only a brief résumé will be presented here.

In the work of Zundel, hydration of thin polyelectrolyte membrane ion-exchangers was studied by infrared observations of the progressive sorption of water vapor. Since most of the materials were in the acid or salt forms, and only a relatively small uptake of "solvent" was involved, the spectroscopic observations give information mainly on the hydration of the polyion charge centers in the presence of closely associated counter-ions or H_3O^+, which are themselves progressively hydrated. The conditions are thus similar to those employed in the thermodynamic sorption studies of Glueckauf and Kitt [84]. The method has the advantage that spectroscopic effects due to secondary, long-range interactions in liquid water, which are difficult to interpret, are avoided.

Working with polysulfonates and selenonates ($-SO_3^-$, $-SeO_3^-$ charge centers on the polymer matrix), Zundel and co-workers first investigated the spectra of a variety of unhydrated polymer salts and established the effects of associated cations on the anion spectrum. Cation association occurs unsymmetrically at $-SO_3^-$ and SeO_3^- anion centers, leading to loss of degeneracy of the antisymmetric vibrations [176]. This effect is important in following the hydration of cation-polyanion association centers and also depends on the assignment of changes of band frequencies in the water molecule itself as it becomes bound. If a water molecule becomes bound to other O centers by H-bonds, the bands $\bar{\nu}_1$ and $\bar{\nu}_3$ of the stretching vibrations are shifted towards smaller wave numbers while the $\bar{\nu}_2$ band associated with the "scissor" bending vibrational mode is shifted toward larger wave numbers compared with the wave numbers for corresponding modes in free H_2O. These effects arise because in the former case the restoring forces for O—H motions are diminished due to the H-bonding of the H in the O—H group to another O center, while in the latter case the restoring force is enhanced by H-bonding. In liquid water these effects become very complex due to Fermi resonance and other factors [174], but by employing HOD in excess, H_2O or D_2O coupling effects between the bending overtone $2\bar{\nu}_2$ and the stretching frequencies are largely eliminated and a simpler spectrum results. In the presence of simple ions the binding associated with hydration causes characteristic infrared shifts dependent on the nature and charge of the ion [181].

Hydration affects the intramolecular bands of the anionic groups and, in polystyrene derivatives, also the vibrations of the benzene ring structure. Since the cations also strongly interact with the anion centers as they become hydrated, sorption of water results in complex changes of the spectra. Interpretation is facilitated, however, by examining a range of salts of the polyacids with cations of various radii and charges.

In the region 2000-4000 cm^{-1}, hydration changes due to the actual molecules of water of hydration are distinguished (3000-3700 cm^{-1} for H_2O: 2200-2750 cm^{-1} for D_2O). The effects associated with sorbed "solvent" can be distinguished from the background spectrum by comparison of the spectra obtained with H_2O and D_2O at various controlled humidities. The band of the O—H stretching vibration of the hydration water molecules is increasingly shifted toward lower wave numbers as the radius of the bound counter-cation in polystyrene sulfonates decreases, e.g., from Ba^{2+} to Be^{2+}, from In^{3+} to Al^{3+} and from La^{3+} to Sc^{3+}. Also, the higher is the valence of the cations, the greater are the shifts. Thus, the intense band of the OH stretching mode of hydration water depends on the nature of the cation, and the position of this band depends on the nature of the anion charge center. The molecules of hydration water are thus directly interacting with both the anionic center and the counter-cation at low degrees of sorption. The OH stretching band is, in fact, that of OH groups in the hydrogen bonds by which the water molecules are attached to the anion centers, but modified by the presence of the interacting anions, as shown in Fig. 34.

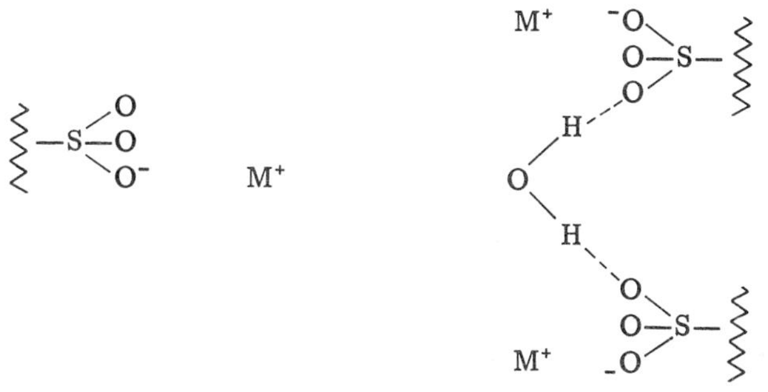

Fig. 34. Hydration of sulfonate residue in cross-linked resin (after Zundel).

The cation interaction effect tends to promote stronger H-bonding between the hydrating water molecules and the O-centers of the anionic groups because of polarizing effects which promote positive charge at the hydrogen atoms of H_2O molecules. Correspondingly, increase of the dipole moment of OH groups through H bridging to anion groups tends to increase the interaction with the cations, so that there is an effect of mutual reinforcement at low degrees of hydration. In fact, the cation-anion binding is found to be directly dependent on the degree of hydration, and even at relatively high degrees of hydration the cations are still preferentially associated with O atoms of the anionic centers on the polymer matrix, but the bond is considerably loosened.

With increasing extent of hydration of salts of polystyrenesulfonic

and polystyreneselenonic acids the position of the OH stretching band
of the water of hydration shifts progressively with relative humidity
and also with integrated extinction due to the scissor vibration. The
changes of the infrared spectrum of the bound water are greater in
going from 1 to 2 water molecules per ion than in going from 2 to 3
or more, as may be expected since the influence of the ion on the
water dipoles and on the H-bonding tendency of OH groups is attenuated.

The spectroscopic results are consistent with the thermodynamic
sorption results of Glueckauf and Kitt [84] and of Dickel and co-
workers [96,178] who found the greatest values of $-\Delta \bar{H}$ and $-\Delta \bar{S}$
for the sorption of the first H_2O molecule per ion pair than for subsequent water uptake.

With higher degrees of hydration, two and subsequently more
"layers" of water molecules become associated with the cation-
anion pairs in the polyelectrolyte structure.

With the unneutralized acids, e.g., polystyrenesulfonic acid itself,
an interesting result is that the initial stages of water sorption
($\leq 1\,H_2O$ per $-SO_3H$ group) do not remove the proton from the acid
group (as H_3O^+); this is only achieved when 2 water molecules are
available per $-SO_3H$ group so that, formally, $H_5O_2^+$ groups are
formed. Under these conditions a continuous absorption is found
below ca. 3500 cm^{-1} for OH groups, or 2600 cm^{-1} for OD groups.
In the $H_5O_2^+$ groups proton tunneling occurs but the two water molecules in this H-bonded complex retains their individuality as far as
internal molecular vibrations are concerned. This is indicated by
the fact that the extinction of the continuous absorption increases
linearly with the integrated extinction of the scissor mode. The observation of the continuous absorption is an interesting proof of the
proton tunneling mechanism proposed for H_3O^+/H_2O proton transfer
in conductance in ice and water itself [179].

Few spectroscopic studies have been carried out on linear polyelectrolytes where the water content can be varied indefinitely to
infinite dilution. However, Bradbury, Price, and Wilkinson [180]
examined the sorption of water by Li^+ and Na^+ salts of DNA by
polarized infrared absorption measurements over a range of relative humidity from 0 to 94%.

Marked changes of spectrum were observed as the water content
increased. The NaDNA was shown to have two forms, one at humidities > 90% where the bases are perpendicular to the helix axis (form B)
and the other at 70-80% humidity where the bases are tilted at an
angle not less than 13° to the helix axis (Form A). For the Li salt,
Form B exists at humidities > 60% while another form, different from

A in the case of the Na salt, exists between 44 and 56% and has the bases tilted at some 4° to the helix axis. Deuteration rates of the Li and Na salts by vapor phase exchange were very rapid, indicating that the H-atoms involved in H-bonding are completely accessible to protons and possibly to water molecules. Detailed interpretations of the mode of binding of the water, along the lines developed by Zundel and co-workers were, however, not attempted; they would, of course, present much greater difficulties than with synthetic polyelectrolyte structures owing to the complex polyfunctional nature of DNA salts where there are phosphate, deoxyribose, and purine and pyrimidine moieties constituting the structure of this macromolecule.

NMR studies, referred to earlier in this review (p. 223) have also been carried out by Migchelson, Berendsen, and Rupprecht [183] with regard to the behavior of water sorbed by DNA. The conclusions regarding chainlike arrangements of water molecules, deduced in the case of collagen [182], are applicable to DNA.

Infrared studies on water in the structure of proteins and polypeptides were made by Chirgadze, Ven'yaminov, and Zimont [185] by examining the spectrum of procollagen films at 0 and 100% relative humidity. In the "fundamental" vibration region (600-3600 cm^{-1}) the main features of the spectrum of the macromolecular material remain unchanged except for interaction effects due to the presence of water. In the overtone region the water exhibits an absorption maximum at 5150 cm^{-1} while CH and amide group vibrations cover the range 3900-5000 cm^{-1}. Sorption of water and hydration of the polypeptide can thus be progressively followed by measurements of the absorption around 5150 cm^{-1}. This peak is also completely displaced when D_2O is used as the solvating species, indicating its association with hydration processes. The infrared dichroism at this frequency allows determination of the orientation of the sorbed water with respect to the axes of the fibrils. Applications to the state of water in tissues have also been made [186].

ACKNOWLEDGMENTS

The facilities of the Universities of Southampton and Newcastle upon Tyne, where this review was written, are gratefully acknowledged. The author is also indebted to Dr. D. Schiffrin for comments and discussion on electrostatic calculations of polyion hydration considered in Section IV.B, and to Professor G. J. Hills and Dr. A. Covington for discussions on evaluation of individual ionic hydration contributions.

230 B. E. CONWAY

References

[1] J. E. Desnoyers and C. Joliecoeur, in Modern Aspects of Electrochemistry, Vol. 5 (J. O'M. Bockris and B. E. Conway, eds.), Plenum, New York, 1969, p. 1.
[2] F. J. Millero, in Structure and Transport Processes in Water and Aqueous Solutions (R. A. Horne, ed.), Wiley (Interscience), New York, 1970, Chap. 15.
[3] B. E. Conway, in Physical Chemistry: An Advanced Treatise, Vol. IX A (Electrochemistry) (H. Eyring, ed.), Academic, New York, 1970, Chap.1.
[4] B. E. Conway and J. O'M. Bockris, in Modern Aspects of Electrochemistry, Vol. 1 (J. O'M. Bockris, ed.), Butterworths, London, 1954, Chap. 2.
[5] M. H. Panckhurst, Rev. Pure Appl. Chem., 19, 45 (1969).
[6] B. E. Conway, Ann. Rev. Phys. Chem., 17, 481, (1966).
[7] G. Nemethy and H. A. Scheraga, J. Chem. Phys., 36, 3382, 3401 (1962).
[8] H. S. Frank and W. Y. Wen, Discussions Faraday Soc., 24, 133 (1957).
[9] H. S. Frank, Proc. Roy. Soc., Ser.A, 247, 481 (1958).
[10] B. E. Conway, J. E. Desnoyers, and R. E. Verrall, Trans. Faraday Soc., 62, 2738 (1966).
[11] B. E. Conway and R. E. Verrall, J. Phys. Chem., 70, 3952 (1966).
[12] R. E. Verrall and B. E. Conway, Ibid., 70, 3961 (1966).
[13] B. E. Conway and L. Laliberte, in Hydrogen Bonded Solvent Systems (A. Covington and P. Jones, ed.), Taylor and Francis, London, 1968, p. 139.
[14] D. J. G. Ives and P. D. Marsden, J. Chem. Soc., 1965, 649.
[15] T. Alfrey, P. W. Berg, and H. Morawetz, J. Polym. Sci., 7, 543 (1951).
[16] J. D. Watson and J. F. Crick, Nature, 171, 964 (1953).
[17] H. Schwander and R. Signer, Helv. Chim. Acta, 34, 1344 (1951).
[18] J. Lawrence and B. E. Conway, J. Phys. Chem., 2353, 2362 (1971).
[19] N. Ise and T. Okubo, J. Amer. Chem. Soc., 90, 4527 (1968).
[20] A. M. Couture and K. J. Laidler, Can. J. Chem., 27, 1423, 1957; 34, 1209 (1956).
[21] D. H. Everett and W. F. K. Wynne-Jones, Proc. Roy. Soc., Ser. A, 177, 499 (1941).
[22] L. Hepler, J. Phys. Chem., 69, 965 (1965).
[23] W. F. K. Wynne-Jones, Proc. Roy. Soc., Ser. A, 140, 440 (1933).
[24] M. Born, Z. Phys., 1, 45 (1920).
[25] D. D. Eley and M. G. Evans, Trans. Faraday Soc., 34, 1093 (1938).
[26] F. Vaslow, J. Phys. Chem., 67, 2777 (1963).
[27] J. D. Bernal and R. H. Fowler, J. Chem. Phys., 1, 515 (1933).
[28] A. D. Buckingham, Disc. Faraday Soc.,24, 151 (1957).
[29] R. G. Pearson, J. Amer. Chem. Soc., 85, 3533 (1963).
[30] E. g., see R. M. Fuoss, in Modern Aspects of Electrochemistry,Vol. 1 (J. O'M. Bockris and B. E. Conway, eds.), Butterworths, London, 1954, Chap. 1.

[31] H. S. Frank, *J. Chem. Phys.*, **23**, 2023 (1955).
[32] F. Booth, *J. Chem. Phys.*, **19**, 391, 1327, 1615 (1951).
[33] J. O'M. Bockris, *Quart. Rev.* (London), **3**, 173 (1949).
[34] O. Ya. Samoilov, *Structure of Aqueous Electrolyte Solutions and the Hydration of Ions*, Consultants Bureau, New York, 1965.
[35] H. S. Frank and M. W. Evans, *J. Chem. Phys.*, **13**, 507 (1945).
[36] J. E. Desnoyers, R. E. Verrall, and B. E. Conway, *J. Chem. Phys.*, **43**, 243 (1965).
[37] A. G. Passynsky, *Acta Physicochim. URSS*, **8**, 385 (1938).
[38] R. Garnsey, R. J. Moe, R. Mahoney, and T. A. Litovitz, *J. Chem. Phys.*, **50**, 5222 (1969).
[39] H. G. Hertz and G. Engel, *Ber. Bunsenges. Phys. Chem.*, **72**, 808 (1968); *cf. Ibid.*, **73**, 542 (1969).
[40] C. H. Haggis, J. B. Hasted, and T. J. Buchanan, *J. Chem. Phys.*, **20**, 1452 (1952).
[41] P. Debye and E. Hückel, *Phys. Z.*, **24**, 49, 185, 305 (1923); **25**, 97 (1924).
[42] H. F. Halliwell and S. C. Nyburg, *Trans. Faraday Soc.*, **59**, 1126 (1963).
[43] D. F. C. Morris, *Structure and Bonding*, Vol. 4, Springer, New York, 1968, p. 63.
[44] H. J. V. Tyrrell and G. L. Hollis, *Trans. Faraday Soc.*, **45**, 411 (1949).
[45] M. Eastman, *J. Amer. Chem. Soc.*, **50**, 283, 292; (1928).
[46] W. G. Breck and J. Lin, *Trans. Faraday Soc.*, **61**, 2223 (1965).
[47] P. Debye, *J. Chem. Phys.*, **1**, 13 (1933).
[48] R. Zana and E. Yeager, *J. Phys. Chem.*, **70**, 954 (1966).
[49] B. E. Conway, J. E. Desnoyers, and R. E. Verrall, *J. Phys. Chem.*, **75**, 3031 (1971).
[50] R. W. Rampolla, R. C. Miller, and C. P. Smyth, *J. Chem. Phys.*, **30**, 566 (1959).
[51] B. E. Conway, J. E. Desnoyers, and A. C. Smith, *Phil. Trans. Roy. Soc., Ser. A*, **256**, 389 (1964).
[52] M. Abraham and R. Becker, *Classical Theory of Electricity and Magnetism*, 2nd ed., Blackie, London, 1950.
[53] R. M. Fuoss, A. Katchalsky, and S. Lifson, *Proc. Nat. Acad. Sci. U.S.*, **37**, 579 (1951).
[54] J. R. Philip and R. A. Wooding, *J. Chem. Phys.*, **52**, 953 (1970).
[55] D. C. Chapman, *Phil. Mag.*, **25**, 475 (1913).
[56] N. F. Mott and R. J. Watts-Tobin, *Electrochim. Acta*, **4**, 79 (1961).
[57] J. O'M. Bockris, M. A. V. Devanathan, and K. Muller, *Proc. Roy. Soc., Ser. A*, **274**, 55 (1963).
[58] J. G. Kirkwood, *J. Chem. Phys.*, **7**, 911 (1939); see also H. Frohlich, *Theory of Dielectrics*, Oxford Univ. Press, New York, 1949, Chap. 2.
[59] T. J. Webb, *J. Amer. Chem. Soc.*, **48**, 2589 (1926).
[60] K. J. Laidler, *Can. J. Chem.*, **37**, 138 (1959).
[61] F. T. Wall and J. Berkowitz, *J. Chem. Phys.*, **26**, 114 (1957).
[62] B. Jacobson, W. A. Anderson, and J. T. Arnold, *Nature*, **173**, 772 (1954).
[63] B. Jacobson, *J. Amer. Chem. Soc.*, **77**, 2919 (1955).

[64]   N. Ise and T. Okubo, *J. Phys. Chem.*, **70**, 2400 (1966).

[65]   R. H. Stokes and E. A. Robinson, *J. Amer., Chem. Soc.*, **70**, 1870 (1948); see also K. Linderstrøm-Lang, *C. R. Trav. Lab. Carlsberg*, **15**, 29 (1924) for applications of ionic theory to proteins.

[66]   A. Ikegami, *J. Polym. Sci.*, **A2**, 907 (1964).

[67]   S. Lapanje, I. Haebig. H. T. Davis, and S. A. Rice, *J. Amer. Chem. Soc.*, **83**, 1590 (1961).

[68]   C. Y. Shen and R. A. Herrmann, *Ind. Eng. Chem., Prod. Res. Develop.*, **5**, 357 (1966).

[69]   B. E. Conway and L. Laliberte, *Trans. Faraday Soc.*, **66**, 3032 (1970).

[70]   W. L. Masterton, *J. Chem. Phys.*, **22**, 1830 (1954).

[71]   J. A. V. Butler, B. E. Conway, and D. W. F. James, *Trans. Faraday Soc.*, **50**, 612 (1954).

[72]   J. R. Huizenga, P. F. Grieger, and F. T. Wall, *J. Amer. Chem. Soc.*, **72**, 2636, 4228 (1950).

[73]   S. O. Hamann, P. J. Pearce, and W. Strauss, *J. Phys. Chem.*, **68**, 375 (1964).

[74]   M. Eigen and K. Tamm, *Z. Elektrochem.*, **66**, 107 (1962).

[75]   S. Goto, *Bull. Chem. Soc. Jap.*, **37**, 1685 (1964).

[76]   T. Isemura and S. Goto, *Ibid.*, **37**, 1690 (1964).

[77]   H. Nomura and Y. Miyahara, *Nippon Kagaku Zasshi*, **88**, 504 (1967); cf. *Chem. Abstr.*, **68**, 3268 (1968).

[78]   I. M. Konyushko, *Issled. Suoistv. Ionobmen. Materialov, Akad. Nauk SSSR Inst. Fiz. Khim.*, **1964**, 59-65.

[79]   P. Debye and J. McAulay, *Phys. Z.*, **26**, 22 (1925).

[80]   J. A. V. Butler, *J. Phys. Chem.*, **33**, 1015 (1929).

[81]   H. P. Gregor, B. R. Sundheim, K. M. Held, and M. H. Waxman, *J. Colloid Sci.*, **7**, 511 (1952).

[82]   A. Despic and G. J. Hills, *Trans. Faraday Soc.*, **51**, 1260 (1955).

[83]   G. J. Hills, J. A. Kitchener, and P. Ovenden, *Trans. Faraday Soc.*, **51**, 719 (1955).

[84]   E. Glueckauf and G. P. Kitt, *Proc. Roy. Soc. Ser. A*, **228**, 322 (1955).

[85]   E. Glueckauf, *Ibid.*, **214**, 207 (1952).

[86]   G. Zundel and H. Metzger, *Z. Phys. Chem.*, **59**, 225 (1968).

[87]   G. Zundel, H. Noller, and G. M. Schwab, *Z. Elektrochem.*, **66**, 122, 129 (1962).

[88]   G. Zundel and A. Murr, *Z. Phys. Chem.*, [N.F.] **54**, 49 (1967); cf. *Z. Naturforsch.*, **21**, 1391 (1966).

[89]   G. E. Boyd and B. A. Soldano, *Z. Elektrochem.*, **57**, 164 (1953).

[90]   T. Westermark, *Acta Chem. Scand.*, **14**, 1858 (1960).

[91]   E. Hogfeldt, *Nature*, **210**, 941 (1966).

[92]   O. N. Myagkoi, V. P. Meleshko, and A. I. Ryaguzov, *Ionity, Ionnyi Obmen, Acta. Nauk SSSR Sb. Statei*, **1966**, 8.

[93]   H. L. Friedman and Y. C. Wu, *J. Phys. Chem.*, **70**, 166 (1966).

[94]   J. Persoz and R. Rosset, *Bull. Soc. Chim. Fr.*, **9**, 2197 (1964).

[95]   I. M. Konyushko and L. I. Konyushko, *Geterogennye Reaktsii i Reakts. Sposobnost, Minsk, Sb.*, **1964**, 48.

[96] G. Dickel and K. Bunzl, *Makromol. Chem.*,79, 54 (1964).
[97] G. L. Starobinets and A. B. Chizhevskaya, *Zhur. Fiz. Khim.*, 40, 1360 (1966).
[98] B. Chu, D. C. Whitney, and R. M. Diamond, *J. Inorg. Nucl. Chem.*, 24, 1405 (1962).
[99] J. T. Edsall, in *The Proteins*, Vol. 1, Part B (H. Neurath and K. Bailey, eds.), Academic, New York, 1953, Chap. 7, p. 567.
[100] J. G. Kirkwood and J. B. Shumaker, *Proc. Nat. Acad. Sci. U.S.*, 38, 855 (1952).
[101] J. H. Wang, *J. Amer. Chem. Soc.*, 76, 4755 (1954).
[101a] W. J. C. Orr and J. A. V. Butler, *J. Chem. Soc.*, 1935, 1273.
[102] J. H. Wang, C. B. Anfinsen, and F. M. Polestra, *J. Amer. Chem. Soc.*, 76, 4763 (1954).
[103] I. M. Klotz, in *The Proteins*,Vol. 1, Part B (H. Neurath and K. Bailey, eds.), Academic, New York, 1953, p. 763.
[104] S. Katz and H. K. Schachman, *Biochem. Biophys. Acta*, 81, 28 (1955).
[105] R. M. Fuoss,*J. Amer. Chem. Soc.*, 80, 5059 (1958); *cf.* J. T. Denison and J. B. Ramsey, *Ibid.*, 77, 2615 (1955).
[106] G. H. Nancollas,*J. Amer. Chem. Soc.*,83, 755 (1961).
[107] G. Scatchard, I. H. Scheinberg, and S. H. Armstrong,*J. Amer. Chem. Soc.*, 72, 535 (1950).
[108] S. Katz,*J. Amer. Chem. Soc.*,78, 300 (1956).
[109] D. J. Cox and V. N. Schumaker, *J. Amer. Chem. Soc.*, 83, 2433, 2439 (1961).
[110] E. P. K. Hade and C. Tanford, *J. Amer. Chem. Soc.*, 89, 5034 (1967).
[111] V. N. Schumaker and D. J. Cox, *J. Amer. Chem. Soc.*, 83, 2445 (1961).
[112] A. Ikegami and N. Imai,*J. Polym. Sci.*, 56, 133 (1962).
[113] P. K. Rawlings and F. W. Schneider, *J. Chem. Phys.*, 52, 946 (1970).
[114] P. Mukerjee, K. Mysels, and P. Kapauau, *J. Phys. Chem.*, 71, 4166 (1967).
[115] A. S. Tombalakian, C. Y. Yeh, and W. F. Graydon, *J. Phys. Chem.*, 71, 435 (1967).
[116] P. Mukerjee,*J. Colloid Sci.*, 19, 722 (1964).
[117] H. K. Schachman and M. A. Lauffer, *J. Amer. Chem. Soc.*, 71, 536 (1949).
[118] S. Katz and H. K. Schachman, *Biochim. Biophys. Acta*, 18, 28 (1955).
[119] N. Nishida, *J.Phys.Soc.Jap.*, 17, 531 (1962).
[120] D. Woodside and H. Eisenberg,*Amer. Chem. Soc. Div. Polym. Chem. Preprints*, 2(1), 120 (1961).
[121] D. L. Drabkin,*J. Biol. Chem.*, 185, 231 (1950).
[122] M. Lauffer, in *Currents in Biochemical Research* (D. E. Green, ed.), Interscience, New York, 1946.
[123] N. E. Dorsey, *Properties of Ordinary Water Substance* (Amer. Chem. Soc. Monograph 81), Reinhold, New York, 1940.
[124] J. Oncley, *Chem. Rev.*, 30, 433 (1942); J. T. Edsall and M. Cohn, *Proteins, Amino Acids and Peptides*, Reinhold, New York, 1943, Chap. 22.

[125] J. Oncley, *J. Amer. Chem. Soc.*, 60, 1122 (1938).
[126] T. J. Buchanan, G. H. Harris, J. B. Hasted, and R. S. Robinson, *Proc. Roy. Soc.*, *Ser.*, A, 213, 379 (1952).
[127] H. N. Ritland, P. Kaesberg, and N. W. Beeman, *J. Chem. Phys.*, 18, 1237 (1950).
[128] M. F. Perutz, *Trans. Faraday Soc.*, 42B, 187 (1946).
[129] H. J. C. Berendsen, *J. Chem. Phys.*, 36, 3297 (1962).
[130] E. H. Grant, *Ann. N.Y. Acad. Sci.*, 125, 418 (1965).
[131] J. Pople and J. Lennard-Jones, *Proc. Roy. Soc.*, *Ser.* A, 202, 163, 323 (1950).
[132] B. E. Conway, *Can. J. Chem.*, 37, 178 (1959).
[133] H. Li and H. P. Schwann, *Ann. N.Y. Acad. Sci.*, 125, 344 (1965), *cf. Advan. Biol. Med. Phys.*, 5 (1966).
[134] H. Fricke, *Phys. Rev.*, 26, 678 (1925).
[135] V. B. Kazanskii, L. Stepin, and P. M. Onishchenko, *Biofiz. i Radiobiol. Akad. Nauk, Ukr. SSR Resp. Mezhvedomstv. Sb.*, 1966, 15; *Chem. Abstr.*, 65, 7498h (1966).
[136] H. M. Dintzis, J. L. Oncley, and R. M. Fuoss, *Proc. Nat. Acad. Sci.*, U.S., 40, 62 (1954).
[137] B. E. Conway and A. Dobry-Duclaux, *Rheology—Theory and Applications*, Vol. 3, Academic, New York, 1959, Chap. 3.
[138] J. Mesnard and M. Vasilescu, *C. R. Congr. Nat. Voc. Savantes*, *Sect. Sci.*, 90(1), 110 (1966); *cf. Chem. Abstr.*, 67, 26964 (1967).
[139] M. Lauffer, *Biochemistry*, 3, 731 (1964).
[140] I. M. Klotz, *Science*, 128, 815 (1958).
[141] T. L. McMeekin and K. Marshall, *Science*, 116, 142 (1952).
[142] D. F. Waugh, *Advan. Protein Chem.*, 9, 325 (1954).
[143] B. Belleau, *Ann. N.Y. Acad. Sci.*, 144(2), 705 (1967).
[144] B. E. Conway and L. G. M. Gordon, *J. Phys. Chem.*, 73, 3609 (1969).
[145] S. B. Horowitz and I. R. Fenickel, *Ann. N.Y. Acad. Sci.*, 125, 572 (1965).
[146] D. T. Warner, *Ibid.*, 125, 605 (1965).
[147] I. Z. Steinberg and H. A. Scheraga, *J. Biol. Chem.*, 238, 172 (1963).
[148] M. Lauffer, *Molecular Basis of Neoplasia*, Univ. of Texas Press, Austin, Texas, 1962, p. 180.
[149] W. L. Peticolas, *J. Chem. Phys.*, 37, 2323 (1962); 40, 1463 (1964).
[150] C. G. Rosen and G. Ahnstrom, *Int. J. Radiat. Biol.*, 9, 435 (1965).
[151] H. A. Scheraga, *Ann. N.Y. Acad. Sci.*, 125, 249 (1965). *Ber. Bunsenges. Phys. Chem.*, 68, 857 (1964).
[152] F. Franks, *Ibid.*, 125, 277 (1965).
[153] D. C. Poland and H. A. Scheraga, *Biopolymers*, 3, 275 (1965).
[154] P. L. Privalov and G. M. Mrevlishvili, *Biofizika*, 12, 22 (1967).
[155] W. Kauzmann, *Advan. Protein Chem.*, 14, 1 (1959).
[156] L. G. Sedykh and N. V. Sedykh, *Biofizika*, 22, 936 (1967).
[157] E. Forslind, *Proc. Swedish Cement Concrete Res. Inst.*, 16 (1952).
[158] B. Jacobson, *Svensk Kem. Tidskr.*, 67, 1 (1955).
[159] A. Szent-Gyorgyi, *Bioenergetics*, Academic, New York, 1957.
[160] B. V. Derjaguin, *Discussions Faraday Soc.*, 42, 109 (1966).

[161] E. R. Lippincott and R. R. Stromberg, *Science*, 164, 1482 (1969).
[162] G. N. Ling, *Ann. N.Y. Acad. Sci.*, 125, 401 (1965).
[163] W. W. Beeman, P. Geil, M. Shurman, and A. G. Malmas, *Acta Cryst.*, 10, 818 (1957).
[164] B. Jacobson, *Svenska Lakartidn.*, 54, 1836 (1957).
[165] B. Jacobson, *Nature*, 172, 666 (1953).
[166] K. W. Kohn and C. L. Spears, *Biochim. Biophys. Acta*, 145, 720 (1967).
[167] K. W. Kohn and C. L. Spears, *Ibid*, 145, 734 (1967).
[168] F. W. Cope, *Bull. Math. Biophys.*, 29, 583 (1967).
[169] R. Santamaria, *Rend. Atti. Accad. Sci. Med. Chir.*, 119, 283 (1965).
[170] R. Suhrmann and F. Breyer, *Z. phys. Chem.*, B20, 17 (1933); B23, 193 (1937).
[171] P. C. Cross, J. Burnham, and P. A. Leighton, *J. Amer. Chem. Soc.*, 59, 1134 (1937).
[172] B. E. Conway, *Ann. Rev. Phys. Chem.*, 17, 481 (1966).
[173] G. E. Walrafan, in *Hydrogen Bonded Solvent Systems* (A. K. Covington and P. Jones, eds.), Chap. 1, Taylor and Francis, London, 1968.
[174] M. Falk and T. A. Ford, *Can. J. Chem.*, 44, 1699 (1966); 46, 3679 (1968).
[175] G. Zundel, *Zh. Strukt. Khim.*, 6, 384 (1965).
[176] G. Zundel and A. Murr, *Electrochim. Acta*, 12, 1147 (1967).
[177] G. Zundel, *Hydration and Intermolecular Interaction*, Academic, New York, 1969.
[178] G. Dickel and J. W. Hartmann, *Z. Phys. Chem.*, [N.F.] 23, 1 (1960); see also *Ibid.*, 20, 121 (1959).
[179] B. E. Conway, J. O'M. Bockris, and H. Linton, *J. Chem. Phys.*, 24, 834 (1956).
[180] E. M. Bradbury, W. L. Price, and G. R. Wilkinson, *J. Mol. Biol.*, 3, 301 (1961).
[181] E.g., see E. R. Nightingale Jr., in *Chemical Physics of Ionic Solutions* (B. E. Conway and R. G. Barradas, eds.), Wiley, New York, 1966, Chap. 7, p. 87.
[182] H. J. C. Berendson, *J. Chem. Phys.*, 36, 3297 (1962).
[183] C. Migchelson, H. J. C. Berendson, and A. Rupprecht, *J. Mol. Biol.*, 37, 235 (1968).
[184] L. P. Kayushin, ed., *Water in Biological Systems*, trans., Consultants Bureau, New York, 1969.
[185] Y. N. Chirgadze, S. Y. Ven'yaminov, and S. L. Zimont, p. 51 in *Water in Biological Systems* (L. P. Kayushin, ed.), trans. Consultants Bureau, New York, 1969.
[186] A. I. Sidorova, I. N. Kochnev, L. V. Moiseeva, and A. I. Khaloimov, *Ibid.*, p. 54.
[187] G. M. Mrevlishvili and P. L. Privalov, *Ibid.*, p. 63.
[188] E. L. Andronikashvili, G. M. Mrevlishvili, and P. L. Privalov, *Ibid.*, p. 67.

Hydrogen Transfer Polymerization with Anionic Catalysts and the Problem of Anionic Isomerization Polymerization

J. P. KENNEDY
Institute of Polymer Science
The University of Akron
Akron, Ohio

T. OTSU
Department of Applied Chemistry
Osaka City University
Sumiyoshiku, Osaka, Japan

I. INTRODUCTION

In 1954 a patent by Matlack [1] and shortly thereafter a paper by Breslow, Hulse, and Matlack [2] described that acrylamide readily polymerizes to fairly high molecular weight poly(β-alanine) (nylon 3) in the presence of anionic initiators such as t-BuONa:

$$n \quad CH_2 = CH - CONH_2 \longrightarrow \ \{CH_2 CH_2 - CO - NH\}_n$$

This interesting polymerization reaction and related systems quickly became the subject of intensive further investigation by many research groups around the world. Since the time of the original observation, a large amount of information has become available and the reviewing and discussion of this material is warranted.

In addition to our discussion on hydrogen transfer polymerization by anionic initiator, we also examine some aspects of intramolecular anionic isomerization polymerization, a field related to the hydrogen transfer process. Both mechanisms afford unusual polymer structures.

While related to our main subject, ring-opening polymerizations of cyclic amides (lactams and N-carboxy-α-amino acid anhydrides) to nylons and polypeptides are not discussed in this paper, since no hydrogen transfer is involved in these systems. Also, this field has been excellently summarized in recent reviews and polymer textbooks. The reader interested in this subject is referred to a select list at the end of the references.

II. HYDROGEN TRANSFER POLYMERIZATION WITH ANIONIC INITIATOR

A. Acrylamide

The first well-authenticated and most investigated hydrogen transfer polymerization by anionic initiator is the polymerization of acrylamide to poly(β-alanine):

$$CH_2 = CH - CONH_2 \longrightarrow \ \sim\!\sim\!CH_2 - CH_2 - CONH \sim\!\sim$$

This system was first described in 1954 in a patent by Matlack [1]. Significantly, Matlack found that when a solution of sodium in t-butyl alcohol and acrylamide are heated in the presence of a radical-polymerization inhibitor, a polyamino acid, poly(β-alanine), is obtained. The cornerstone of the proof of the structure was that on hydrolysis with sulfuric acid the polymer yeilded β-alanine.

Shortly thereafter, in 1957, Breslow, Hulse, and Matlack [2] discussed this system and raised some of the fundamental questions research workers are still intensively studying. Before we begin a discussion of these questions, it is necessary to examine the gist of the findings of these authors.

The conversion of acrylamide to poly(β-alanine) can be viewed as an example of the well-known Michael reaction. This reaction is essentially a base-catalyzed addition of a nucleophilic species (i.e., carbanion or amide ion) to the α,β double bond of an unsaturated ketone, ester, amide, or nitrile:

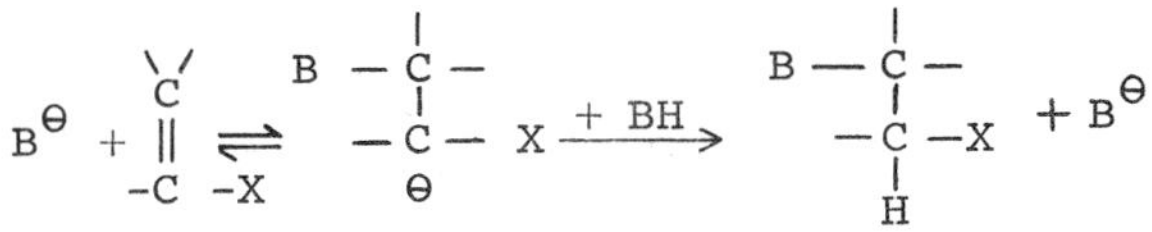

$$B^\ominus + \underset{-C\ -X}{\overset{\diagup}{\underset{\|}{C}}} \rightleftharpoons \underset{\ominus}{\overset{B\ -\ C\ -}{\underset{-C\ -\ X}{|}}} \xrightarrow{+\ BH} \underset{H}{\overset{B\ -\ C\ -}{\underset{-C\ -X}{|}}} + B^\ominus$$

As the α-carbon is substituted with an electron withdrawing group, attack by $B^\ominus$ will always be at the β-carbon and the new nucleophilic site will be formed on the α-carbon. Proton capture completes the reaction. "Cyanoethylation" with acrylonitrile is a well-known example of the Michael reaction. In the case of acrylamide the initial addition can be visualized as:

$$B^\ominus + \underset{CH\ -\ CONH_2}{\overset{CH_2}{\underset{\|}{\|}}} \longrightarrow \underset{\ominus CH-CONH_2}{\overset{B\ -\ CH_2}{|}}$$

However, the next event, that of proton capture, is still a controversial step, as discussed in detail later, since it may occur intramolecularly:

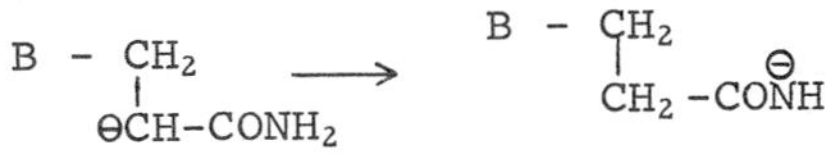

$$\underset{\ominus CH-CONH_2}{\overset{B\ -\ CH_2}{|}} \longrightarrow \underset{CH_2\ -CO\overset{\ominus}{N}H}{\overset{B\ -\ CH_2}{|}}$$

or intermolecularly:

$$\underset{\ominus CH-CONH_2}{\overset{B\ -\ CH_2}{|}} \xrightarrow{+BH} \underset{CH_2\ -\ CONH_2}{\overset{B\ -\ CH_2}{|}} + B^\ominus$$

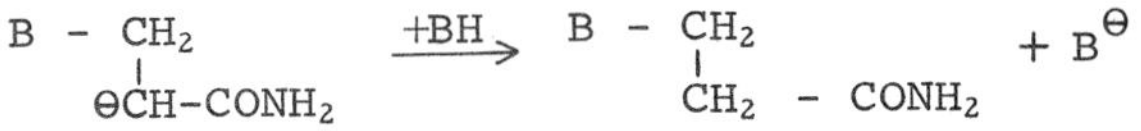

In the latter case BH can be the monomer.

According to Breslow et al. [2], when acrylamide is polymerized with a strong base (i.e., t-C_4H_9ONa, CH_3ONa, $NaNH_2$, etc.) in inert solvents (i.e., t-butanol, acetonitrile, pyridine, etc.) in the presence of radical inhibitors (i.e., hydroquinone, phenyl-β-naphthylamine, etc.) at 83 to 200°, poly(β-alanine) is formed. The polymer could be fractionated into water-soluble and insoluble fractions of respectable molecular weights (the weight-average molecular weight of a sample was $\sim$ 80,000). Both the water-soluble and insoluble fractions were highly crystalline and melted at about 325 and 340°C, respectively, with considerable decomposition. Both polymer fractions showed the same x-ray diffraction pattern; however, they exhibited different degrees of crystallinity. The water-insoluble high polymer was soluble in formic acid, dichloroacetic acid, phenol, and concentrated aqueous salt solution, known solvents for polyamide. The over-all repeat unit of the polymer was determined by acid hydrolysis which yielded $\sim$ 90% β-alanine based on acrylamide. Other significant findings were that the end groups were either olefinic double bonds or $-CONH_2$ groups and that the nonpolymerized material was unconverted monomer and a dimer, $CH_2{=}CHCONHCH_2CH_2CONH_2$.

With these hard facts on hand the authors were able to propose two alternatives for each of the fundamental mechanisms of initiation and propagation:

Initiation:

I_1) $B^{\ominus} + CH_2{=}CHCONH_2 \rightleftharpoons BH + CH_2{=}CHCON\overset{\ominus}{H}$

I_2) $B^{\ominus} + CH_2{=}CHCONH_2 \rightleftharpoons B{-}CH_2\overset{\ominus}{C}HCONH_2 \rightleftharpoons B{-}CH_2CH_2CON\overset{\ominus}{H}$

Propagation:

P_1) $\sim\!\!\sim\!CH_2CH_2CON\overset{\ominus}{H} + CH_2{=}CHCONH_2 \longrightarrow \sim\!\!\sim\!CH_2CH_2CONHCH_2\overset{\ominus}{C}HCONH_2$

$\longrightarrow \sim\!\!\sim\!CH_2CH_2CONHCH_2CH_2CON\overset{\ominus}{H}$

P_2) $CH_2{=}CHCON\overset{\ominus}{H} + CH_2{=}CHCONH_2 \longrightarrow$
$$
\begin{array}{c}
CH_2{=}CHCONH \\
\vert \qquad\quad \ominus \\
CH_2{-}CHCONH_2 \\
\text{(I)}
\end{array}
$$

(I) $+$ $CH_2{=}CHCONH_2 \longrightarrow$
$$
\begin{array}{c}
CH_2{=}CH{-}CONH \\
\vert \\
CH_2CH_2CONH_2 \\
\ominus \\
+\ CH_2{=}CHCON\overset{\ominus}{H}
\end{array}
$$

By formulating these alternatives Breslow and his coworkers [2] outlined much of the research which ensued for many years by various groups.

Thus initiation can occur either by proton transfer to the base $B^{\ominus}(I_1)$ or by direct attack of the base $B^{\ominus}$ on the monomer (I_2); in both cases the final product, the growing active species, would possess $—CO\overset{\ominus}{N}H$ endgroups. Breslow and coworkers [2] suggested that I_1 is the actual initiation mechanism with sodium or potassium t-butoxide as catalyst, because they were able to identify an unsaturated dimer in the reaction mixture and because they found evidence for the presence of terminal olefinic unsaturation in the high polymer.

Contrary to these conclusions, Japanese workers [3-6] argued in favor of the I_2 initiation mechanism. Ogata [3] repeated the work by Breslow et al. [2] and presented some infrared evidence for the presence of ether linkage in the polymer and showed that olefinic terminal unsaturation decreases during the initial stages of the polymerization. Also some kinetic experiments indicated that the rate of the polymerization was proportional to the monomer concentration and that the relative viscosity (in 98% sulfuric acid) of the polymer did not change significantly with conversion; these are characteristic features for chain growth polymerizations. While the value of viscosity measurements of poly(β-alanines) in strong sulfuric acid is questionable, the rest of these various observations argue in favor of a chain growth process with initiation by I_2. Some data of Tani et al. [6] corroborated Ogata's conclusion in regard to initiation by I_2. Tani and coworkers [6] reacted acrylamide with stoichiometric amounts of sodium methoxide and isolated from the reaction mixture 3-methoxypropionamide, $CH_3OCH_2CH_2CONH_2$. According to Ogata [4] the methoxide ion adds to acrylamide to give intermediate anion III, similar to a 1,4-addition to a conjugate bond:

$$CH_3O^{\ominus} + CH_2=CHCONH_2 \longrightarrow$$

$$\left[\begin{array}{ccc} \underset{\overset{|}{\underset{\overset{\|}{O}}{\overset{|}{C}-NH_2}}}{CH_3O-CH_2\overset{\ominus}{CH}} & \longleftrightarrow & \underset{\overset{\|}{\underset{O^{\ominus}}{C-NH_2}}}{CH_3O-CH_2\overset{\|}{CH}} \end{array}\right] \longrightarrow \underset{\overset{\|}{\underset{O}{C}-\overset{\ominus}{NH}}}{CH_3O-CH_2\,CH_2}$$

$$\qquad\qquad II \qquad\qquad\qquad\qquad III$$

where II is the enolate form of the carbanion. This enolate anion is unstable and easily undergoes intramolecular proton shift to give the more stable amide anion III.

In contrast to the results obtained with sodium methoxide, Tani et al. [6] isolated a mixture of N-benzylacrylamide ($CH_2=CH-CONHCH_2C_6H_5$) and 3-t-butoxypropionamide [$(CH_3)_3COCH_2CH_2CONH_2$] from the reaction of acrylamide with sodium t-butoxide in dioxane and then neutralization with benzyl chloride. This indicates a duality of initiation possibilities by either I_1 or I_2.

Recently Trossarelli et al. [7] polymerized acrylamide with alcohol-free sodium t-butoxide in aprotic solvents, such as dioxane, dimethylformamide, and 1-methyl-2-pyrollidone, at 100° and recovered the theoretical amount of t-butyl alcohol from the reaction mixture. Similarly, Leoni et al. [8] investigated the polymerization of acrylamide in the presence of a variety of anionic catalysts (sodium t-butoxide, n-butyllithium, lithium benzophenone ketyl, etc.) and were able to isolate β-acrylamidopropionamide ($CH_2=CHCONHCH_2CH_2CONH_2$) from the reaction mixture in each case. These findings, of course, strongly support Breslow et al.'s original initiation hypothesis.

More recently Bush and Breslow [9] have argued that initiation in the t-butoxide-catalyzed polymerization of acrylamide occurs by I_1 and that the carbanion of acrylamide, which is formed by a conventional addition of t-butoxide ion to acrylamide, abstracts a proton from an acrylamide molecule:

$$t\text{-BuO-CH}_2\overset{\ominus}{\underset{|}{\text{CH}}} \quad + \quad CH_2=\overset{|}{\underset{|}{\text{CH}}} \quad \longrightarrow \quad t\text{-BuO-CH}_2\overset{|}{\underset{|}{\text{CH}_2}} \quad + \quad CH_2=\overset{|}{\underset{|}{\text{CH}}}{}_\ominus$$
$$\qquad\quad CONH_2 \qquad\qquad CONH_2 \qquad\qquad\qquad CONH_2 \qquad\qquad CONH$$

It is very difficult to discuss the conflicting evidence presented in favor of the two initiation mechanisms I_1 or I_2. While the weight of the data and particularly those of more recent vintage seem to favor mechanism I_1, the results described by Ogata et al. [4] and (partly) substantiated by Tani et al. [6] are still unchallenged and might have validity under certain conditions. Since this polymerization reaction is carried out above 100°, it may be impossible to avoid side reactions. More work is needed to clarify this picture.

Similarly to the initiation mechanism, propagation in the base-initiated proton-transfer polymerization of acrylamide may also proceed by two fundamentally different mechanisms: by intramolecular or intermolecular proton transfer, P_1 or P_2. In the intramolecular process the negative charge on the carbon could be transferred to the nitrogen directly by the following mechanism [10]:

The driving force for this rearrangement is provided by the formation of a more stable (less basic) amide ion from the less stable (more basic) secondary carbanion. The arrangement of the atoms in the proposed transition state seems to be favorable for proton transfer. Another possibility for intramolecular proton shift has been proposed [11] and is shown by the following sets of resonances and equilibria:

$$- CH_2-CH-\overset{\overset{\ominus}{|}}{\underset{\underset{O}{\|}}{C}}-NH_2 \longleftrightarrow CH_2-CH=\underset{\underset{O^\ominus}{|}}{C}-NH_2 \rightleftharpoons -CH_2-CH=\underset{\overset{\diagdown}{OH}}{C}-\overset{\ominus}{NH} \rightleftharpoons$$

$$\sim\!\!\sim CH_2-CH_2-\underset{\underset{O}{\|}}{C}-\overset{\ominus}{NH}$$

On the basis of molecular orbital calculations, Yonezawa et al. [11] prefer the above propagation mechanism.

If propagation would in fact proceed by an intramolecular proton transfer mechanism, the resulting polymer would probably be a copolymer of rearranged and unrearranged units (1,4- and 1,2-enchainment) produced by propagation via monomer addition plus proton migration, and propagation via conventional vinyl addition. Nakayama et al. [12-15] presented evidence that acrylamide when polymerized with strong bases such as sodium sec-butoxide and n-butyllithium gives a polymer with 1,2- and 1,4-units:

$$-CH_2-\underset{\underset{CONH_2}{|}}{CH}- \qquad\qquad -CH_2-CH_2-CONH-$$

1,2-unit   1,4-unit

The presence of these repeat structures was explained by the following competition:

$$\sim\!\!CH_2-\underset{\underset{CONH_2}{|}}{CH}\underset{\overset{\diagdown}{\underset{H\ trans-\atop fer}{}}}{\overset{\ominus\ \ +\ M}{\nearrow}}\begin{array}{l}\sim\!\!CH_2-\underset{\underset{CONH_2}{|}}{CH}-CH_2-\overset{\ominus}{\underset{\underset{CONH_2}{|}}{CH}} \\[2em] \sim\!\!CH_2-\underset{\underset{\underset{CONH}{|}}{\ominus}}{CH_2}\xrightarrow{\ +\ M\ } \sim\!\!CH_2-\underset{\underset{\overset{\ominus}{CONHCH_2\,CHCONH_2}}{|}}{CH_2}\end{array}$$

The relative proportions of these units in the polymers were determined by measuring the primary amide groups and the nitrogen content, and the yield of β-alanine in the hydrolyzed product [12].

Infrared spectroscopy was also used in quantitative structure analysis. The product ratios, T

$$T = \frac{1,4\text{-unit}}{1,4\text{-unit} + 1,2\text{-unit}}$$

were determined in polymers obtained with sodium sec-butoxide in toluene at 100°. The T value fell in the range 0.8-0.9, indicating that the polymers contained mainly 1,4-units [13]. The melting points of the polymers were largely dependent on T and not on reduced viscosities (Fig. 1) [12].

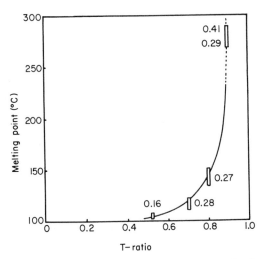

Fig. 1. Relationship between T-ratio and melting point of polymers obtained from the polymerization of acrylamide with sodium sec-butoxide in toluene at 100°C. The numbers indicate the reduced viscosity determined in 1% formic acid solution at 30°C [13].

The effect of monomer and catalyst concentration on the polymer structure was also investigated. It was found that T decreased from 0.8 to 0.6 with monomer concentration in the range from about 0.3 to 1.4 M, but increased to 0.9 with catalyst concentrations up to 10 M and remained constant beyond this value [13] (Fig. 2). This might indicate that the production of 1,4-units was favored with increasing catalyst concentration and with decreasing monomer concentration. In monosubstituted benzene solvents such as toluene, chlorobenzene, and nitrobenzene, T decreased with increasing solvent polarity (i.e., dielectric constant), but increased in other solvents

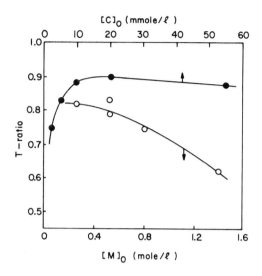

Fig. 2. Effects of monomer and catalyst concentrations on the structure of polymers obtained from the polymerization of acrylamide with sodium sec-butoxide in toluene at 100°C for 2 hr. In the plots with monomer and catalyst concentrations, $[C]_0$ = 5.6 mmole/liter and $[M]_0$ = 0.56 mole/liter were used, respectively [13].

such as dioxane, pyridine, and dimethylformamide. Similar results were observed with $(sec\text{-}BuO)_2Ca$ as initiator; however, the initiating activity of $(sec\text{-}BuO)_3Al$ was quite low and remained unaffected by the nature of the solvent [13]. Solvation of the amide group-catalyst complex was considered to have an important effect on the formation of 1,4-units.

With n-butyllithium initiator in toluene solvent [14] the T ratio, the reduced viscosity, and the yield of polymers increased with increasing temperatures from 40 to 100°C. However, the T ratios in the resulting insoluble polymers remained almost unaffected by the solvent employed. The solvent did not affect T when phenyl magnesium bromide was used as the initiator at 100°. It was noted that n-butyllithium actively induces the polymerization at low temperature (40°C) and gives a polymer with T = 0.52.

With n-butyllithium and phenyl magnesium bromide in pyridine, a large amount of the unsaturated dimer, $CH_2{=}CHCONHCH_2CH_2CONH_2$, and a small amount of the high polymer with mainly 1,4-enchainment was obtained. In contrast to this, in toluene only a minor amount of the dimer was formed [15]. A large amount of this dimer is produced in the early stages of the reaction; however, the concentration of the dimer gradually decreases with time and a high polymer is formed. On the basis of these facts, Nakayama et al. [15] concluded that the polymerization of acrylamide with n-butyllithium is determined by the solvent: in toluene the polymerization probably proceeds by a chain-growth mechanism involving intramolecular proton transfer, while in pyridine a step-growth mechanism by intermolecular proton abstraction is the dominant reaction.

Bush and Breslow [9] also investigated the propagation of acrylamide polymerization. They recognized that the two different propagation mechanisms P_1 and P_2 will give rise to two fundamentally different kinetic expressions: the intramolecular path would give kinetic expressions identical to those obtained with simple chain-growth polymerization, whereas the intermolecular mechanism would lead to step-growth kinetics. On the basis of a few simple experiments these authors established that the polymerization of acrylamide with sodium t-butoxide in dry sulfolane at 100° proceeds by a step-growth mechanism (acrylamide monomer disappears long before high polymer is formed) and therefore proved that in this system propagation proceeds by intermolecular proton transfer (P_2).

Leoni et al. [8] isolated unsaturated acrylamide dimers and trimers (n = 1 and 2) from polymerization charges. These authors used a variety of basic initiators (i.e., sodium t-butoxide, n-butyllithium, lithium benzophenone ketyl, etc.) in dioxane solution in the range 20 to 100°. The dimers and trimers were subsequently polymerized by free radical and anionic initiators to different structures:

$$CH_2 =CH \quad \xrightarrow{R\cdot} \quad \sim\!\!CH_2-CH\!\!\sim$$

$$\begin{array}{c} CH_2 =CH \\ | \\ CONH(CH_2\,CH_2\,CONH)_n H \\ (n\ =\ 1,2) \end{array} \xrightarrow[B^{\ominus}]{R\cdot} \begin{array}{c} \sim\!\!CH_2-CH\!\!\sim \\ | \\ CONH(CH_2\,CH_2\,CONH)_n H \\[1em] \sim\!\!-CH_2-CH_2 \\ | \\ CONH(CH_2\,CH_2\,CONH)_{\overline{n}}\!\sim \end{array}$$

These findings also strongly argue in favor of an intermolecular growth process.

Thus two possible initiation and propagation steps, as described above, would lead to complicated structures, i.e., to a homopolymer of β-alanine repeat units or to copolymers of β-alanine and conventional vinyl-addition units.

The above, sometimes conflicting observations might have been due to a variety of side reactions produced by the relatively high temperatures employed in these investigations. In addition, Glickson and Applequist [16] have reported recently from proton magnetic resonance and infrared absorption studies that the water soluble polymers obtained by the t-BuO$^\ominus$-initiated polymerization of acrylamide are branched copolymers of β-alanine and β,β'-iminodipropionic acid with primary amide end groups:

$$\sim\!\!\sim\!\!CH_2\ CH_2\ CON\!-\!CH_2\ CH_2\ CONH\!-\!\sim\!\!\sim\!\!\sim\!\!CONH_2$$
$$\mid$$
$$CH_2\ CH_2\ CONH\!-\!\sim\!\!\sim\!\!\sim\!\!CONH_2$$

They also found that the water solubility of the polymers increased with increasing branching and decreasing molecular weight.

Masamoto et al. [17,18] wanted to produce high molecular weight, regular poly(β-alanine) by carrying out the polymerization in a homogeneous system. A homogeneous initiator dispersion was prepared by mixing an alcohol solution of the alkoxide and the solvent, followed by evaporation of the alcohol. By using calcium propoxide catalyst in o-dichlorobenzene at 115°, these authors obtained the highest molecular weight poly(β-alanine) to date ($\eta_{sp}/c = 3.04$) containing less than about 2% of 1,2-units [17]. Moreover, they found that high molecular weight poly(β-alanine) can be produced with t-BuOK in o-dichlorobenzene in conjunction with some inorganic salts such as LiCl and CaCl$_2$. The function of these salts is to increase the solubility of the growing poly(β-alanine) chains [18].

The base-catalyzed hydrogen transfer copolymerization of acrylamide with ϵ-caprolactone and acrylonitrile has been investigated by Ito et al. [19]. In a copolymerization with ϵ-caprolactone by using t-BuOLi catalyst in toluene at 100° for 7 hr, 48.7% of a copolymer was obtained and the product contained β-alanine units. This product was fractionated to an acetone-soluble (85.7%, softening point 44-46°) and -insoluble fraction (14.3%, softening point 265-277°).

Besides the hydrogen transfer polymerization of acrylamide, poly(β-alanine) and its derivatives have also been prepared by other reactions from various starting materials. This field is summarized in Table 1 [20]. Although the polymer obtained from the base-initiated polymerization of acrylamide by Breslow et al. [2] showed a weight-average molecular weight of 76,000, its specific viscosity in formic acid was only 0.639. Thus the number-average molecular weight of this polymer is too low for the production of nylon-3 fiber. The highest molecular weight nylon 3 ($\eta = 4$-5 dl/g, $\overline{M}_W = 500,000$) was obtained from the anionic polymerization of β-propiolactam in dimethylsulfoxide at room temperature. Similarly, various alkyl-substituted β-propiolactams were found to give high molecular weight polymers.

Table 1

Preparation of Poly-β-amides (Nylon 3)

Starting material	Reaction conditions	Molecular weight
$H_2N-CH_2-CH_2-COOH$	Condensation at 200°	< 5,000
$H_2N-CH_2-CH_2-COO_2H_5$	Self-condensation at 20°	< 5,000
$H_2N-CH_2-CH_2-COCl$	Thermal condensation under vacuum	< 5,000
$HN-CH_2-CH_2-COOH$ $\quad\mid$ $CO-SC_6H_5$	In dioxane at 60-80° with pyridine catalyst	< 5,000
N-Carboxy-β-alanine anhydride	Thermal decomposition at 150°	~7,000
$H_2N-CH_2-C(CH_3)_2-COOH$	In cresol at 190°	~10,000
$CH_2=CH-CO-NH_2$	In pyridine at 100° with alkaline catalyst	76,000
CH_2-CH_2 $\mid\qquad\mid$ $CO\;-NH$	Anionic polymerization in dimethylsulfoxide at room temperature	500,000

These polymers differ from commercial nylons in that the amide groups are much more closely spaced. They are the nearest among synthetic polyamides to natural silk.

Poly(β-alanine) and its methyl-substituted derivatives, poly(β-valine) and poly(β-aminobutyric acid), are highly crystalline and are readily soluble in formic acid. Indeed, formic acid solutions of these polymers give good fibers by wet spinning. If highly regular and high molecular weight poly(β-alanine) could be synthesized, acrylamide could become an important raw material for the production of interesting fibers.

Finally, the following bimolecular hydrogen transfer could also be envisioned. The success of proton transfer polymerization of acrylamide depends on (a) a suitable acidic amide hydrogen as the proton-source, and (b) a relatively electrophilic vinyl group, i.e., a $CH_2=CH-$ group conjugated with an electron-withdrawing system, as the proton target. It is not necessary that these two groups be directly coupled as in acrylamide. Indeed, as will be discussed later, in spite

of the fact that in certain systems, e.g., $CH_2=CH-\!\!\left\langle\bigcirc\right\rangle\!\!-CONH_2$, these two functions are separated, proton transfer polymerization proceeds readily. Therefore, theoretically, the vinyl and amide groups could be reacted as bifunctional species, e.g.,

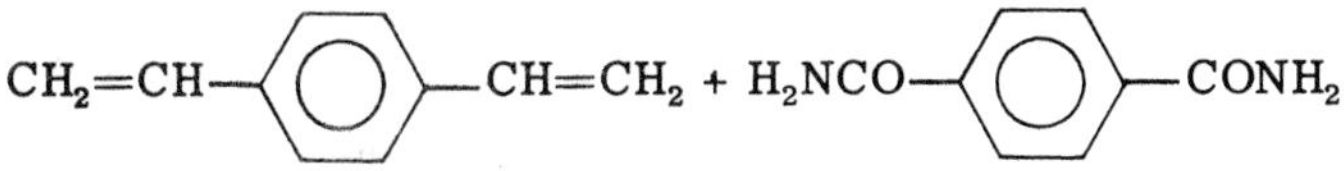

$$CH_2=CH-\langle\bigcirc\rangle-CH=CH_2 + H_2NCO-\langle\bigcirc\rangle-CONH_2, \text{ and the}$$

following polymerization could ensue:

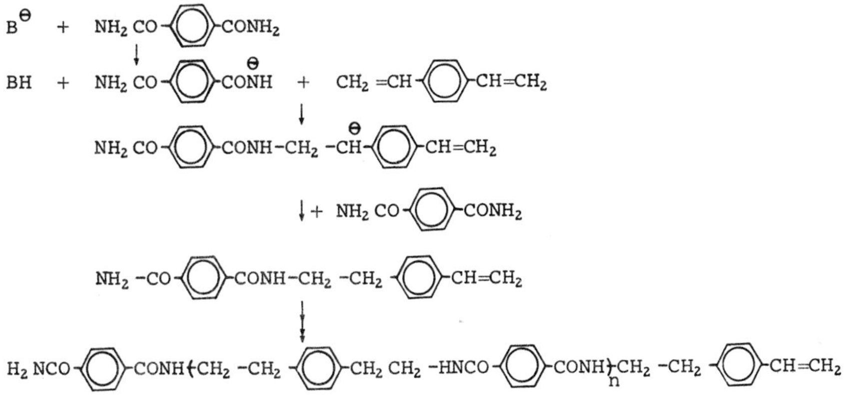

$$B^{\ominus} + NH_2CO-\langle\bigcirc\rangle-CONH_2$$
$$\downarrow$$
$$BH + NH_2CO-\langle\bigcirc\rangle-CONH^{\ominus} + CH_2=CH-\langle\bigcirc\rangle-CH=CH_2$$
$$\downarrow$$
$$NH_2CO-\langle\bigcirc\rangle-CONH-CH_2-CH^{\ominus}-\langle\bigcirc\rangle-CH=CH_2$$
$$\downarrow + NH_2CO-\langle\bigcirc\rangle-CONH_2$$
$$NH_2-CO-\langle\bigcirc\rangle-CONH-CH_2-CH_2-\langle\bigcirc\rangle-CH=CH_2$$
$$\downarrow$$
$$H_2NCO-\langle\bigcirc\rangle-CONH(CH_2-CH_2-\langle\bigcirc\rangle-CH_2CH_2-HNCO-\langle\bigcirc\rangle-CONH)_nCH_2-CH_2-\langle\bigcirc\rangle-CH=CH_2$$

Although similar polyaddition reaction between α,ω-divinyl compounds and α,ω-dithiol compounds with peroxide initiator to give a polyalkylene sulfide structure have been reported [21], systems like these have not yet been described in the scientific literature. The relation between the structures of the proposed polyamides conceivably obtainable by the above reaction sequence and those obtainable from p-vinyl benzamide are related to each other as, e.g., nylon 66 is related to nylon 6, i.e., —X—NHCO—X—CONH— vs. —X—CONH—. Similar examples to this approach have been reported in the base-initiated hydrogen transfer polymerization between tetracarboxylic diimide and divinyl sulfone (cf. Sect. II.E).

B. N-Substituted Acrylamides

Many N-substituted acrylamides readily give polymers by proton transfer mechanism under conditions similar to those used for the polymerization of the parent compound acrylamide. As branched poly(β-alanine) can be regarded as an N-substituted acrylamide, it is interesting that branched poly(β-alanines) were first mentioned only in 1969 [16]. Up to this recent date none of the authors who examined the polymerization of acrylamide found or mentioned any evidence for the formation of branched structures. During the period from 1954, the discovery of H-transfer polymerization of acrylamide, till 1969, it was assumed that growth is either exclusively by intramolecular proton transfer involving only the $-CONH_2$ terminus of the growing polymer or by intermolecular proton transfer involving only primary amide groups. Secondary amide groups ($-CONH-$) have not been considered as proton sources in spite of their much larger concentration in the polymer. As mentioned in the previous section, Glickson and Applequist [16] pointed out in 1969 that the water-soluble product isolated from the base-catalyzed polymerization of acrylamide is a highly branched polymer, indicating that proton transfer could also involve secondary amides in the polymer chain.

Available data on the polymerization of N-substituted acrylamides are compiled in Table 2. Significantly, the rates of polymerization and the molecular weights (viscosities) of the polymers are substantially lower for the N-substituted acrylamides than for the parent monomer, indicating the sluggishness of these polymerizations. As pointed out by Yokota et al. [22], the order of the ease of hydrogen transfer polymerization of N-substituted phenylacrylamides increases with the increasing acidity of the N—H bond, i.e., with the increasing electron-withdrawing character of the substituent on the nitrogen. With the electron-donating N-cyclohexyl derivative, conventional vinyl polymerization took place exclusively.

Leoni et al. [23] prepared highly regular, crystalline, relatively high metling but low molecular weight polymers of N-methyl-, N-phenyl-, and N-isopropylacrylamide. The melting points of these three polymers were, respectively, ~200, ~203, and ~129°. Polymerizations could be carried out to high conversions even at room temperature with highly basic initiators (n-butyllithium) in dioxane solvent. All the products had 1,4-structures and contained amide groups in the main chain.

N-Acryloyl- and N-methacryloylglycinamides (IV) and N-acryloyl and N-methacryloylalaninamides (V) were polymerized by Iwakura et al. [24] with base initiators. It was theorized that if hydrogen transfer propagation involving the terminal amide group would occur exclusively, alternating copolymers of α- and β-amino acid would be obtained:

$$CH_2 = CR-CONH-CH_2 CONH_2 \longrightarrow \sim\sim CH_2 CHRCONHCH_2 CONH\sim\sim$$

$$(IV, \quad R = H \text{ or } CH_3)$$

$$\text{CH}_2=\overset{\underset{\displaystyle |}{\text{CH}_3}}{\text{CR}}-\text{CONH}-\overset{\underset{\displaystyle |}{}}{\text{CH}}\text{CONH}_2 \longrightarrow \sim\!\sim\!\text{CH}_2\,\text{CHRCONH}\overset{\underset{\displaystyle |}{\text{CH}_3}}{\text{CH}}\text{CONH}\!\sim\!\sim$$

(V, R = H or CH₃)

The polymers obtained were of low molecular weight and hydrogen transfer propagation, in competition with conventional vinyl polymerization, was demonstrated. For example, with IV (R = H) in the presence of n-butyllithium in DMF at 100° a polymer with 28% hydrogen-migrated structure was obtained.

Sekiguchi [25] investigated the polymerization of N-acetonyl-acrylamide, $\text{CH}_2=\text{CH}-\text{CONH}-\text{CH}_2\text{COCH}_3$, under conditions most favorable for proton transfer propagation with acrylamine (t-BuONa in o-dichlorobenzene at 78°). In spite of this, structure analysis, mainly by hydrolysis and paper chromatography, indicated that the polymer was predominantly of a conventional vinyl enchainment:

$$\sim\!-\text{CH}_2-\underset{\underset{\displaystyle \text{CONH}-\text{CH}_2\,\text{COCH}_3}{|}}{\text{CH}}-\sim$$

Sebille [26a] polymerized N-methyl- and N-methoxyacrylamide to very low molecular weight products with sodium hydride in a variety of polar (THF, hexamethylphosphoramide) and nonpolar (benzene) solvents. The initiating species was $\text{CH}_2=\text{CH}-\underset{\underset{\displaystyle \text{R}}{|}}{\text{CON}^\ominus}\text{Na}^\oplus$

where (R = CH₃ or OCH₃). Infrared evidence indicated that under a variety of conditions growth by proton transfer took place, giving rise to amide enchainment in the main chain.

In a short report in 1959 Shields and Coover [26b] described that N-isopropylacrylamide could be polymerized with metal alkyl/transition metal halide catalysts in hydrocarbon, chlorinated hydrocarbon, and ether solvent to a crystalline water-, acetone-, and dimethyl-formamide-insoluble polymer. This polymer had a specific gravity of 1.118 and softening range of 170-200°. The specific gravity and softening range of an amorphous polymer produced by radical initiator were 1.070 and 100-125°, respectively, and it was soluble in the above solvents. The possibility of hydrogen transfer polymerization has not been recognized by these authors. It has been described that N,N-dialkyl-substituted acrylamides homopolymerize only at the vinyl site with metal alkyls dispersed in hydrocarbons to highly crystalline isotactic polymers having softening points higher than 300° [26c].

Table 2

Polymerization of N-Substituted Acrylamides

R Substituent in $CH_2=CHCONHR$	Catalyst	Solvent	Temp. (°C)	η_{sp}/c	Mp (°C)	Predominant enchainment	Ref.
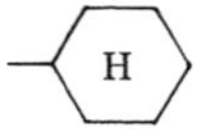 H (phenyl)	t-BuONa	Toluene	105	0.05	83-87	Vinyl	22
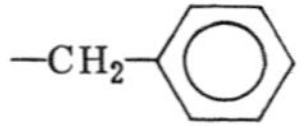 $-CH_2$-(phenyl)	t-BuONa	Toluene	105	0.05	92-94	H transfer	22
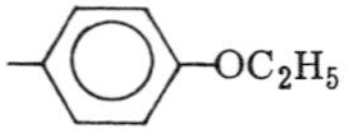 OC_2H_5-(phenyl)	t-BuONa	Toluene	105	0.05	119-124	H transfer	22
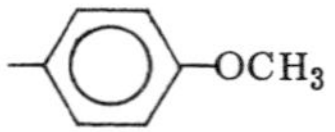 OCH_3-(phenyl)	t-BuONa	Toluene	105	0.05	130-145	H transfer	22
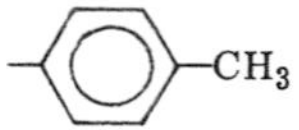 CH_3-(phenyl)	t-BuONa	Toluene	105	0.04	90-100	H transfer	22
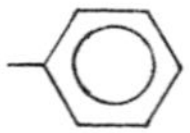 (phenyl)	t-BuONa	Toluene	105	0.05	109-120	H transfer	22

 Cl-phenyl–CH$_3$	t-BuONa	Toluene	105	0.02	118–127	H transfer	22
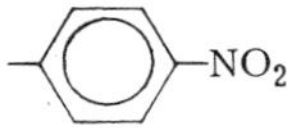 NO$_2$-phenyl–CH$_3$	t-BuONa	Toluene	105	0.04	202–205	Vinyl	22
—CH$_3$	NaH	THF, HMPA, etc.	18–90	~0.11	—	H transfer	26a
—OCH$_3$	NaH	THF, HMPA, etc.	18	~0.05	—	H transfer	26a
—CH$_3$	n–BuLi, t–BuONa, etc.	Dioxane, benzene, etc.	25–10	0.10	~200	H transfer	23
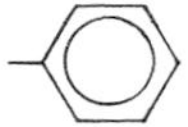 phenyl	n–BuLi, t–BuONa, etc.	Dioxane, benzene, etc.	25–10	0.08	~203	H transfer	23
—CH$<$CH$_3$/CH$_3$	n–BuLi, t–BuONa, etc.	Dioxane, benzene, etc.	25–10	0.045	~129	H transfer	23
—CH$<$CH$_3$/CH$_3$	RMe/MeX	Hydrocarbon, chlorohydrocarbon, etc.	—	—	170–200	Vinyl?	26b
—CH$_2$COCH$_3$	t–BuONa	Dichlorobenzene	78–117	—	—	Vinyl	25
—CH$_2$CONH$_2$	t–BuONa, n–BuLi	DMF, Py, DMSO	100	0.03–0.08	—	Vinyl + H transfer	24
—CH(CH$_3$)CONH$_2$	t–BuONa, n–BuLi	DMF, Py, DMSO	100	—	—	Vinyl + H transfer	24
—(CH$_2$CH$_2$CONH)$_n$H (where n = 1 or 2)	t–BuONa, n–BuLi, etc.	Dioxane	20–100	—	—	H transfer	23

Thus in the base-initiated polymerization of N-substituted acryl-amides, two completely different sets of observations emerge (cf. Table 2): depending on the structure and polymerization conditions, vinyl polymerization leading to a conventional structure or H-trans-fer polymerization giving rise to amide enchainment may arise. This difference may be due to a change in polymerization mechanism from step growth to chain growth. The most important parameter which determines the course of the reaction seems to be the nature of the substituent on the N atom. An electron-repelling substituent (e.g., alkyl) would stabilize the charge on the N, causing the base to attack preferentially the double bond and to produce a covalent bond by chain-growth mechanism. Conversely, an electron-attracting sub-stituent (aromatic ring) helps to stabilize the charge on the N and consequently promotes intermolecular H transfer by a step-growth mechanism. In general terms, polymerization by step growth would lead to 1,4-enchainment and low molecular weights. Conversely, a predominantly chain-growth mechanism would result in increasing amounts of conventional 1,2-enchainment. Clearly more detailed investigations are needed to better correlate reaction conditions with structure.

C. α- and β-Substituted Acrylamides

The polymerization of α- and β-substituted acrylamides has been investigated by many research groups. A compilation of the available literature is shown in Table 3.

Hydrogen transfer polymerization occurs readily in α- or β-sub-stituted acrylamides. The polymerization is somewhat slower and the molecular weights are much lower with these derivatives than with the acrylamide parent. Qualitatively, it appears that substitution on the nitrogen causes the largest rate-retarding and molecular weight-reducing effect followed by substitution on the β-carbon and finally on the α-carbon [2]. The reason could be that alkyl mono-substitution on nitrogen renders the remaining hydrogen in the —CONHR group more basic (less acidic) and consequently more re-luctant to sustain proton transfer propagation. This effect is more important in reducing rates and molecular weights than the effect of β-substitution which is probably a steric hindrance effect, i.e., diffi-culty in attacking an internal double bond. This is evidenced by the fact that both electron-releasing and attracting substituents reduce rates and molecular weights.

More in particular, Nakayama et al. [27] polymerized methacryl-amide with sec-BuONa and n-BuLi in toluene and polar solvents at 100° and reported that the rate of polymerization was much slower than that of acrylamide. Propagation involved an intermolecular step-growth process. This was independently found by Wexler [28a] who carried out the polymerization with sodium methoxide in chlorobenzene solvent. Guaita and Thomas [28b] isolated a crystalline trimer, cyclic tri-α-methyl-β-alanine (VI), from the t-butoxide-initiated hydrogen transfer polymerization of methacrylamide in 1-methyl-2-pyrrolidone or dimethylsulfoxide. The structure was confirmed by NMR spectra:

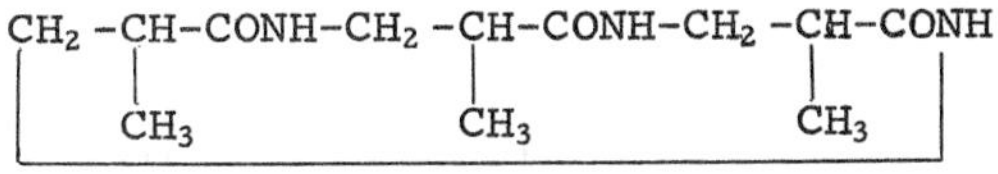

$$CH_2-CH-CONH-CH_2-CH-CONH-CH_2-CH-CONH$$
$$\quad\quad |\quad\quad\quad\quad\quad\quad | \quad\quad\quad\quad\quad\quad |$$
$$\quad\quad CH_3\quad\quad\quad\quad\quad\quad CH_3 \quad\quad\quad\quad\quad CH_3$$

(VI)

According to these authors, the polymerization was initiated by proton abstraction from the amide group, followed by propagation via intramolecular proton transfer mechanism. If the growing amide anion adds to the double bond attached to the other growing end, this trimer would be produced.

The polymerization of α-benzylacrylamide [29] and α-phenylacrylamide [30] proceeds by hydrogen transfer. With the latter monomer (atropamide) steric compression by the pendant phenyl group is so large that conventional vinyl polymerization is completely prevented. Evidently the $-CH_2-\overset{\ominus}{\underset{C_6H_5}{C}}-CONH_2$ ion is too bulky to attack the monomer so that growth occurs exclusively by proton transfer:

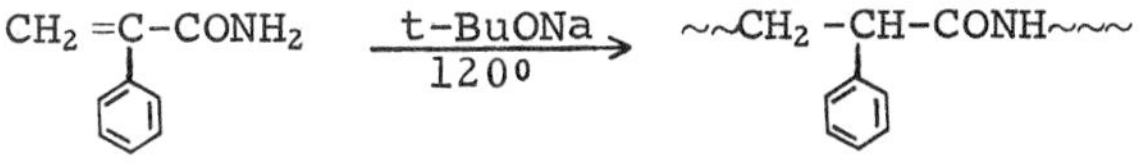

$$CH_2=C-CONH_2 \quad \xrightarrow[120^0]{t-BuONa} \quad \sim\sim CH_2-CH-CONH\sim\sim$$

The base-initiated hydrogen transfer polymerization of β-substituted acrylamides was also investigated and was confirmed in crotonamide [31], cinnamide [32], and β-vinylacrylamide (VII) [33]. The latter two monomers lead to poly-δ-amino acids:

$$R-CH=CH-CH=CH-CONH_2 \quad \longrightarrow \quad \sim\sim CH-CH=CH-CH_2\,CONH\sim\sim$$
$$\quad\quad\quad\quad\quad\quad\quad\quad\quad\quad\quad\quad\quad\quad\quad\quad\quad\quad |$$
$$(VII,\ R=H:\ VIII,\ R=CH_3)\quad\quad\quad\quad R$$

Table 3

Polymerization of α- and β-Substituted Acrylamides

R Substituent	Catalyst	Solvent	Temp. (°C)	η_{sp}/c	Mp (°C)	Predominant enchainment	Ref.
In $CH_2=CR-CONH_2$							
—CH₃	n–BuLi, s–BuONa	Toluene, DMF, pyridine	100	0.08–0.09	—	H transfer	27
—CH₃	t–BuONa	Dioxane	100	0.1	< 257	—	2
—CH₃	CH₃ONa	Chlorobenzene	~120	—	~300	H transfer	28a
(phenyl)	Na/K, t–BuONa	Toluene, pyridine	120	—	—	H transfer	30
—CH₂(phenyl)	n–BuLi, t–BuONa	Xylene	100	0.04–0.05	280–290	H transfer	29
In $RCH=CH-CONH_2$							
—CH₃	K, t–BuONa, t–BuOK	Pyridine, chlorobenzene, o-dichlorobenzene, xylene	100–115	0.08–0.1	—	H transfer	31

Monomer	Catalyst	Solvent	Temp.			Type	Ref.
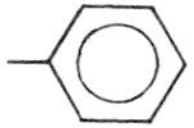 [phenyl]—CH=CH$_2$	n-BuLi, Na, t-BuONa	DMF, pyridine	120–140	0.04–0.07	—	H transfer	32
—CH=CH—CH$_3$	n-BuLi, t-BuONa	Bulk, xylene, o-dichlorobenzene	140–170	0.01–0.1	160–190	H transfer	33
	n-BuLi, t-BuONa	Bulk, toluene, DMF, pyridine, etc.	120–130	—	—	H transfer	33
—CONH$_2$	n-BuLi, t-BuONa	DMF	20–90	—	258–268	H transfer	34
—COOCH$_3$	n-BuLi, t-BuONa	Toluene, DMF	20–90	—	—	H transfer	34
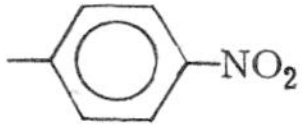 [phenyl]—NO$_2$	n-BuLi, t-BuONa	DMF, dioxane	90	0.09	—	H transfer + vinyl	35a
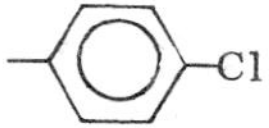 [phenyl]—Cl	n-BuLi, t-BuONa	DMF, dioxane	90	0.1	—	H transfer + vinyl	35b
In R$_1$—CH=C—CONH$_2$, R$_2$; R$_1$=CH$_3$, R$_2$=CONH$_2$	n-BuLi, t-BuONa	DMF	20–90	—	—	H transfer	34

These were amorphous; the polymer of VII was insoluble whereas that of VIII was soluble initially but became insoluble on standing in air.

Recently, it has been found that α,β-dimethylacrylamide undergoes hydrogen transfer polymerization when heated in the presence of n-BuLi in pyridine at 110° [36]:

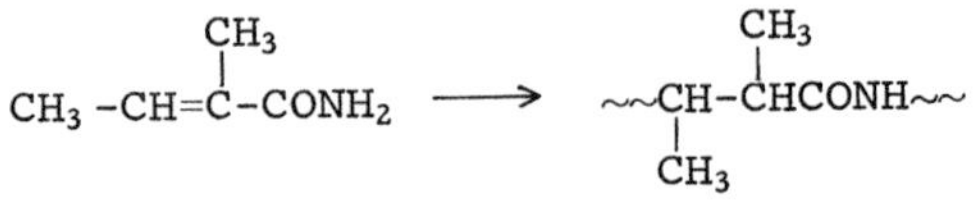

$$\underset{\overset{\textstyle CH_3}{\textstyle |}}{CH_3-CH=C-CONH_2} \longrightarrow \underset{\overset{\textstyle |}{\textstyle CH_3}}{\sim\!\sim\!CH-\overset{\textstyle CH_3}{\overset{\textstyle |}{C}}HCONH\sim\!\sim}$$

Bamford and co-workers [34] described an interesting synthesis for the preparation of α-polypeptides by base-initiated hydrogen transfer polymerization. The basic idea was to force the propagating anion to attack the α-carbon (in preference to the β-carbon) by introducing a strongly electron withdrawing group X in the β-position:

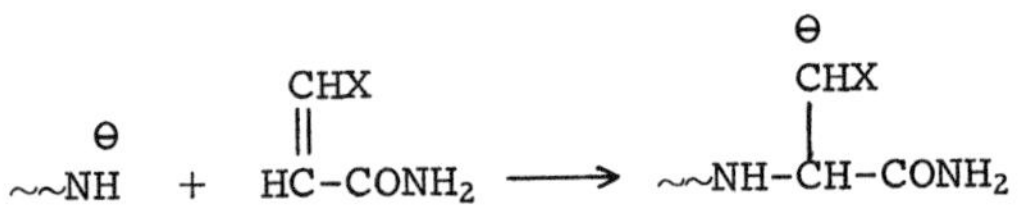

$$\sim\!\sim NH^{\ominus} + \underset{\overset{\textstyle ||}{\textstyle HC-CONH_2}}{\overset{\textstyle CHX}{}} \longrightarrow \sim\!\sim NH-\underset{}{\overset{\overset{\textstyle \ominus}{\textstyle CHX}}{\textstyle CH-CONH_2}}$$

followed by the well-known proton transfer, giving rise to a propagating α-peptide chain:

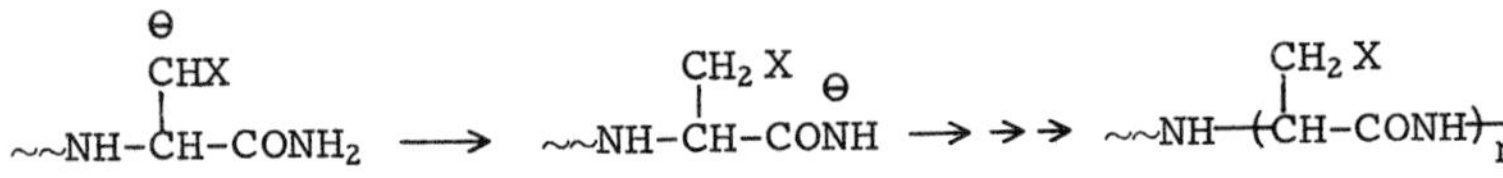

$$\sim\!\sim NH-\underset{}{\overset{\overset{\textstyle \ominus}{\textstyle CHX}}{\textstyle CH-CONH_2}} \longrightarrow \sim\!\sim NH-\underset{}{\overset{\textstyle CH_2X}{\textstyle CH-CONH}}{}^{\ominus} \rightarrow \twoheadrightarrow \sim\!\sim NH\!-\!\!\left(\underset{}{\overset{\textstyle CH_2X}{\textstyle CH-CONH}}\right)_{\!\!n}$$

This ingenious scheme was tested with several monomers e.g., maleamide and mesaconamide:

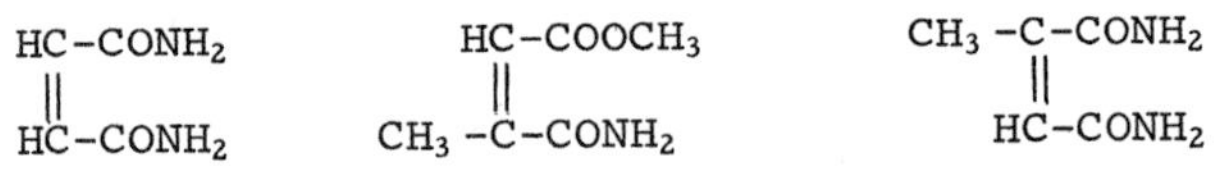

$$\underset{\overset{\textstyle ||}{\textstyle HC-CONH_2}}{\overset{\textstyle HC-CONH_2}{}} \qquad \underset{\overset{\textstyle ||}{\textstyle CH_3-C-CONH_2}}{\overset{\textstyle HC-COOCH_3}{}} \qquad \underset{\overset{\textstyle ||}{\textstyle HC-CONH_2}}{\overset{\textstyle CH_3-C-CONH_2}{}}$$

For example, by substituting the β-carbon with an ester group, a strong electron acceptor, and reinforcing the inductive effect by a CH_3-group on the α-carbon (mesaconic ester amide), the authors were able to achieve a measure of the desired 1-addition; however, the undesirable 2-addition also occurred:

$$
\overset{\ominus}{\text{~NH}} + \underset{\text{CH}_3-\overset{\|}{\text{C}}-\text{CONH}_2}{\overset{\text{HC-COOCH}_3}{\|}}
\begin{cases}
1 & \begin{array}{c} \overset{\ominus}{\text{HC-COOCH}_3} \\ | \\ \text{~NH-C-CONH}_2 \\ | \\ \text{CH}_3 \end{array} \xrightarrow{\sigma} \begin{array}{c} \text{CH}_2\text{-COOCH}_3 \\ | \quad \ominus \\ \text{~NH-C-CONH} \\ | \\ \text{CH}_3 \end{array} \xrightarrow{\ggg} \alpha \text{ peptide} \\
2 & \begin{array}{c} \text{~NH-CH-COOCH}_3 \\ | \\ \text{CH}_3-\text{C-CONH}_2 \\ \ominus \end{array} \xrightarrow{\sigma} \begin{array}{c} \text{~NH-CH-COOCH}_3 \\ | \quad \ominus \\ \text{CH}_3-\text{CH-CONH} \end{array} \xrightarrow{\ggg} \beta \text{ peptide}
\end{cases}
$$

The occurrence of the detrimental 2-addition was indicated by the presence of α- and β-aspartic acids after hydrolysis and paper chromatography of the final peptide.

This lead was later followed by Imanishi et al. [35a,35b] who substituted the β-carbon with p-nitrophenyl or p-chlorophenyl, strong electron attractors. However, with the p-nitrophenyl derivatives, trans-p-nitrocinnamide, unforeseen complications have occurred because the product not only contained derivatives of 1- and 2-additions but also there was evidence for competing vinyl polymerization giving rise to C—C linkages:

$$
\begin{array}{cccc}
\text{O}_2\text{N}-\bigcirc-\overset{\text{CH}}{\underset{\text{HC-CONH}_2}{|}} & \rightarrow & \text{O}_2\text{N}-\bigcirc-\overset{\text{CH}_2}{\underset{\text{~CH-CONH~}}{|}} & \quad \text{O}_2\text{N}-\bigcirc-\overset{\text{CH~}}{\underset{\text{CH}_2-\text{CONH~}}{|}} & \quad \text{O}_2\text{N}-\bigcirc-\overset{\text{CH~}}{\underset{\text{~CH}}{|}} \\
& & & \underset{\text{CONH}_2}{|}
\end{array}
$$

| 1 addition | 2 addition | vinyl addition |

The significance of these pioneering investigations is that they show a possible way of synthesizing α-polypeptides from vinyl monomers. These first trials are by no means discouraging as they demonstrate the feasibility of obtaining α-peptide linkages by a new method. Perhaps by combining the directive influence of the inductive effect with the prohibitive influence of steric compression, future workers will be able to force uniform attack on the α-carbon:

$$
\overset{\ominus}{\text{~NH}} \searrow \quad \underset{\text{HC-CONH}_2}{\overset{\text{X-C-Y}}{\|}}
$$

where X is strong electron acceptor and Y is bulky group or combination of these.

D. Miscellaneous Amides and Related Compounds

The polymerization of aromatic amides has been investigated by numerous research groups (see Table 4). Kojima, Yoda, and Marvel [37] polymerized p-vinylbenzamide with t-BuONa and on the basis of the amount of ammonia gas evolved on NaOH treatment, they concluded that the polymer consisted of ~17% conventional vinyl units:

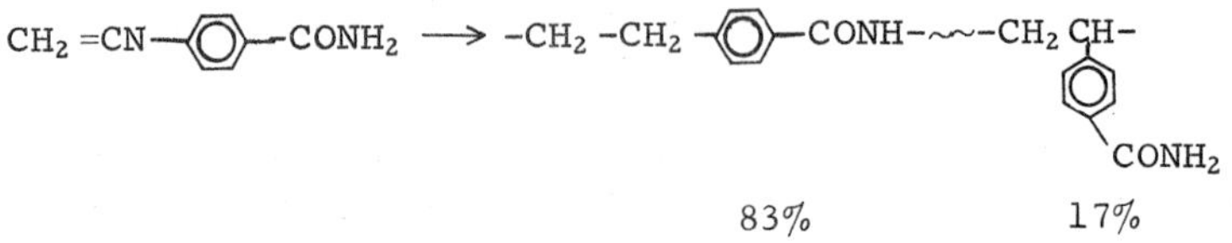

$$CH_2 =CN-\langle O \rangle-CONH_2 \longrightarrow -CH_2 -CH_2 -\langle O \rangle-CONH-\sim\sim-CH_2 \underset{\underset{CONH_2}{\overset{|}{\langle O \rangle}}}{CH}-$$

83%   17%

Just about the same time Negishi and Tamura [38] carried out a more thorough investigation on the basis of which they showed conclusively that this monomer polymerizes predominantly by hydrogen transfer. These investigations with p-vinylbenzamide are also significant in regard to the question of intra- vs. intermolecular proton transfer during propagation of unsaturated amides in general. Considering the spatial arrangement of the atoms of the initially formed carbanion in p-vinylbenzamide, it is very difficult to visualize a reasonable path for intramolecular proton transfer:

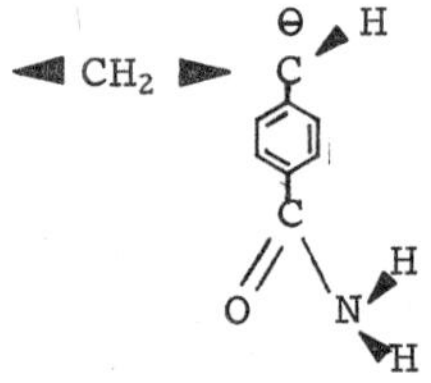

In other words, at least in this system, negative reasoning alone compels us to decide against an intramolecular propagation mechanism. Negishi and Tamura's findings [38] directly corroborate this expectation. These authors found a large amount of dimer

$$CH_2=CH-\langle O \rangle-CO-NH-CH_2CH_2-\langle O \rangle-CONH_2 \text{ in the}$$

alkoxide-catalyzed polymerization charge. According to infrared evidence, the end groups of the dimer were a vinyl group and an amide group, respectively. Significantly, this dimer could be polymerized to a powdery product, the infrared spectrum of which was

identical to that of a poly(vinylbenzamide) obtained by direct polymerization of the monomer. These findings are strong corroboration
for Breslow's views [2] concerning the initiation mechanism and
argue against Ogata's mechanism [4]. In this context it is interesting to contemplate that intramolecular proton shift did not occur
even in the o-vinylbenzamide system [38], a system, the transition
state configuration of which, would have been much more favorable
for intramolecular $H^{\oplus}$ shift than that in acrylamide:

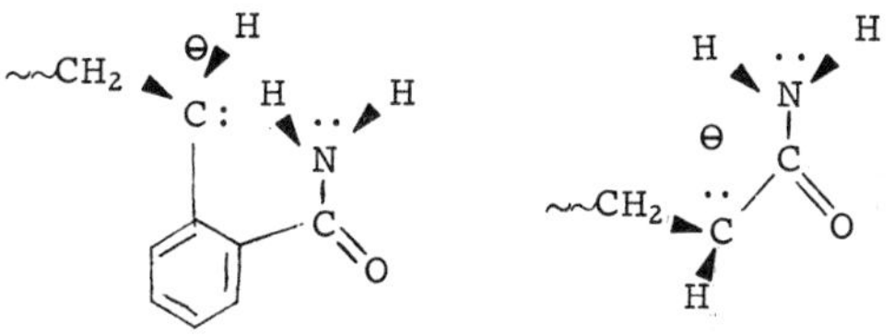

Indeed the present authors consider this finding by analogy very
strong evidence for the general validity of the intermolecular propagation mechanism in acrylamide derivatives as well. o-Vinylbenzamide did not give polymer at all under the conditions in which the
p-derivative underwent polymerization to respectable molecular
weights (see Table 3). A possible explanation is that the initially
formed amide anion, instead of propagating by proton transfer,
internally attacks the o-vinyl double bond [38]:

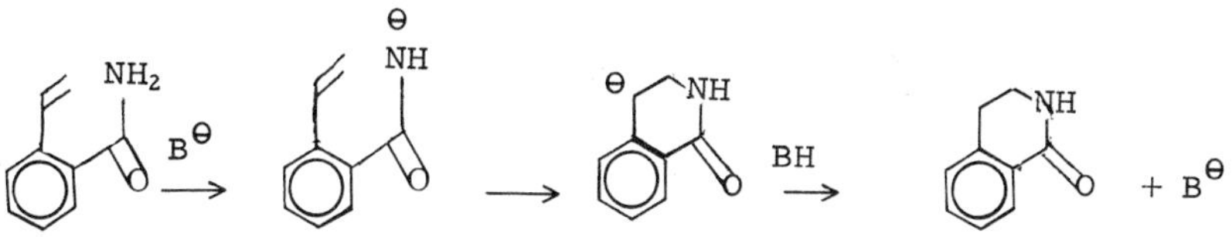

The meta isomer was found to be extremely sluggish toward polymerization (traces of polymer even after 19 hr at 150°). This behavior
was attributed by the authors [38] to the reactivity-reducing inductive
effect of the m-vinyl substituent.

Against this background it is, therefore, disturbing to read about
1 year later Nakayama et al.'s [39] report according to which p-
vinylbenzamide gives predominantly conventional vinyl enchainment
in the presence of such typical anionic initiators as phenyl magnesium
bromide and n-butyllithium in toluene or pyridine. However, closer
examination of the data of these authors reveals that these controversial conclusions were reached on the basis of rather poorly resolved infrared spectra and therefore might be in error.

Table 4

Anionic Polymerization of Miscellaneous Amides and Related Compounds

Formula	Catalyst	Solvent	Temp. (°C)	η_{sp}/c	Mp (°C)	Predominant enchainment	Ref.
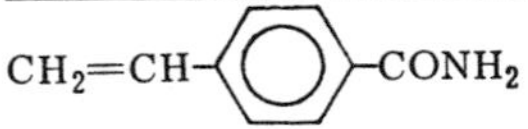 $CH_2{=}CH{-}$⬡${-}CONH_2$	t-BuONa	DMA, pyridine, toluene, p-chlorobenzene	80–100	0.04–0.43	—	H transfer	37
	PhMgBr, Na, K, Li, n-BuLi	Toluene, pyridine, DMF	80–120	0.1–0.3	—	Vinyl + H transfer	39
	t-BuONa	DMSO	110–160	0.1–0.2	>340	H transfer	38
	t-BuOC$_5$	HMPA, DMA	~130	0.12–0.16	—	H transfer	40–43
	t-BuOC$_5$/LiCl	DMA	~130	~0.6	—	Vinyl	40–43
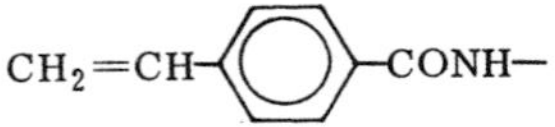 $CH_2{=}CH{-}$⬡${-}CONH{-}$	t-BuOK	DMA	150	—	—	H transfer	38
${-}(CH_2CH_2)_n$⬡${-}(CONH)_n{H}$ (n = 1–2)							
$CH_2{=}CH{-}$⬡${-}$ H_2NOC	t-BuONa	DMF	150	—	—		38
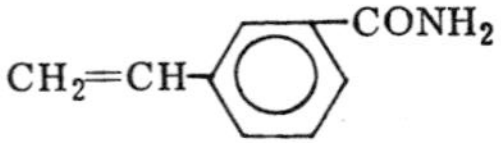 $CH_2{=}CH{-}$⬡${-}CONH_2$	K, t-BuONa	DMF	150	—	—	Trace yield	38
$CH_2{=}CHCH_2CONH_2$	t-BuONa, n-BuLi	Pyridine, toluene	80–100	0.05	—	H transfer + allylic isomerization	45

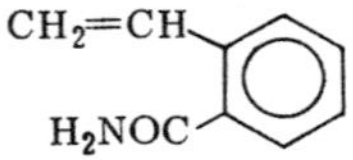

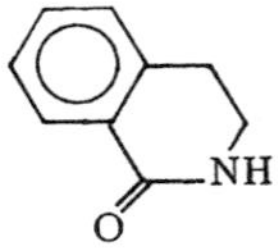

Monomer	Catalyst	Solvent	Temp.			Notes	Ref.
CH₂=CHCOOCH₂CH₂CONH₂	t-BuOK	o-Dichlorobenzene	120	—	—	Vinyl + H transfer	44
CH₂=CHSO₂NH₂	Na	Bulk	100	0.079	~100		2
	t-BuOK	DMF	60–160	0.08–0.9	>276	Different from radical polymer	47
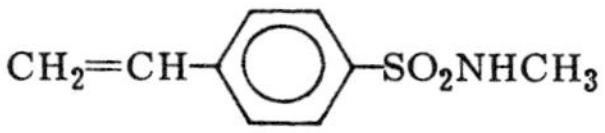 CH₂=CH–C₆H₄–SO₂NHCH₃	t-BuOLi	DMF	80–130	0.02–1.5	—	Vinyl + 20–40% H transfer	48
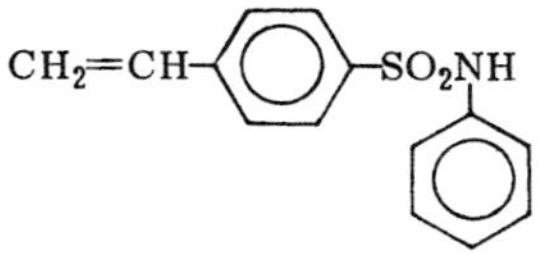 CH₂=CH–C₆H₄–SO₂NH–C₆H₅	t-BuOLi	DMF	130	0.1–0.4	—	Vinyl + 20–30% H transfer	48
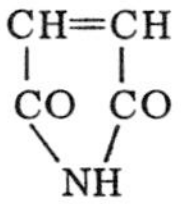 CH=CH / CO–CO \ NH	t-BuONa, etc.	DMF, etc.	100	0.03–0.036	—	H transfer	50
	n-BuLi	Toluene	~40	Very low	—	H transfer	51
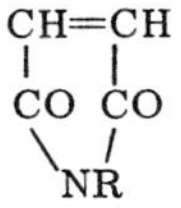					—	Vinyl complex	51
CH=CH / CO–CO \ NR	n-BuLi	THF, toluene	0–70	~0.1	—	Vinyl	52

The p-vinylbenzamide system has also been extensively studied by Asahara et al. [40-43]. These authors reconfirmed the fact that under anionic polymerization conditions this monomer gives about 90% hydrogen transfer polymerization, and in addition demonstrated that in the presence of a complexing inorganic salt i.e., LiCl, the course of the polymerization can be changed toward exclusively vinyl enchainment:

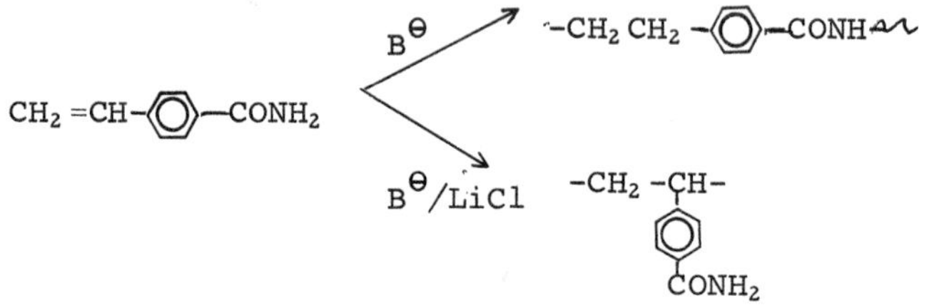

$$CH_2 =CH-\langle O \rangle-CONH_2 \quad \overset{B^{\ominus}}{\underset{B^{\ominus}/LiCl}{\bigg\langle}} \quad \begin{array}{l} \nearrow -CH_2 CH_2 -\langle O \rangle-CONH\sim \\ \\ \searrow -CH_2 -CH- \\ \qquad\quad \langle O \rangle \\ \qquad\quad CONH_2 \end{array}$$

While this redirecting effect is quite dramatic, it is by no means specific to LiCl. $CaCl_2$, $CuCl_2$, $ZnCl_2$, etc. gave similar results. Interestingly, acrylamide polymerization proceeds by hydrogen transfer even in the presence of LiCl. These major findings and many supporting observations are plausibly explained by the authors as follows: LiCl or other salts are able to complex strongly vinyl-benzamide by the amide group so that the polymerization is forced to commence by a nucleophilic attack of the anionic initiator on the vinyl unsaturation; complexation by the LiCl might even enhance by resonance the polarity of the vinyl group:

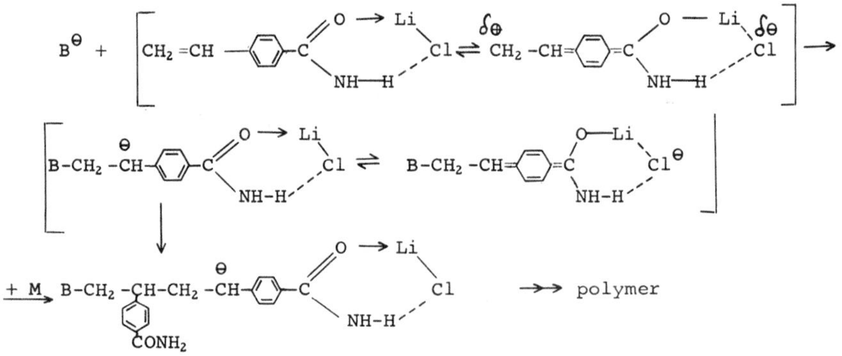

$$B^{\ominus} + \left[CH_2 =CH -\langle O \rangle-C \overset{O \to Li}{\underset{NH-H}{\diagdown}} Cl \rightleftarrows \overset{\delta\ominus}{CH_2 -CH}=\langle O \rangle=C \overset{O - Li}{\underset{NH-H}{\diagdown}} Cl \right]^{\delta\ominus} \rightarrow$$

$$\left[B-CH_2 -\overset{\ominus}{CH}-\langle O \rangle-C \overset{O \to Li}{\underset{NH-H}{\diagdown}} Cl \rightleftarrows B-CH_2 -CH=\langle O \rangle=C \overset{O-Li}{\underset{NH-H}{\diagdown}} Cl^{\ominus} \right]$$

$$\underset{+ M}{\Big\downarrow}$$

$$\overset{+ M}{\longrightarrow} B-CH_2 -\underset{CONH_2}{\underset{|}{CH}}-CH_2 -\overset{\ominus}{CH}-\langle O \rangle-C \overset{O \to Li}{\underset{NH-H}{\diagdown}} Cl \quad \longrightarrow\longrightarrow polymer$$

The coordinated amide group cannot function as an effective source of protons because of its hydrogen bridge to the chlorine. In this manner the carbanion is forced to attack the polarized monomer, etc. Evidently the complexing between acrylamide and LiCl must be much weaker than with p-vinylbenzamide as LiCl had no directing influence on that polymerization.

With this background, it would be interesting to investigate the effect of inorganic salts on Michael reactions in general, in particular to learn if the preparative yield of this reaction could be increased in the presence of LiCl or other coordinating salts.

α-Acryloyloxypropinionamide is expected to produce a copolymer with alternating ester and amide linkages through hydrogen transfer polymerization:

$$CH_2 = CHCOOCH_2\ CH_2\ CONH_2\ \longrightarrow\ \sim\sim CH_2 - CH_2\ COOCH_2\ CH_2\ CONH\sim\sim$$

When polymerized with t-BuOK in o-dichlorobenzene at 120°, a copolymer with 35% hydrogen migration was obtained, but in other solvents such as pyridine, chlorobenzene, toluene, and dimethylformamide only vinyl polymerization took place [44].

An interesting case of "anionic-allylic-isomerization-combined-with-proton-transfer-polymerization" with vinylacetamide, $CH_2 = CH - CH_2 - CONH_2$, has been described by Nakayama et al. [45]. These authors polymerized vinylacetamide with n-BuLi or t-BuONa in pyridine and toluene solvent and thoroughly characterized the polymer structure by infrared and NMR spectroscopy and thin-layer chromatography of the hydrolyzates. These studies led to the following structure:

$$CH_3 - CH=CH-CONH\{CH=CH-CONH\}_{8-9}^{\overset{CH_3}{|}}H$$

Experiments demonstrated qualitatively that crotonamide formed during the polymerization of vinylacetamide and, vice-versa, vinylacetamide formed during the polymerization of crotonamide. These facts led the authors to conclude that the growth of vinylacetamide proceeds by an initial allylic isomerization to crotonamide which is then immediately polymerized:

$$CH_2 = CH - CH_2 - CONH_2 \longrightarrow CH_3 - CH=CH - CONH_2 \longrightarrow polymer$$

(probably cis isomer)

This theory was directly confirmed by polymerizing crotonamide and determining the structure of the product. The infrared and NMR spectra of polycrotonamide and the polymer obtained from vinyl-acetamide were virtually undistinguishable, indicating the identity of these two materials. The spectroscopic results have independently been confirmed by thin-layer chromatography of the hydrolyzates of the two polymers.

Independent experiments showed, however, that vinylacetamide polymerized somewhat faster than crotonamide under identical conditions. To explain this observation, the authors assumed that the first intermediate to form from vinylacetamide is the more reactive cis isomer, isocrotonamide, which would polymerize faster than the more stable trans isomer, crotonamide. This very attractive theory has not yet been directly confirmed.

The above reaction sequence qualifies the vinylacetamide system to be a "polymerization with isomerization of monomer preceding propagation," a subject recently reviewed by the present authors [46].

Monomers having a sulfonamide group, i.e., ethylenesulfonamide [2], p-styrenesulfonamide [47], and N-methyl or N-phenyl-p-styrenesulfonamide [48], have been investigated for proton-transfer polymerization in the presence of alkaline initiators:

$$CH_2 = CH \text{-} \langle \bigcirc \rangle \text{-} SO_2 NHR \longrightarrow \sim\sim\sim CH_2 - CH_2 - \langle \bigcirc \rangle - SO_2 NR \sim\sim$$

$$(R = H, CH_3, C_6 H_5)$$

With p-styrenesulfonamide derivatives the resulting polymer was probably a copolymer of proton transferred units and conventional vinyl enchainment. The base-catalyzed copolymerization of p-styrenesulfonamide with p-vinylbenzamide was studied by Asahara et al. [49]. These workers obtained aromatic copolyamides and noted that the relative extent of vinyl or H-transfer polymerization could be influenced by the relative concentrations of the monomers in the charge and the catalyst employed.

Marvel and co-workers [50] found that hydrogen transfer polymerization occurs with maleimide in the presence of t-BuONa in dimethylformamide. The low molecular weight polymer obtained consisted mainly of the hydrogen-migrated structure. Nakayama and Smets [51] confirmed Marvel's data:

$$
\begin{array}{ccc}
\text{CH}{=}{=}\text{CH} & & \sim\!\!\sim\!\text{CH}\!-\!\text{CH}\!-\!\sim\!\!\sim\!\!\sim\!\!\sim\!\!\text{-CH-CO}\!\!\diagdown \\
\mid\quad\mid & & \mid\quad\mid\qquad\qquad\mid\qquad\diagup\!\text{N}\!\sim\!\!\sim \\
\text{CO}\quad\text{CO} & \longrightarrow & \text{CO}\quad\text{CO}\qquad\text{CH}_2\text{-CO} \\
\diagdown\diagup & & \diagdown\diagup \\
\text{N} & & \text{N} \\
\text{H} & & \text{H}
\end{array}
$$

$$15 \sim 25\% \qquad 75 \sim 85\%$$

and reported 70-75% hydrogen-migrated structure in the polymale-
imide obtained with alkaline initiators at 20°C. Moreover, they
found that the rate was zero-order in monomer which was explained
by assuming a rapid complex formation between the propagating
species and the monomer followed by a slow intramolecular rearrangement of the complex to a new propagating anion. N-n-Butyl-
maleimide rapidly reacts with n-BuLi in toluene at −40°; however,
the final yield of polymer is very low because of side reactions involving the opening of the ring.

Cubbon [52] examined the polymerization of eight N-substituted
maleimides, e.g., ethyl, isopropyl, n-butyl, t-butyl, n-octyl, benzyl
and phenyl, with n-butyllithium initiator in THF and toluene solvents in temperatures from 0 to −70°. Structure analysis in this
instance involved only x-ray diffractometry which showed two inter-
planar spacings for all polymers. One of the spacings at ~5 Å was
common to all poly(N-substituted maleimides) and was attributed
to the backbone repeat unit. The other, larger and variable (from
10.6 to 18.9 Å) spacing was assigned to the spacing between the polymer chains since it increased with the size of the substituent. Although a more comprehensive structure analysis has not been carried out, it was assumed that the repeat unit was the conventional
vinyl structure:

$$
\begin{array}{cc}
\text{- CH - CH -} \\
\mid\qquad\mid \\
\text{CO}\quad\text{CO} \\
\diagdown\diagup \\
\text{N} \\
\mid \\
\text{R}
\end{array}
$$

E. Monomers Having Other Groups than Amide

In analogy with the proton transfer polymerization of acrylamide,
efforts have been made to carry out similar reactions with mono-

mers having suitable functional groups other than amide. Available information is compiled in Table 5. The first report concerning hydrogen transfer polymerization of compounds other than amides appeared in 1963 by Iwatsuki et al. [54] who set out to polymerize methyl vinyl ketone with bases in the presence of an inhibitor for radical polymerization. These authors used t-BuONa in toluene and phenyl-β-naphthylamine inhibitor at 0° for 50 hr. The polymer was a low molecular weight soluble product, the structure of which was investigated making use of the Schmidt reaction, i.e., treatment of the polymer with sodium oxide, hydrolysis, and fragment analysis by paper chromatography. The Schmidt rearrangement followed by hydrolysis yields a mixture of two amides from an unsymmetric ketone. The key finding of Iwatsuki et al. [54] was the isolation and analysis of γ-aminobutyric acid by the above method. This is con-

vincing evidence for $R-\overset{\displaystyle O}{\overset{\|}{C}}-CH_2-CH_2-CH_2-\overset{\displaystyle O}{\overset{\|}{C}}-R'$ units in the chain which in turn indicates that at least part of the original polymer was formed by hydrogen transfer propagation. γ-Aminobutyric

acid could not have been formed from $-CH_2-\overset{\displaystyle |}{CH}-COCH_2-$ units in the backbone.

Contrary to these findings by Japanese investigators, Italian workers, Trossarelli et al. [55], claim that methyl vinyl ketone when polymerized with t-BuONa in N-methylpyrrolidone in the range of 0 to 120° gives vinyl enchainment which then further reacts by intramolecular aldolization and dehydration:

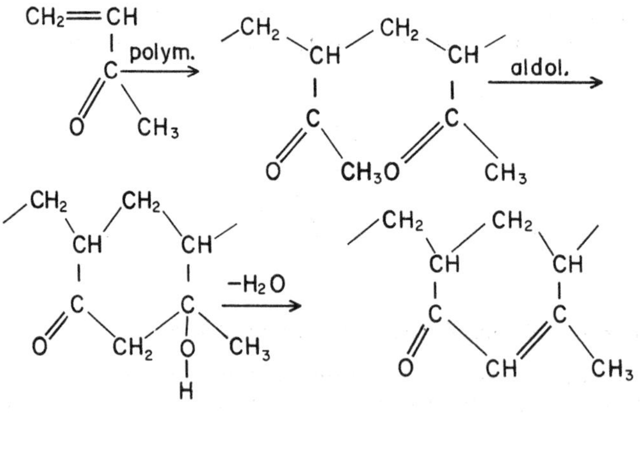

Table 5

Polymerization of Monomers Having Other Groups than Amide

Monomer	Catalyst	Solvent	Temp. (°C)	η_{sp}/c	Predominant enchainment	Ref.
$CH_2=CH—COCH_3$	t-BuONa	Toluene	0	0.012	H transfer	54
$CH_2=CH—CO—CH_3$	t-BuONa	N-Methylpyrrolidone	0–120	—	Vinyl + aldol	55
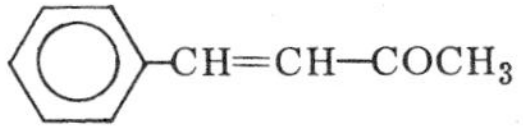 $\bigcirc$—CH=CH—COCH$_3$	Li (−)menthoxide	—	—	(mp 185–195°C)	H transfer	56
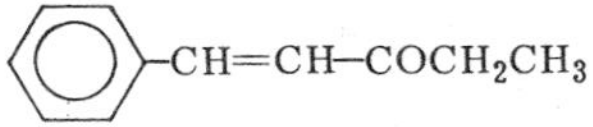 $\bigcirc$—CH=CH—COCH$_2$CH$_3$	Li (−)menthoxide	—	—	—	H transfer	56
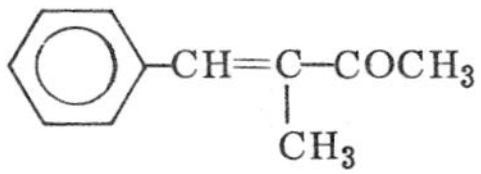 $\bigcirc$—CH=C—COCH$_3$ with CH$_3$	Li (−)menthoxide	—	—	—	H transfer	56
$CH_2=CHCH_2CN$ / CH_3CHO	n-BuLi Na/Hg	Toluene —	−78 0	— (MW ~300)	Allylic Isomerization —CH$_2$—CHOH—	45 57~60
CH_3CHO	Li/Hg	Toluene	0	(MW ~680)	—CH$_2$—CHOH—	57~60
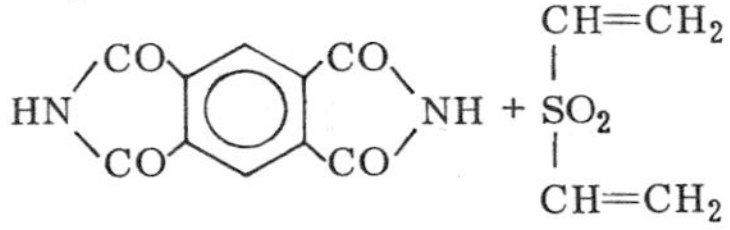 (imide–SO$_2$ monomer with CH=CH$_2$ and CH=CH$_2$ groups)	t-BuONa	DMF, pyridine	18–100	0.09–0.17	H transfer	61

Infrared evidence which indicated the presence of conjugated and
nonconjugated carbonyl groups was shown. By increasing the polymerization temperature, the units formed by aldolization and dehydration were increased. Significantly, the infrared spectra of anionically
polymerized material and that obtained by free radicals followed by
treatment with t-BuONa were similar.

It is very difficult to explain the apparent disagreement between
these findings. The only major difference between the syntheses is
in the nature of the solvent: Iwatsuki et al. [54] used toluene whereas
Trossarelli et al. [55] employed N-methyl-pyrrolidone. It would be
of interest to establish by independent experiments whether or not
this effect of the solvent on reaction mechanism is real.

Recently, Aliev et al. [56] studied the hydrogen transfer polymerization of β-phenyl vinyl ketone derivatives, $C_6H_5CH=CR-COCH_2R'$
(where R = H, R' = H; R = H, R' = CH_3; and R = CH_3, R' = H), with
lithium (-)menthoxide catalyst. From IR and UV spectra, the resulting polymer was found to consist of the following hydrogen transferred structure with $[\alpha]_{375\ m\mu} = +4\text{-}7°$ and mp = 185-195°.

$$C_6H_5\,CH{=}\underset{\underset{R}{|}}{C}{-}COCH_2\,R' \longrightarrow \quad \sim\!\!\sim\!CH{-}\underset{\underset{R}{|}}{CH}{-}\underset{\underset{O}{\|}}{\overset{\overset{C_6H_5}{|}}{C}}{-}\overset{\overset{R'}{|}}{CH}\!\sim\!\!\sim$$

It is interesting that optically active polymer can be obtained in
these polymerizations.

Imoto et al. [57-60] in a series of papers claimed that acetalde-
hyde in the presence of alkali metal amalgams or evaporated sodium
gives low degree of polymerization, $\sim 3\text{-}13$, viscous liquids or tacky,
water-soluble solids which they believe are of the polyvinyl alcohol
type:

$$\underset{\underset{O}{\|}}{CH_3\,CH} \longrightarrow \quad \sim\!\!\sim\!CH_2{-}\underset{\underset{OH}{|}}{CH}\!\sim\!\!\sim$$

The mechanism of this polymerization is thought to proceed by
intermolecular proton transfer, similar to the aldol condensation.

A very interesting hydrogen transfer polymerization has recently
been described by Yuki et al. [53]. These workers were able to
polymerize p-methyl-α-methylstyrene to respectable molecular
weight products with n-BuLi or Na-K alloy in THF at 60° or in
benzene even at 120°. At first glance this is startling considering
that the structurally very closely related α-methylstyrene cannot be

polymerized to high molecular weights above 61°, its ceiling temperature. Structure analysis of the polymers holds the key to the understanding of these observations.

The low temperature (−78°) anionic polymerization of p-methyl-α-methylstyrene gives a conventional enchainment as indicated by NMR spectroscopy:

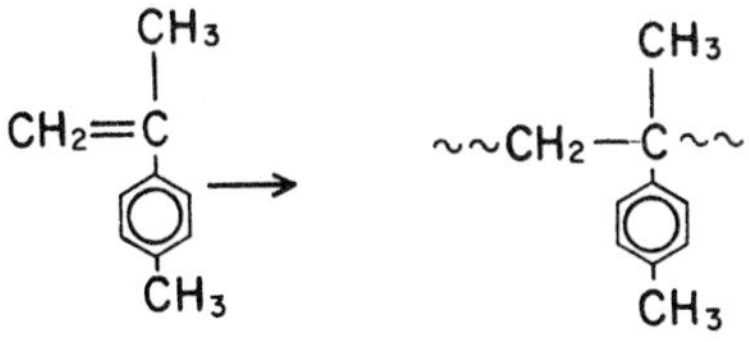

$$CH_2\!=\!\underset{\underset{CH_3}{|}}{\overset{\overset{CH_3}{|}}{C}} \longrightarrow \sim\!\sim\!CH_2\!-\!\underset{\underset{CH_3}{|}}{\overset{\overset{CH_3}{|}}{C}}\!\sim\!\sim$$

However, NMR and IR spectroscopic analysis of the high temperature (120 or 60°) polymer led the authors to conclude that the repeat

unit was $-CH_2-\underset{\overset{|}{CH}}{\overset{\overset{CH_3}{|}}{}}-\!\!\bigcirc\!\!-CH_2\,-.$ To explain this structure

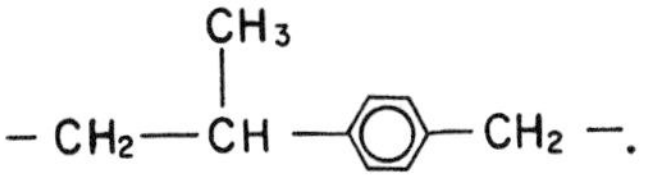

within the framework of the available data the following polymerization mechanism could be postulated (somewhat different from that proposed by Yuki et al.):

Initiation:

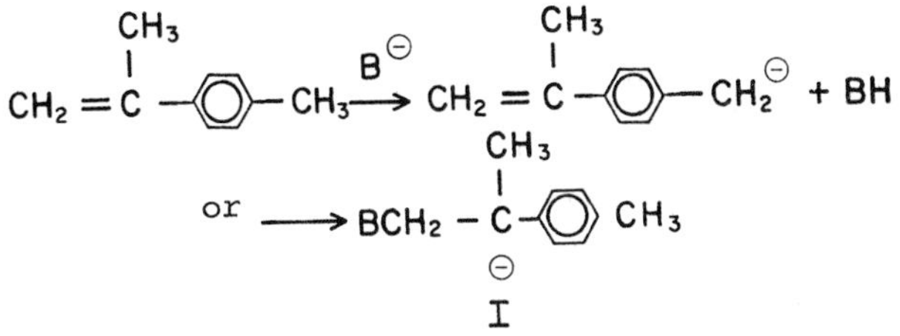

$$CH_2=\underset{\underset{CH_3}{|}}{\overset{\overset{CH_3}{|}}{C}}\!-\!\!\bigcirc\!\!-CH_3 \xrightarrow{B^{\ominus}} CH_2=\underset{\underset{CH_3}{|}}{\overset{\overset{CH_3}{|}}{C}}\!-\!\!\bigcirc\!\!-CH_2^{\ominus} + BH$$

$$\text{or} \longrightarrow BCH_2-\underset{\underset{\ominus}{|}}{\overset{\overset{CH_3}{|}}{C}}\!-\!\!\bigcirc\; CH_3$$

$$\mathbf{I}$$

Propagation:

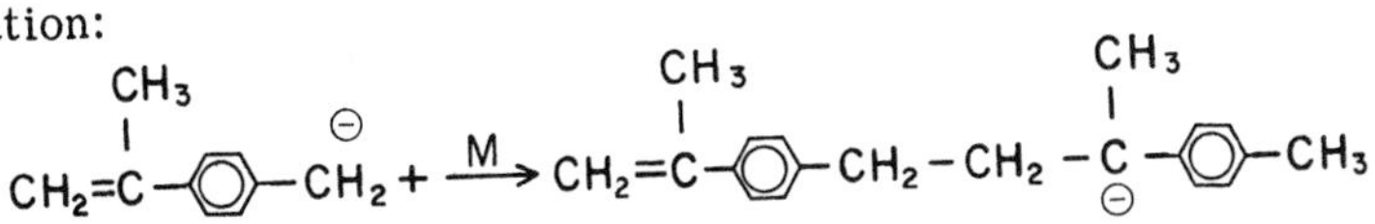

$$CH_2=\underset{\underset{CH_3}{|}}{C}\!-\!\!\bigcirc\!\!-CH_2^{\ominus} + \xrightarrow{M} CH_2=\underset{\underset{CH_3}{|}}{C}\!-\!\!\bigcirc\!\!-CH_2-CH_2-\underset{\underset{\ominus}{|}}{\overset{\overset{CH_3}{|}}{C}}\!-\!\!\bigcirc\!\!-CH_3$$

Proton Transfer:

$$\mathbf{I} + M \to CH_2=\underset{\underset{CH_3}{|}}{C}\!-\!\!\bigcirc\!\!-CH_2-CH_2-\overset{\overset{CH_3}{|}}{CH}\!-\!\!\bigcirc\!\!-CH_3 + CH_2=\underset{\underset{CH_3}{|}}{C}\!-\!\!\bigcirc\!\!-CH_2^{\ominus}$$

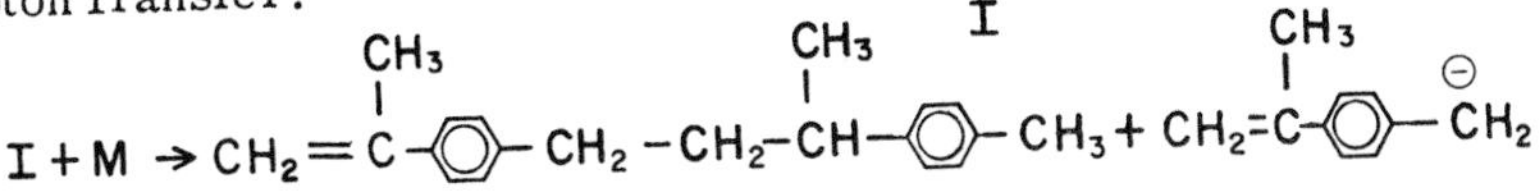

The possibility that the proton is released by the α-methyl has been examined. Had the α-methyl group functioned as the proton source, the repeat unit of the polymer would have been $- CH_2- \overset{\overset{\textstyle H}{|}}{\underset{\underset{\textstyle CH_3}{|}}{\underset{\textstyle \bigcirc}{C}}} - CH_2 -$.

However, this structure did not agree with the spectroscopic findings. Another piece of supporting evidence for the proposed hydrogen transfer polymerization of p-methyl-α-methylstyrene is the fact that p-methylstyrene produces cross-linked polymer when polymerized above 120°, probably by the following mechanism:

Some of the results of the polymerization of p-methyl-α-methyl-styrene are summarized in Table 6.

Table 6

Polymerization of p-Methyl-α-Methylstyrene[a]

Solvent	Catalyst	Temp. (°C)	Time (days)	Total conversion (%)[b]	DP	Softening point (°C)
THF	n-BuLi	−95	1	94.3	96	240
THF	n-BuLi	−78	12	84.5	100	240
THF	n-BuLi	−20	10	99.2	23	200
THF	n-BuLi	0	10	98.0	17	170
THF	n-BuLi	60	20	99.9	26	180
THF	Na/K	60	10	97.8	31	85
C_6H_5	Na/K	120	10	96.2	8.5	55
−	Na/K	120	10	99.5	12	75

[a]Conditions: monomer, 1 g; solvent, 7.0 ml.
[b]The polymers consist of benzene-insoluble, methanol-insoluble, and methanol-soluble fractions.

Recently Italian researchers described the synthesis of linear polyimides by hydrogen transfer propagation starting with tetracarboxylic acid diimide and divinyl sulfone [61]. The polymerization mechanism was proposed to proceed as follows:

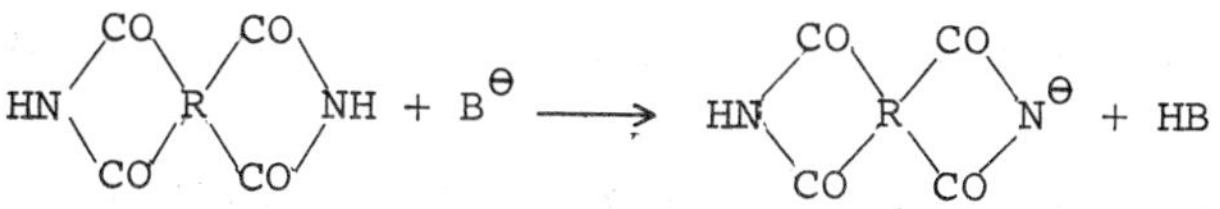

$$\text{HN}\underset{CO}{\overset{CO}{\diagup}}R\underset{CO}{\overset{CO}{\diagdown}}\text{NH} + \text{B}^{\ominus} \longrightarrow \text{HN}\underset{CO}{\overset{CO}{\diagup}}R\underset{CO}{\overset{CO}{\diagdown}}\text{N}^{\ominus} + \text{HB}$$

I

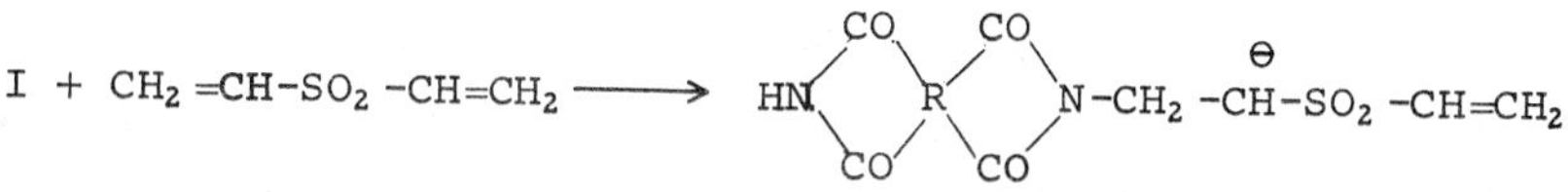

$$\text{I} + \text{CH}_2\!=\!\text{CH}-\text{SO}_2-\text{CH}\!=\!\text{CH}_2 \longrightarrow \text{HN}\underset{CO}{\overset{CO}{\diagup}}R\underset{CO}{\overset{CO}{\diagdown}}\text{N}-\text{CH}_2-\text{CH}\overset{\ominus}{-}\text{SO}_2-\text{CH}\!=\!\text{CH}_2$$

II

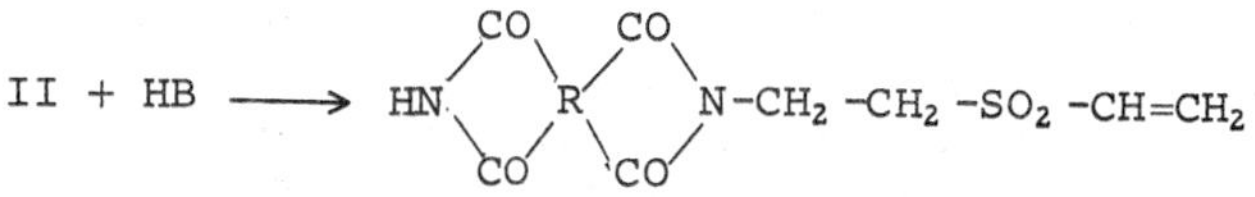

$$\text{II} + \text{HB} \longrightarrow \text{HN}\underset{CO}{\overset{CO}{\diagup}}R\underset{CO}{\overset{CO}{\diagdown}}\text{N}-\text{CH}_2-\text{CH}_2-\text{SO}_2-\text{CH}\!=\!\text{CH}_2$$

where R = [structures], or [structure]-CO-[structure].

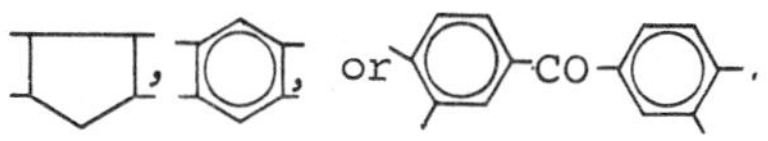

The concept involved in this mechanism is the same as that discussed previously in conjunction with bimolecular proton transfer (see Sect. II.A). According to the authors these polyimides are infusible, concentrated H_2SO_4 soluble, crystalline solids; they are stable up to 300° under vacuum.

Similar polyaddition reactions have recently been reported by Danusso et al. [62]. They prepared various tertiary amine polymers by the polyaddition of bifunctional compounds containing active hydrogen atoms with divinyl compounds having electrophilic double bonds in the presence of base catalysts.

In this context it is of interest that a polymerization of the mono-
mer-isomerization-preceding-propagation type [46] has also been
postulated with allyl cyanide by Nakayama et al. [45]. In this instance $CH_2=CH-CH_2-CN$ was polymerized with n-butyllithium at
$-78°$ and a rather low molecular weight (DP ~11) methanol-insoluble
product was obtained. Infrared evidence (i.e., the presence of CH_3-

and $-CN$ groups) indicated that the repeat unit is probably $-\overset{\displaystyle CH_3}{\underset{\displaystyle CN}{\overset{|}{\underset{|}{CH}}}}-CH-$

which in turn would indicate that under polymerization conditions the
monomer first isomerizes to croton cyanide $CH_3-CH=CH-CN$
which then polymerizes immediately.

III. THE PROBLEM OF INTRAMOLECULAR ANIONIC
ISOMERIZATION POLYMERIZATION

Cations isomerize readily and the literature of cationic rearrangements is quite voluminous [63]. In comparison to the wealth of information on cationic isomerizations, very few anionic rearrangements have been described. This apparent contradiction was recognized by Wittig and Clausnitzer [64] in 1954 and their observation
remains fully valid up to the present time. The early authors also
discussed the influence of the nature of the migrating group on intramolecular isomerizations and recognized that electropositive substituents (e.g., $p-CH_3O-C_6H_4-$) migrate preferentially during
cationic rearrangements whereas electronegative groups (e.g.,
$p-NO_2-C_6H_4-$) shift preferentially in anionic isomerizations. Progress in this area of small organic molecules during the intervening
years has been less than spectacular: some quantum-chemical calculations have been made to explain certain aspects of these observations [65], but fundamental experimental progress has been sparse
and the number of authentic anionic isomerizations remains few.
Much more progress has been made in the area of large molecules
and a new field of study has opened: that of hydrogen or proton transfer polymerization initiated by anionic catalysts, the main subject of
this review.

While many types of carbonium ion isomerizations, e.g., electrophilic migrations of hydrogen, methyl or phenyl groups, are certainly
among the most thoroughly investigated and best understood organic
chemical reactions, anionic rearrangements are comparatively rare;
simple $C_1 \rightarrow C_2$ alkyl or aryl shifts which are quite common among
cationic rearrangements are virtually unknown in anionic chemistry.

Indeed, these authors found only one well-authenticated case of 1,2-carbon-to-carbon anionic migration in the literature. Thus according to Grovenstein and Wentworth [66], 1,2-phenyl migration occurs in the rearrangement of 2,2,2-triphenylethyllithium to 1,1,2-triphenyl-ethyllithium in tetrahydrofuran solution:

$$\phi\text{-}\underset{\displaystyle\phi}{\overset{\displaystyle\phi}{\underset{|}{\overset{|}{C}}}}\text{-}CH_2\,Li \longrightarrow \left[\underset{\phi}{\overset{\phi}{C}} \text{---} \underset{H}{\overset{H}{C}} \ \ Li \ \overset{\oplus}{} \right] \longrightarrow Li\underset{\displaystyle\phi}{\overset{\displaystyle\phi}{\underset{|}{\overset{|}{C}}}}\text{---}\underset{\phi}{\overset{\phi}{C}}H_2$$

The same authors also showed that the rearrangement of 2,2,3-triphenylpropyllithium to 1,1,3-triphenylpropyllithium, which was previously thought to occur by intramolecular benzyl anion migration, did in fact involve elimination-readdition:

$$CH_2-\underset{\displaystyle\phi}{\overset{\displaystyle\phi}{\underset{|}{\overset{|}{C}}}}-CH_2-Li \longrightarrow CH_2-Li + CH_2=\underset{\displaystyle\phi}{\overset{\displaystyle\phi}{\underset{|}{\overset{|}{C}}}} \longrightarrow Li-\underset{\displaystyle\phi}{\overset{\displaystyle\phi}{\underset{|}{\overset{|}{C}}}}-CH_2-\overset{\phi}{CH_2}$$

The driving force for the isomerization of hydrocarbons by cationic mechanism arises from the considerable stability difference between the primary $<$ secondary $<$ tertiary carbonium ions, in that order. This driving force is responsible for the cationic intramolecular isomerization polymerization of a large number of diverse monomers leading to various unique polymer structures [10]. The 3-methyl-1-butene system is an outstanding example of such a polymerization reaction and has been explored in detail [10]:

$$CH_3=\underset{\underset{CH_3}{\diagup}\underset{CH_3}{\diagdown}}{\overset{|}{CH}}CH \xrightarrow{R^{\oplus}} R\text{-}CH_2\text{-}\overset{\oplus}{\underset{\underset{CH_3}{\diagup}\underset{CH_3}{\diagdown}}{\overset{|}{CH}}}CH \ \curvearrowright \ R\text{-}CH_2\text{-}CH_2\underset{\underset{CH_3}{\diagup}\underset{\oplus}{\diagdown}CH_3}{\overset{|}{C}} \ \text{- - - -} \rightarrow \sim CH_2\text{-}CH_2\text{-}\underset{CH_3}{\overset{CH_3}{\underset{|}{\overset{|}{C}}}}\text{-}\sim$$

$$\qquad\qquad\qquad\qquad I \qquad\qquad\qquad\qquad II$$

In this case a nonspecific electrophile $R^{\oplus}$, which can be the proton during initiation or the growing carbonium ion during propagation, attacks the π system of the monomer and produces a secondary carbonium ion (I). This ion rearranges, by intramolecular hydride shift, to a tertiary carbonium ion (II) prior to propagation. Finally the newly formed stable tertiary carbonium ion attacks the monomer and completes the propagation step. Plesch calls these polymers phantom polymers because the polymer does not have a "monomer" [67].

In contrast to carbonium ions, the various carbanions do not represent substantial stability differences and, consequently, isomerization polymerizations, particularly intramolecular shifts, analogous to the cationic 3-methyl-1-butene system, are as yet unknown with carbanions. A possible (electrophilic) proton-shift polymerization, analogous to the (nucleophilic) hydride-shift system discussed above would be the anionic 1,3-polymerization of allylbenzene or 3-phenylallylbenzene:

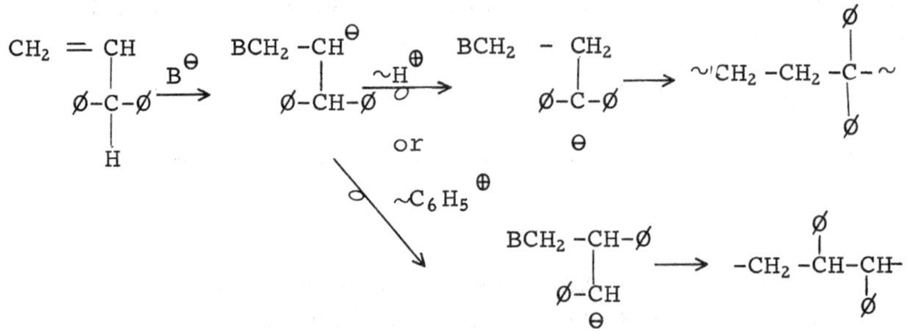

Of the two possible rearrangement polymerizations, proton or phenonium shift, the latter appears to be more favorable because (a) phenyl is a better migrating group than the proton, (b) phenyl shift is statistically favored over that of proton migration by a factor of 2 (proton extraction by the base with concurrent diphenyl allyl anion formation might be a disturbing side reaction).

At this point the question arises: Why do carbonium ions have such a high propensity for rearrangement while carbanions do not? Zimmerman and Zweig [65] considered this question and estimated the energetics of various carbon-to-carbon migrations by using a simple Huckel LCAO molecular orbital calculation. Five $C_1 \rightarrow C_2$ shifts were considered:

A: alkyl shifts between aliphatic carbons
B: phenyl shifts between aliphatic carbons

C: alkyl shifts from a phenyl-bearing C_1 to a nonphenyl-bearing C_2

D: phenyl shifts from a phenyl-bearing C_1 to a nonphenyl-bearing C_2

E: phenyl shift from a two-phenyl bearing C_1 to a nonphenyl-bearing C_2

By making some simple reasonable assumptions as to the hybridizations involved, geometry of orbitals, location and number of electrons for the half-migrated species, etc., the energetics of the above migrations involving carbonium ions, free radicals, and carbanions were calculated. A key assumption was that the bridging energy is inversely related to the ease of migration. The results may be summarized as shown in Table 7.

Evidently the number of electrons involved in bridge-formation strongly influences the over-all energetics. For example, in the first system (A) with alkyl shifts between aliphatic carbons, the number of delocalized electrons in the bridged transition state is $2 + n$ where the 2 indicates the two σ electrons originally between C_1 and R and $n = 0, 1$, or 2 depending on the nature of the active species carbonium ion, free radical, or carbanion, respectively. In this system, then, the bridging energy is quite favorable for carbonium ion shifts (-0.40β) but is prohibitive for carbanion mechanisms $(+1.22\beta)$. According to this theory [65] the propensity for rearrangement is always strongest with carbonium ions, weaker with free radicals, and weakest with carbanions. For anionic alkyl migrations (cases A and C) the energetics are unfavorable by 1.22β or 0.08β, respectively, but phenyl migrations (cases B, D, and E) are allowed and, indeed, the above-mentioned example of the Grovenstein-rearrangement of 2,2,2-triphenyllithium is energetically quite favorable with -1.35β. The above proposed phenonium shift polymerization would be favorable with -0.88β.

As unconjugated (unstabilized) aliphatic carbanions are extremely elusive species and, indeed, might not even exist, it is not too surprising that anionic $C \rightarrow C$ migrations are extremely rate (hydrogen and alkyl shifts are as yet unknown and only one authentic aryl migration system has been described). In contrast to this, carbanions stabilized by conjugation to various groups, e.g., oxygen, nitrogen, vinyl, and phenyl, are quite common and anionic oxygen-to-carbon $(O \rightarrow C)$ or nitrogen-to-carbon $(N \rightarrow C)$ shifts are well-known reactions. The driving force in these intramolecular reactions is provided by the stability difference between the anions of carbon and oxygen, and carbon and nitrogen, respectively. Examples for the

Table 7

	Ground state	Bridge structure	No. of electrons involved	Bridging energy (kcal/mole)
A	R—C_1—C_2*	R C_1====C_2	2 + n	$E = (-0.40 + 0.81n)\beta$ $= -0.40\beta$ for $C^{\oplus}$ $= +0.41\beta$ for $C\cdot$ $= +1.22\beta$ for $C^{\ominus}$
B	C_6H_5—C_1—C_2*	C_6H_5 C_1====C_2	8 + n	$E = (-1.18 + 0.33n)\beta$ $= -1.18\beta$ for $C^{\oplus}$ $= -0.81\beta$ for $C\cdot$ $= -0.51\beta$ for $C^{\ominus}$
C	R—C_1(C_6H_5)—C_2*	R C_1(C_6H_5)—C_2	8 + n	$E = (-0.98 + 0.53n)\beta$ $= -0.98\beta$ for $C^{\oplus}$ $= -0.45\beta$ for $C\cdot$ $= +0.08\beta$ for $C^{\ominus}$
D	C_6H_5—C_1(C_6H_5)—C_2*	C_6H_5 C_1(C_6H_5)====C_2	14 + n	$E = (-1.46 + 0.29n)\beta$ $= -1.46\beta$ for $C^{\oplus}$ $= -1.17\beta$ for $C\cdot$ $= -0.88\beta$ for $C^{\ominus}$
E	C_6H_5—(H_5C_6—C_1)(C_6H_5)—C_2*	C_6H_5 H_5C_6=C_1(C_6H_5)====C_2	20 + n	$E = (-1.87 + 0.26n)\beta$ $= -1.87\beta$ for $C^{\oplus}$ $= -1.61\beta$ for $C\cdot$ $= -1.35\beta$ for $C^{\ominus}$

N→C shift are various Stevens rearrangements:

and for the O→C migrations the well-characterized Wittig ether rearrangements, for example [68]:

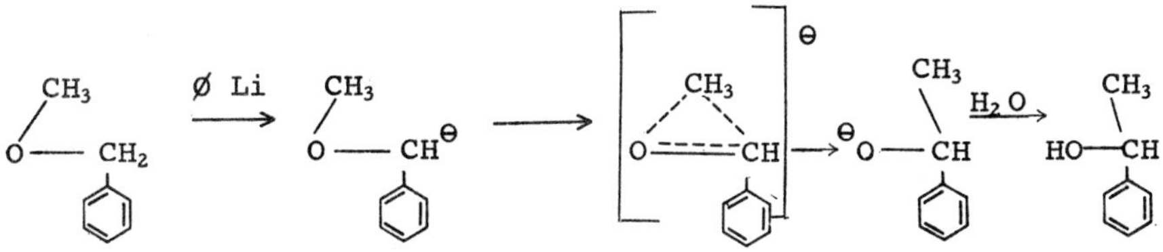

Grovenstein and Wentworth [66], who extended Zimmerman and Zweig's MO calculations [65] to the Stevens rearrangement case, concluded that alkyl shifts may proceed with increasing facility in the $C \rightarrow C < O \rightarrow C < N \rightarrow O$ series because of the increasingly favorable electron delocalization in the transition states involved, i.e.,

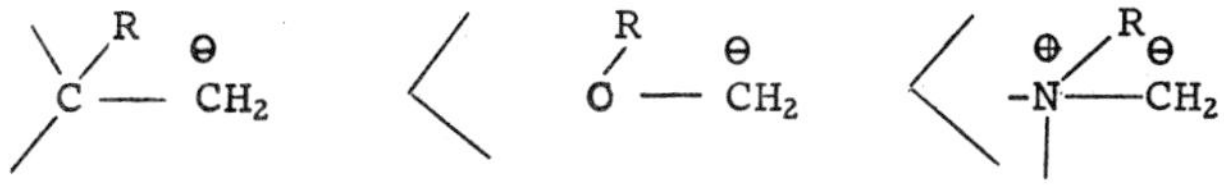

It is conceivable that the Wittig ether rearrangement would lead to anionic isomerization polymerization in the α-methoxystyrene system:

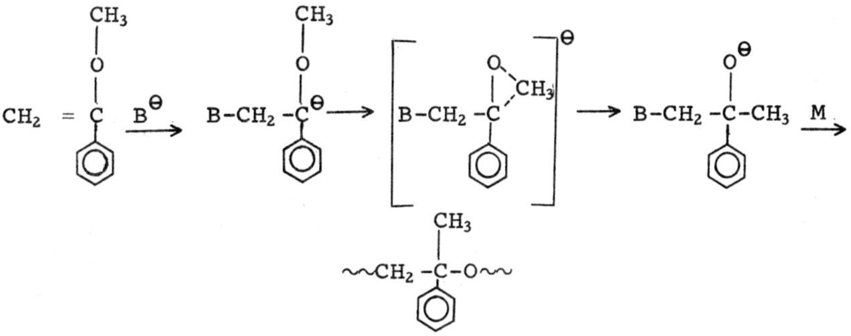

The driving force for this reaction is the same as in the Wittig rearrangements, namely an $O \rightarrow C$ shift. It is quite conceivable that the alkoxide ion will be able to propagate the chain. However, this isomerization polymerization has not yet been described.

IV. CONCLUSIONS

The base-initiated polymerization of acrylamide to poly(β-alanine) or nylon 3, first reported in 1954 by Matlack and explored by Breslow and their associates, has opened up a new field of fruitful investigation in polymer science. While initially there was some confusion as to the reaction mechanism of this polymerization, today the weight of evidence tends to indicate that this polyreaction proceeds by intermolecular (in contrast to intramolecular) proton transfer. Since the original publication, many attempts have been made to synthesize new polyamides and polyamide derivatives from various vinyl monomers with amide groups by this technique. In most cases the available evidence is strong that in these systems conventional anionic chain-growth propagation operates besides the step-growth by proton-transfer mechanism and, consequently, most of the products are mixtures (copolymers?) of the two possible repeat units: amide and conventional 1,2-enchainment. One circumstance which contributed to this state of events is that most workers in order to increase polymerization rates, employed elevated temperatures ($> 100°$) which in turn gave rise to secondary reactions and reduced selectivity. While information is starting to accumulate on how to control propagation to desirable end products, more direct experimentation is needed to define better the relationship between polymerization conditions and structure.

The molecular weights and conversions are still too low. Therefore more information is needed to understand the reasons for this and to improve all the important parameters. One possibility for the preparation of high molecular weight products may be the polymerization of highly purified higher oligomers in solution or homogeneous dispersion or in conjunction with certain complexing agents to aid solubilizing the system. For obvious reasons there is great incentive for the synthesis of high molecular weight, regular nylon 3 or related products. It is a matter of record that these polymers are highly crystalline and that they can be spun. Very little is known about the molecular weight distributions of these systems, even for the simplest and best-characterized members of this class of polymers.

Research workers in this field have uncovered a large number of intriguing polymerizations and copolymerizations. Some of these systems might turn out to be useful; e.g., the conceptually novel synthesis of α-polypeptides from substituted amides.

Hydrogen transfer polymerizations could obviously be used for the synthesis of valuable α,ω-amino acids from vinyl amides. The

process would comprise two steps: a polyreaction and a subsequent hydrolysis.
Finally, some aspects of the problem of intramolecular molecular anionic isomerizations have been considered. The parallelism between anionic and cationic isomerization polymerization of branched olefins was explored and the reason for the scarcity of the formers was discussed.
New leads for further research and some possibilities for the synthesis of new types of polymer structures have been suggested.

References

[1]   A. S. Matlack, U.S. Patent 2,672,480 (1954) to Hercules Powder Co.
[2]   D. S. Breslow, G. E. Hulse, and A. S. Matlack, *J. Amer. Chem. Soc.*, **79**, 3760 (1957).
[3]   N. Ogata, *Bull. Chem. Soc. Jap.*, **33**, 906 (1960).
[4]   N. Ogata, *Makromol. Chem.*, **40**, 55 (1960).
[5]   N. Ogata, *J. Polym. Sci.*, **46**, 271 (1960).
[6]   H. Tani, N. Oguni, and T. Araki, *Makromol. Chem.*, **76**, 82 (1964).
[7]   L. Trossarelli, M. Guaita, and C. Camino, *Ibid.*, **105**, 285 (1967).
[8]   A. Leoni, S. Franco, and G. Polla, *J. Polym. Sci., Part A-1*, **6**, 3187 (1968).
[9]   L. W. Bush and D. S. Breslow, *Macromolecules*, **1**, 189 (1968).
[10] J. P. Kennedy, in *Encyclopedia of Polymer Science and Technology*, Vol. 7, Wiley (Interscience), 1967, p. 754.
[11] T. Yonezawa, K. Shimizu, H. Kato, and K. Fukui, *Nippon Kagaku Zasshi*, **87**, 20 (1966).
[12] H. Nakayama, T. Higashimura, and S. Okamura, *Chem. High Polym.*, **23**, 433 (1966).
[13] H. Nakayama, T. Higashimura, and S. Okamura, *Ibid.*, **23**, 439 (1966).
[14] H. Nakayama, T. Higashimura, and S. Okamura, *Ibid.*, **23**, 537 (1966).
[15] H. Nakayama, T. Higashimura, and S. Okamura, *Ibid.*, **24**, 42 (1967).
[16] J. D. Glickson and Y. Applequist, *Macromolecules*, **2**, 628 (1969).
[17] J. Masamoto, K. Yamaguchi, and H. Kobayashi, *Chem. High Polym.*, **26**, 631 (1969).
[18] J. Masamoto, C. Ohizumi, and H. Kobayashi, *Ibid.*, **26**, 638 (1969).
[19] K. Ito, K. Baba, and Y. Yamashita, *Kogyo Kagaku Zasshi*, **68**, 703 (1965).
[20] H. Bestian, *Angew. Chem. Int. Ed.*, **7**, 278 (1968).
[21] C. S. Marvel and P. H. Aldrich, *J. Amer. Chem. Soc.*, **72**, 1978 (1950).
[22] K. Yokota, M. Shimizu, Y. Yamashita, and Y. Ishii, *Makromol. Chem.*, **77**, 1 (1964).
[23] A. Leoni, M. Guaita, and C. Saini, *Chim. Ind.* (Milan), **47**, 373 (1965).
[24] Y. Iwakura, F. Toda, Y. Torii, and R. Sekii, *J. Polym. Sci., Part A-1*, **5**, 1585 (1967).
[25] H. Sekiguchi, *Bull. Soc. Chim. Fr.*, **8**, 337 (1968).

[26a] B. Sebille,*C. R. Acad. Sci., Paris, Ser. C.*, **269**, 1194 (1969).
[26b] D. J. Shields and H. W. Coover, Jr., *J. Polym. Sci.*, **39**, 532 (1959).
[26c] K. Butler, P. R. Thomas, and G. Jylex, *J. Polym. Sci.*, **48**, 357 (1960).
[27] H. Nakayama, Y. Yamazawa, T. Higashimura, and S. Okamura,*Chem. High Polym.*, **24**, 296 (1967).
[28a] H. Wexler, *Makromol. Chem.*,**115**, 262 (1968).
[28b] M. Guaita and L. F. Thomas, *Ibid.*, **117**, 171 (1968).
[29] H. Tani and H. Takeda, *Ann. Rept. Fiber Res. Osaka Univ.*, **13**, 134 (1960).
[30] H. Lüssi, *Kolloid-Z.*,**212**, 28 (1966).
[31] K. Fufii and S. Kudo, *Chem. High Polym.*,**21**, 613 (1964).
[32] Y. Iwakura, N. Nakabayashi, K. Sagara, and Y. Ichikura, *J. Polym. Sci., Part A-1*, **5**, 675 (1967).
[33] T. Tsunetsugu, T. Matsuo, and J. Furukawa, *Makromol. Chem.*, **107**, 222 (1967).
[34] C. H. Bamford, G. C. Eastmond, and Y. Imanishi, *Polymer*, **8**, 651 (1967).
[35a] Y. Imanishi, T. Andoh, and S. Okamura, *J. Polym. Sci., Part A-1*, **7**, 773 (1969).
[35b] Y. Imanishi, T. Andoh, and S. Okamura, *Chem. High Polym.*, **25**, 708 (1968).
[36] T. Otsu, B. Yamada, and M. Itahashi, Unpublished Result.
[37] K. Kojima, N. Yoda, and C. S. Marvel, *J. Polym. Sci., Part A-1*, **4**, 1121 (1966).
[38] S. Negishi and Y. Tamura,*Ibid.*, **5**, 2911 (1967).
[39] H. Nakayama, T. Sogo, T. Higashimura, and S. Okamura,*Bull. Chem. Soc. Jap.*, **41**, 520 (1968).
[40] T. Asahara and N. Yoda, *J. Polym. Sci., Part B*, **4**, 921 (1966).
[41] T. Asahara and N. Yoda,*J. Polym. Sci., Part A-1*, **6**, 2477 (1968).
[42] T. Asahara, K. Ikeda, and N. Yoda,*Ibid.*, **6**, 2489 (1968).
[43] T. Asakara, *Ibid.*,**7**, 2489 (1968).
[44] H. Yuki and Y. Taketani, *Chem. High Polym.*,**25**, 515 (1968).
[45] N. Nakayama, T. Higashimura, and S. Okamura, *J. Macromol. Sci.— Chem.*,**A2**, 53 (1968).
[46] J. P. Kennedy and T. Otsu, *Advan. Polym. Sci.*, **7**, 369 (1970).
[47] N. Yoda and C. S. Marvel, *J. Polym. Sci., Part A*, **3**, 229 (1965).
[48] A. Konishi, N. Yoda, and C. S. Marvel, *Ibid.*,**3**, 3833 (1965).
[49] T. Asahara, N. Yoda, H. Saito, and K. Nukata, *Kogyo Kagaku Zasshi*,**70**, 1974 (1967).
[50] K. Kojima, N. Yoda, and C. S. Marvel,*J. Polym. Sci., Part A-1*, **4**, 1121 (1966).
[51] Y. Nakayama and G. Smets,*Ibid.*, **5**, 1619 (1967).
[52] R. C. P. Cubbon,*Polymer*, **6**, 419 (1965).
[53] H. Yuki, K. Kosai, and K. Ohtsu,*Kogyo Kagaku Zasshi*, **70**, 1963 (1967).
[54] S. Iwatsuki, Y. Yamashita, and Y. Ishii,*J. Polym. Sci., Part B*, **1**, 545 (1963).

[55] L. Trossarelli, M. Guaita, and A. Priola, *Ric. Sci. Rend.*, 7, 451 (1964).
[56] A. D. Aliev, T. K. Khanmendov, and B. A. Krentsel, *Vysokomol. Soedin.*, 11, 329 (1969).
[57] T. Imoto and T. Matsubara, *J. Polym. Sci.*, 56, S4, (1962).
[58] T. Imoto and T. Matsubara, *J. Polym. Sci.*, *Part A*, 2, 4573 (1964).
[59] T. Matsubara and T. Imoto, *Makromol. Chem.*, 117, 215 (1968).
[60] T. Matsubara and T. Imoto, *Ibid.*, 120, 27 (1968).
[61] M. Russo and L. Mortillaro, *J. Polym. Sci.*, *Part A-1*, 7, 3337 (1969).
[62] F. Danusso and P. Ferruti, *Polymer*, 11, 88 (1970).
[63] P. de Mayo, ed., *Molecular Rearrangements*, Wiley (Interscience), New York, 1967.
[64] G. Wittig and R. Clausnitzer, *Justus Liebigs Ann. Chem.*, 558, 145 (1955).
[65] H. E. Zimmerman and A. Zweig, *J. Amer. Chem. Soc.*, 83, 1196 (1961).
[66] E. Grovenstein, Jr., and G. Wentworth, *Ibid.*, 89, 1852 (1967).
[67] P. H. Plesch, ed., *The Chemistry of Cationic Polymerization*, Macmillan, New York, 1963, p. 233.
[68] D. J. Cram, *Fundamentals of Carbanion Chemistry*, Academic, New York, 1965.

Ring-Opening Polymerization of Lactams and N-Carboxy-α-Amino
Acid Anhydrides

G. D. Fasman, N. Tooney, and Y. Shalitin, in *Encylopedia of Polymer Science and Technology*, Vol. 2, Wiley (Interscience), 1965, p. 837.
R. W. Lenz, *Organic Chemistry of Synthetic High Polymers*, Wiley (Interscience), New York, 1967, p. 461.
G. Odian, *Principles of Polymerization*, McGraw-Hill, New York, 1970, p. 479.
A. Ravve, *Organic Chemistry of Macromolecules*, Dekker, New York, 1967, p. 273.
R. A. Patsiga, *J. Macromol. Sci.–Rev. Macromol. Chem.*, C1, 223 (1967).
M. Szwarc, *Carbanions, Living Polymers, and Electron Transfer Processes*, Wiley (Interscience), New York, 1968, Chap. 10, p. 558.
M. Szwarc, *Polyamides in Encyclopedia of Polymer Science and Technology*, Wiley (Interscience), New York, 1971, In Press.

Author Index

H

Subject Index

A

Acrylamides, hydrogen transfer polymerization of, 238-259
Adhesion rheology, 85-112
  of bonding, 99-101
  definitions in, 85-86
  fracture mechanics in, 87-91
  locus of failure in, 91-92
  molecular criteria for adhesion, 101-107
  polymer-fracture micromechanics, 91-98
Adhesives, from polyquinoxalines, 25-27
Amides, hydrogen transfer polymerization of, 260-267
Anionic catalysts, hydrogen transfer polymerization with, 237-286
Anionic isomerization polymerization, hydrogen transfer polymerization and, 274-279

B

Batch fractionation, of polymers, 67-68
Bonding, rheology of, 99-101

C

Column fractionation, of polymers, 68-70
Composites, from polyquinoxalines, 21-25

Computer, use to form index of polyamides, 34-40

D

Dibenzils, properties of, 15
Dielectric studies of biochemical polyelectrolytes, 211-219

E

Equilibrium sedimentation methods for polymer fractionation, 74-75

F

Failure, locus of, 91-92
Films and fibers, from polyquinoxalines, 19-21
Fractionation techniques for polymers, 51-83
  batch fractionation, 67-68
  column fractionation, 68-70
  gel permeation chromatography, 52-67
  sedimentation methods, 70-75
  turbidimetry, 75-76
Fracture mechanics, 87-91

G

Gel permeation chromatography for polymer fractionation, 52-67
  data treatment, 59-65
  new developments in, 66-67

303